9.50

THE INDIVIDUAL IN HIS FAMILY

An Adaptational Study

THE INDIVIDUAL IN HIS FAMILY

An Adaptational Study

By

ALFRED A. MESSER, M.D.

Professor of Psychiatry, Emory University
Chief, Family Studies Laboratory
Georgia Mental Health Institute
Department of Public Health
Atlanta, Georgia

CHARLES C. THOMAS • PUBLISHER
Springfield • Illinois • U.S.A.

Published and Distributed Throughout the World by

CHARLES C THOMAS • PUBLISHER

Bannerstone House

301-327 East Lawrence Avenue, Springfield, Illinois, U.S.A.

Natchez Plantation House

735 North Atlantic Boulevard, Fort Lauderdale, Florida, U.S.A.

With **THOMAS BOOKS** *careful attention is given to all details of
manufacturing and design. It is the Publisher's desire to present books
that are satisfactory as to their physical qualities and artistic possibilities
and appropriate for their particular use.* **THOMAS BOOKS** *will be true
to those laws of quality that assure a good name and good will.*

Printed in the United States of America
EE-16

iv

To My Parents

Preface

Looking back over forty years in psychiatry and psychoanalysis, Franz Alexander contemplated the future of psychotherapy and enjoined his colleagues to consider ".... man as *a biologic organism, a personality, and a member of a social system.*" He went on to note, in this last essay before his death, "Neglecting any of these three major parameters" would result in "unsatisfactory personality theory and therapy" (1964, p. 23). [*Italics mine.*]

This observation is in harmony with the awareness today that psychotherapy which involves one person and neglects his family and community in the overall treatment is inadequate. Only when a designated patient is seen together with his family does one realize how often the "wrong" person is referred for psychotherapy.

Imagine, if you will, a patient who is referred to a psychiatrist because of depression, inability to adjust on the job, and periods of sexual impotence. He is a single man in his thirties, in good physical health, and has had psychotherapy previously for several years without significant benefit. After interviewing the patient alone, he is seen with his family. The psychiatrist discovers that his father is a brutal, denigrating individual, who has always castigated his son. The father says repeatedly, "The only thing wrong with him is that he's lazy." However, as the family is seen over a period of time, it becomes apparent that the father has great doubts about his own capacity as a man. He therefore makes cutting remarks whenever his son tries to assert himself, for this threatens the older man's impaired sense of masculinity.

Rather than challenging the father's authoritarianism, the entire family bows to his rule. The son is cast into the role of scapegoat for family conflicts, i.e. focusing on his problems does away with the necessity for dealing with more pervasive family conflicts. His "symptoms" preserve the family equilibrium. This situation forces us to ask the question, Who is sick?—the father, the mother, the son, or the family unit? It becomes necessary to rethink the whole concept of the pathogenesis of illness. Frequently, as in this example, one member of a family is "designated" the scapegoat (or patient) for some other disturbed family member, and the method selected for therapy, i.e. psychoanalysis, family therapy, etc., must take these factors into account.

The choice between individual therapy, including psychoanalysis, and family treatment is not an either/or proposition. As a matter of fact, a patient can be in analysis while he is also undergoing family treatment. There are clinical indications for each. In other words, it is sometimes necessary to deal mainly with the interactional elements in a person's environment and at other times to deal primarily with the phantasies and perceptions in one individual. The psychiatrist must therefore be able to shift back and forth with some flexibility, depending on the clinical indications.

Our experience in screening draftees and classifying many as emotionally disturbed during World War II has forced us to focus on more than the perceptions of the individual before deciding about the presence or absence of psychiatric illness. Over ten million men were psychiatrically screened using pre-World War II standards, and by these indices, almost half of the group were "unacceptable" for military service. This situation necessitated a revision of psychiatric screening standards. Further, many men had functioned adequately in their home environment; only after being drafted did they turn up with disabling symptoms. (The converse was also true, but to a lesser extent: many men who showed typical sociopathic personality disturbance in civilian life did well in the military service.) Clearly, psychiatric evaluation and diagnosis had to be broadened to include a study of the individual's environment as well as study of his phantasies and perceptions. While this procedure now appears obvious, for most of the past century patients have been sent off to state hospitals for treatment and, when improved, have been sent back to the same environment from which they came. It is not surprising that the relapse rate has been extremely high.

One of the purposes of this book is to emphasize that behavior must be studied on more than one level. Four levels of functioning are suggested, and there are mechanisms of adaptation at each level. (These mechanisms of adaptation are described in detail in the chapters on individual and family adaptation.) There is (a) the basic hormonal, clinical, or physiological level, where the organism automatically regulates its internal environment; (b) the pain and pleasure level (*hedonic* level), at which the organism automatically adjusts itself to the immediate external environment; (c) the emotional level, at which there are alerting messages and anticipatory reactions to energize the organism for interaction with its environment; and (d) the intellectual level, which is characterized by long-range thought and planning. Without attempting to correlate structure with function or to deal with genetic determinants of behavior, it is worth noting that these levels correspond roughly to the functions mediated by the four great anatomic divisions of the nervous system: (a) the spinal cord, (b) the hindbrain, (c) the limbic system, and (d) the neocortex.

Could there be any correlation between these four levels and subjective experience? Any individual who is introspective for a moment recognizes that there are times when he wants to be left alone to eat, sleep, and vegetate; times when he desires the intimate (emotional) contact of family or friends; and times when he wants to be challenged intellectually—by productive activity, philosophic discussion, or creative endeavor. Each of the higher levels can modify responses at a lower level; this fact helps explain the impact of social experience on basic biological functioning. The student who is called upon to recite in class may suddenly gasp and sense his heart pounding, but as he begins reciting, he usually regains "intellectual" control. The individual brought up to feel that sex is ladened with guilt will run from an encounter that, "biologically speaking," should attract him and enhance his feeling as a human being. As will be stressed in Chapter II, lower levels can sometimes override higher levels: in "brainwashing," functioning at the intellectual and emotional levels is knocked out; the individual becomes mainly a "hedonic" being. His ability to use critical judgment has been impaired.

The focus of this volume is primarily clinical. My own clinical training includes residency in psychiatry, neurology, psychosomatic medicine, and psychoanalytic medicine. During psychoanalytic training, I found myself particularly influenced by the teaching and writings of three pioneer analysts: Drs. Sandor Rado, Abram Kardiner, and David Levy. Their approach forms the basis of what is now called *adaptational psychodynamics,* in which attention is focused on the *interaction* between the organism and its environment.

Some five years after psychoanalytic training, I was for two years clinical director of a community mental health center. Here the orientation was the study of the community and the patient as a part of his total community, as well as the patient as an individual. At this center, treatment was most effective when done immediately, with the patient remaining a member of his "unit"— family or school. This approach parallels the experience of psychiatrists treating battle fatigue in wartime. Immediate treatment of a casualty near his unit led to more rapid recovery. Removal of the man to a distant hospital for treatment served to make his illness more intractable. He had lost his identity as a member of a fighting unit.

I then worked for two years with Dr. Nathan Ackerman at a family treatment center. Seeing the patient as part of a family group draws attention to disturbances in the interaction among family members. Symptoms in one member are often a direct reflection of these interfamilial disturbances.

Using the adaptational framework, mental illness can be defined as an impairment of functioning. This impairment can be at any level. It may stem from structural changes in the brain, as in multiple sclerosis. Disturbances in the hedonic (pain and pleasure) mechanisms are notable in schizophrenia. Disturbances in the emotional mechanisms of adaptation are prominent in the common garden-variety neurotic. Impairments in these three categories are most generally reflected by clinical symptoms or disturbed behavior within one individual. In addition, the community (or culture) can adjudge an individual's behavior as being deviant and label this deviance "mental illness." Depending on the particular culture, the deviant behavior can be defined in a number of ways, including mental illness, juvenile delinquency, alcoholism, or criminality. For example, mental illness during the Middle Ages was defined by the Church as heresy; during the 1930's, some social psychologists defined neurosis as being nonconforming behavior. A knowledge of the "definer" therefore becomes mandatory for a total perspective of mental illness.

Chapter I, the introductory chapter, is entitled, "Who Is Sick and Who Is Treated?" It contains a brief overview of some of the ways in which mental illness has been defined, as well as a description of mental illness as an impairment of functioning. The sickest person is the one who has the most permanent kind of impairment or limitation of functioning. Stressed is the fact that sickness in one culture may be viewed as health in another culture.

Chapter II deals with individual adaptation. Reflex, hedonic, emotional, and intellectual levels are described, as well as the mechanisms involved in the functioning at each level. How does the individual cope with stress? Some correlation between the levels described and neurological structure is suggested.

Chapter III discusses pathological (maladaptive) behavior and failures in coping. There is a detailed description of the adaptive mechanisms as they function in health and in pathology. Some of the effects of social institutions on behavior are outlined. A rationale for psychotherapy of maladaptive behavior is presented.

Chapter IV concerns family adaptation or, as preferred here, family homeostasis. Homeostasis refers to the maintenance of internal equilibrium. The term "homeostasis" (and "homeostatic mechanism") is used here in preference to the term "family adaptation," since it can be argued that organizations such as families, or even societies, can in themselves be considered instruments of adaptation, i.e. they enhance survival of the organism and the species. In order to maintain equilibrium in a family, homeostatic mechanisms are utilized. Examples of family homeostatic mechanisms are formation of alliances and coalitions in a family, scapegoating of one individual, rigidification within the family unit, and dispersion of the family members. A distinction is made between "homeostatic mechanisms" and "family defenses." Homeostatic mechanisms have an open-ended quality which allows for resolution of conflict. Defenses tend to be permanent and fixed impairments. The concept of adaptation is particularly useful in family study.

Chapter V deals with emotional role. A family functions as a unit by having its members assume various roles. However, the fact that a man is forced to take over the duties of the woman in the household may be only half as important as how he feels about this change. If he is comfortable in a "feminine" role, fine; if he is not, what provisions has the family made for resolution of this conflict?

Chapter VI, on family therapy, includes a clinical description of family treatment of a school-phobic child. Rationale for the family therapeutic approach is discussed, as well as points of technique. In the case outlined, it was necessary to interrupt family therapy in order to deal with one member's intrapsychic conflicts which were interfering with treatment of the family as a whole. Following individual psychotherapy, the family was once again treated as a unit.

Chapter VII considers family therapy and psychoanalysis. A patient who had two previous extensive periods of individual treatment was treated as part of his family unit. From the outset, the major focus of treatment turned out to be the father's own deep-seated psychopathology. As the father improved, so did the son.

Chapters VI and VII point out the fact that the traditional model of one-person psychotherapy must be modified; the therapist must be able to shift back and forth between individual treatment and family therapy, depending on the clinical indications. A further suggested modification stems from the existence of complementary relationships. If one member in this relationship undergoes a significant personality change during psychotherapy, it is bound to have repercussions in the mate or other members of the family.

The suggestion made is that, when practicable, the person referred for individual psychotherapy be seen at the *first* interview accompanied by the person(s) with whom he has a complementary relationship. The therapist can then determine whether the pathology is primarily a reflection of the present complementary relationship or whether it is a long-standing conflict in one individual necessitating psychoanalytic exploration. On the basis of this initial evaluation, the therapist can appraise the situation and decide upon the best level of intervention. By so doing, treatment of the "wrong patient" is avoided.

Chapter VIII deals with social homeostasis, i.e. the mechanisms by which society regulates itself. Two clinical descriptions are presented in which a synthesis of individual, family, and societal factors is necessary for a proper understanding of the patient's symptoms.

Chapter IX, "For Better But Not for Worse: Marriage Dynamics and Marriage Therapy," deals with problems in marriage, both nonpathological and pathological.

Chapter X explores future developments in clinical psychiatric practice. More and more, the team approach will be utilized, with experts not only from the traditional fields of psychodynamics and psychopharmacology but with geneticists, learning theorists, physiological chemists, and group dynamicists.

The planning of any mental health program must also take into account the needs of the general public. More and more, it appears that a basic knowledge of mental health will be as important to the average citizen as were hunting and planting to the frontier family. We are being engulfed by population, by technological change and automation, and by a feeling of isolation. Less and less is man the master of his own fate. Therefore, whether it be himself, his family, his neighbors, the town leaders, the secretary of state or defense, or the president of a country, each man will need to know something about the motivation of behavior and how to assess behavior in himself and in others. In my own experience, particularly in the field of community psychiatry, I have found that the support of interested and intelligent laymen is a prerequisite to the success of any undertaking.

Acknowledgments

Grateful thanks are due many individuals who aided significantly in the development of this book. The debt to my teachers has been acknowledged in the paragraphs above. I must express my appreciation to Dr. Bernard Holland, Chairman of the Department of Psychiatry at Emory University, for his support and encouragement and also for making time and facilities available to complete this undertaking. Dr. Richard S. Ward, Professor of Child Psychiatry at Emory, and Dr. H. Lee Hall, Chief of Psychoanalytic Medicine at Emory, have always been available for advice and as discussants of ideas. Clinical work cited in these pages was done at Emory and at the Georgia Mental Health Institute, to whose staffs I am grateful. The book has been read and criticized thoughtfully by Drs. Herbert Hendin, Thomas Manchester, and Frank Pittman. Beverly Pease, my research assistant, has been of inestimable help in preparation of the manuscript, as well as assisting in family interviews. Jeanne Shaw, my secretary, has cheerfully typed and retyped the manuscript. Lastly, thanks are due my wife and children for their encouragement as well as patience and understanding.

Contents

Preface _____ vii

Chapter

   I Who Is Sick and Who Is Treated?
     An Introduction to the Adaptational
     Frame of Reference _____ 1

  II Adaptation in the Individual
     How the Individual Copes With Stress _____ 15

 III Pathological (Maladaptive) Behavior
     Psychotherapy for Maladaptive Behavior _____ 51

 IV Family Equilibrium (Homeostasis)
     How Families Operate in Health and in Conflict__ 67

   V Emotional Role _____ 109

  VI Family Therapy: An Adaptational Approach ____ 137

 VII Psychoanalysis and Family Therapy _____ 176

VIII Social Homeostasis
     Individual—Family—Social Interaction _____ 194

  IX For Better, But Not For Worse
     Marriage Dynamics and Therapy _____ 212

   X Regarding The Future _____ 244

References _____ 252

Index _____ 259

THE INDIVIDUAL IN HIS FAMILY

An Adaptational Study

Chapter I

Who Is Sick and Who Is Treated?
An Introduction to the Adaptational Frame
of Reference

Nick's behavior had changed markedly over the past year. Now fifteen, his boisterous and raucous behavior stood in sharp contrast to the quiet and cooperative young man of a year ago. His grades were failing, but more disturbing to his teachers was his constant "chasing after girls." His behavior led to referral for psychiatric evaluation.

The clinic to which he was referred had the policy of seeing children together with their parents at the first interview. At this first session, Nick's school activities and peer relationships were reviewed. The parents, Mr. and Mrs. D., spent most of the first hour berating the boy for his lack of cooperation and "bad behavior," both at home and at school.

During the second session, an evening hour, the three came in together again. Nick stated at the outset that he would like to leave early because he had promised to take his current girlfriend to a dance. The dance was a school prom, and the boy could not gracefully excuse himself from this date. The therapist agreed.

Nick's father immediately launched an attack on the boy, accusing him of being uninterested in the family's welfare or in their desire for psychiatric treatment. Finally, when the boy got up to leave, he asked his father for a dollar "spending money." The father muttered something inaudible, whereupon the mother beckoned to Nick, opened her pocketbook, gave him five dollars, and pinched him on the buttocks as he left. The therapist called Mrs. D.'s attention to this act, since it was more a seductive pinch than a "motherly" one. Was she always this intimate with Nick? What was Mr. D.'s reaction? Both spouses flushed and sputtered, but in short order a pertinent fact was uncovered: for the past year the father had been having an extramarital liaison with a woman in the neighborhood.

The D. family were originally from the south of Italy. Because of this cultural heritage, Mrs. D. felt she could do nothing about her husband's philandering except suffer in silence. However, Nick's social activities were of great interest to her. She would wait up for him until he returned home at 1:00 or 2:00 A.M. Then they would then sit to-

1

gether in the kitchen while the boy described the evening's events to her in minute detail. The pleasure she derived at this recounting, albeit vicarious, was immediately evident. Mother was, in effect, giving the son "signals" to go out and behave in a provocative way with girls.

The problem confronting the therapist was to decide where the pathology lay in this family. Was it merely an adolescent problem, or was it primarily a problem in marital interaction which was being reflected in the son's behavior? Further, in terms of treatment, at which level should one attempt to intervene—with the boy, the father, the mother, the couple, or with the entire family?

The tradition in psychiatry has been to label one individual as the patient and treat him in the privacy of a therapist's office or, if his behavior or symptoms warranted, in a hospital setting. What would be a suitable approach in this situation? Besides the family picture already obtained, one should pose certain questions about the boy himself—his personality, his reaction to puberty, competitive feelings toward peers, attitudes toward sex—and the parents—their individual characteristics, the early history of their marriage, and their present marital and kinship relationship. One would also want to elaborate on the cultural background of the family and to determine prevalent attitudes in the community toward the father's behavior, i.e. what are the acceptable social standards of conduct in the community?*

Should Nick be singled out as the "patient" in this instance? The boy was obviously not in need of hospitalization and would therefore remain at home and continue in school. But the relationship between the parents could go on as described, the father in extramarital embrace, the mother brooding resentfully and achieving some degree of vicarious pleasure through Nick. In individual psychotherapy, if Nick became aware of the messages his mother was sending, would his behavior change? Perhaps in time. A more expeditious approach, however, might be treating the couple together and allowing Nick to "slide out from under."

In short, several areas of investigation in this clinical situation

---

*It is interesting that some psychiatric texts are attempting to take the environment into account by establishing a diagnostic entity, "dyscultural anxiety reaction." This implies that an anxiety reaction may occur when an individual feels he is not living up to the dictates of his culture.

are apparent: the boy and his parents as individual personalities, the marital relationship, the family interaction, and community attitudes. Perhaps there are others as well. Before considering these areas in detail in subsequent chapters, a brief description of how symptoms in an individual have been viewed in the past might be appropriate here.

HISTORICAL NOTES ON PSYCHOPATHOLOGY

The early Greeks viewed mental illness as a reflection of the flow of humors (fluids) in the body. Changes in the humors resulted in disease. Hippocrates stated that a superabundance of black bile caused melancholia; on the other hand, a state of exhilaration was due to the predominance of warmth and dampness in the brain. Hence, in this view, climatic conditions could be the root of mania and melancholia.

These beliefs are similar to those of the Taoists of China: man is under the control of two antagonistic forces—Yin and Yang—that shape all life and matter. Yin is the shady side of life—female, dark, cold, and negative, typified by organs such as the lungs, spleen, and kidneys. Yang is the sunny side of life—male, bright, warm, and positive, represented by the skin, heart, and liver. The forces of Yin and Yang travel through the body via fourteen mysterious channels, and these can be tapped (acupuncture) using gold or silver needles which vary in length from an inch to a foot. Their points are so sharp that they neither draw blood nor inflict pain.

In the Middle Ages, because of the influence of religion, psychopathology was part and parcel of theological writings. The mentally-ill person was "possessed" by the Devil, and in the highly important *Malleus Maleficarum*, ways of exorcising the evil spirits are described.

In the eighteenth and nineteenth centuries, the invention of the microscope and the perfection of histological staining techniques ushered in the period, particularly in Europe, in which diseases were classified as *heredodegenerative*. Pathology was traced to constitutional elements and constitutional weakness. Structural changes in the brain accounted for symptomatology in individuals. Later on, the great psychiatric classifier, Kraepelin, began gathering symptoms together under specific nosologies. The presence of various symptoms indicated a particular disease or syndrome. This approach is still used today in many mental hospitals.

Although many patients can be classified in Kraepelinian fashion, the difficulty with this descriptive approach is knowing where to draw the line. There are some patients who are overtly ill and whose symptoms fit a particular syndrome; yet many of these same symptoms appear in individuals who are not judged to be overtly ill.

As will be pointed out in detail in Chapter VIII, there are two evaluations by which persons are labeled "mentally ill." The first is a *societal evaluation*: behavior is adjudged deviant or pathological by the family or some other agency. Second comes a *psychiatric evaluation* when the individual is seen by a psychiatrist. Of course, the societal evaluation is bypassed when the individual himself seeks psychiatric help. The psychiatrist may or may not make a diagnosis of mental illness, depending on his own clinical findings. Deviant behavior does not necessarily imply mental illness, and therefore preliminary social screening is necessary. In our time, confusion over what kinds of behavior signify mental illness reached its zenith in the Midtown Study done in New York (Srole, *et al.*, 1962). In this investigation, it was found that 84 per cent of the people studied had symptoms which could be classified as pathological using the Kraepelinian scheme. However, despite these symptoms, they functioned adequately in day-to-day living at home and at work. How can one explain these startling statistics? In the Midtown Study there was only psychiatric screening, without benefit of prior societal evaluation; therefore the startling finding of 84 per cent morbidity.

Sigmund Freud was the first to bring the subjective frame of reference to classification of psychopathology in a systematic manner. He derived his data from listening to the patient's own recounting of what he experienced and felt. Freud made certain theoretical inferences from these data, and his monumental work on the psychopathology of everyday life, interpretation of dreams, principles of free association, and infantile sexuality will forever stand as a tribute to his genius. Most of his clinical observations remain as fresh and incisive today as when they were first written. It is with regard to Freud's later metapsychological speculations, e.g. libido theory, that reevaluations are taking place. Freud postulated that arrest of the libido at the oral, the anal, or the phallic level interferes with the flow of libido and leads to neurotic fixation at a particular level of psychosexual development. But this same phenomenon—blockage in the flow of libido—is discernible in both neurotic and healthy individuals. The same is true for the defense mechanisms described by Freud. They can be seen in healthy as well as disordered behavior.

Freud's data were derived mainly from adult patients, yet his theories were conceptualized almost entirely in terms of the developing child. According to the libido theory, very little personality development takes place beyond adolescence. However, from current studies in ego psychology and family life, it is clear that there can be changes in the personality throughout adulthood. Otto Fenichel emphasized the capacity to achieve complete genital sexuality (orgasm) as a criterion of health in an individual. This definition of health led to great preoccupation about sexual functioning. But many individuals who experience orgasm still have their hang-ups in other areas of life.

Recent years have been marked by advances in the sciences of biochemistry and molecular genetics. Heath (1963) believes that a psychotoxic factor (taraxein), extracted from the blood of schizophrenics, will produce "psychotic" symptoms in normals. Kallmann (1946) and Heston (1970) have detailed the genetic hypothesis about etiology of mental illness. Impetus for study in these areas also come from the advent of effective drug therapy for psychiatric illness. Also, it is apparent that many organic conditions, particularly cancers of the pancreas and parathyroid glands, can first be manifested by anxiety and depression.

ENVIRONMENTAL FACTORS

In the day of the asylum, there was little necessity for studying mental illness. The definition was made by observing the behavior of an individual, and if the proper authority deemed the behavior aberrant, the person was locked away. No specific diagnosis was required. However, investigations such as the Midtown Study demonstrated that many persons outside the hospital have the same symptoms as persons inside a mental hospital. It became necessary, therefore, to investigate other factors before labeling people "mentally ill."

Over the past three decades, sociology and social psychiatry have had great impact on the study of psychopathology. In the 1930's Karen Horney (1937) wrote about the "neurotic personality," stating, in essence, that a person is neurotic if his behavior is significantly different from the behavior of others in the community. In other words, "conformity is health and nonconformity is neurosis." Neurosis, then, would be totally different from culture to culture; what is labeled sickness in one culture might be considered healthy behavior in another culture. The problem is that Horney's definition of sickness does not take into account the subjective perceptions of individuals; rather, emphasis is on the study of behavior as viewed from the outside environment. Further, as will be stressed later in this chapter, conformity itself may represent an impairment in functioning.

Too often, the spectre of mental illness is raised as a means of penalizing nonconformity. How many adolescents are sent to the mental health counselor because they do not conform in the classroom? It is easy to call the individual who is different "sick," and this then becomes a club in the hands of the wielder. (In many ways, psychiatry itself is to blame for this situation. In the classical psychoanalytic explanation of creativity, the suggestion is made that a creative genius is one who uses creativity as an alternative outlet for sublimated libido.) Nonconformity may indeed represent mental illness when it stems from an impairment of functioning, but nonconformity may also represent selective behavior on the part of a healthy, independent individual. In our time, nonconformity often becomes an escape or a rationalization for those who seek to avoid certain realistic challenges in life. In this instance, nonconformity does represent an impairment of functioning or of flexibility. In order to get a realistic appraisal of the individual's behavior, one must resort to the psychiatrist's tool of listening to the individual describe his subjective (inner) perceptions. Is the nonconformity an avoidance or an escape, or does it spring from a feeling of strength and conviction? How much internal stress and anxiety result from the nonconforming behavior?

Ever since the discovery of bacteria, the physician has been directly concerned with his patient's environment. How are infectious diseases transmitted, what factors in the environment favor this transmission, and what factors deter it? In our time, the psychiatric physician is similarly concerned with the social environment. What are the pathogenic factors in an individual's surroundings that may destine him to become mentally ill? It is worth recounting the difference here in the approach to this problem by the psychiatrist and by the sociologist. The psychiatrist, in harmony with his training, is interested in such matters as who is sick, who is not sick, how widespread the illness is, and how contagious it is. (In a sense, mental illness is "contagious" in that one person's fear or anxiety is readily communicated to another person. A very tense mother "infects" her children with tension; a schoolteacher who feels upset on a particular day will find that her class is unruly that day.)

Psychiatry has always focused on the study of pathology in an individual. Why? Because it is the pathology that limits the responses to stimuli; the greater the pathology, the more inflexible the individual. A person with minimal anxiety can go about his daily life with minimal, occasionally moderate, discomfort. A person with severe street phobia cannot venture out of his dwelling; thus, his entire life is changed by this severe symptom.

This situation is analogous to the patient with heart disease. The heart disease may be minor and interfere with the patient's activity only when he attempts strenuous exercise; or, on the other hand, the heart disease may be so severe that the patient's whole life centers around the need to take preventive measures to stay alive.

In the days when psychiatry was centered mainly in the state hospital, most patients admitted showed a rather stereotyped picture of schizophrenia, mania, or organic brain disease. As more and more patients become outpatients and are seen earlier or with their families, it will not be as easy to predict the course of their illness or to quantify their disabilities.

One of the difficulties encountered in assessing personality (or pathology) only on the basis of behavior is the fact that the *cause* of behavior is not investigated. An individual may behave in a certain way because he attempts to fill a social role; or, he may behave in a different way in order to conform or to ingratiate himself. Thus, an understanding of the motivation for behavior is crucial.

The sociologist looks at illness differently. What factors make it possible for some people to become mentally ill and what factors make it possible for them to go on to become patients? What criteria does society use to define "sickness" and "patienthood"? (The concepts of *sick role* and *patient role* are discussed at length in Chapter V.) In one respect, the psychiatrist views symptoms in an individual, and the sociologist views deviance in society, in a similar banner. By recognizing that certain symptoms (behavior) constitute illness, society vests the physician with the task of establishing criteria for defining health. Similarly, by recognizing certain behavior as deviant, society (through its agents, such as sociologists) defines what constitutes "normal" (nondeviant) behavior.

In our society, there are specialized agencies to screen and label deviant behavior. The legal and medical professions are in the forefront. In our legal system, a person is judged innocent or guilty by a jury of peers—a group of average citizens who presumably represent a consensus of what society feels at any given point in time. The accused is considered innocent until proven guilty. Many sociologists feel that this does not work in the same way with regard to psychiatry: psychiatrists see mainly those who have already been labeled deviants by themselves or by the social process, and it is the job of the psychiatrist to "second the nomination" of illness. This focuses one's attention on the study of society and social process as being important in understanding both deviance and mental illness.

The fact that societal reactions change over time is aptly illustrated in the reaction of citizens in Frankfurt to Ehrlich's discovery of Salvarsan[x] as a cure for syphilis. There was great resistance to accepting the drug because many people felt that those with syphilis had been cursed for their sexual promiscuity. (Perhaps, also, this resistance was a product of inordinate rigidity and inflexibility in a group of people at a given time in history.) Once the capacity to cure syphilis was recognized and the benefit to society at large understood, Salvarsan became acceptable.

Sociologic study of mental illness received great impetus during World War II. Some eleven million men and women were screened by the psychiatric standards then in existence. Using these standards, half of this population was found to be unacceptable for military service. This state of affairs necessitated a drastic revision of screening standards. This change was also precipitated by the fact that many individuals whom psychiatrists had classified as mentally ill functioned adequately in civilian life. No one had ever "nominated" them to the status of "sickness" or "patienthood" prior to military service. How can one explain this dilemma?

All of these questions come sharply into focus in the school classroom, in the community mental health center, in the child guidance clinic, in work with juvenile delinquents, and in counseling at social agencies. The problem is immediate and ever present—What is sickness and what is health, and how can one measure the degree of each? (In a state hospital, the diagnosis of mental illness has already been made prior to admission. Hence the concern shifts to treatment of the illness, how long the patient will need to be hospitalized, and so forth.)

THE ADAPTATIONAL FRAME OF REFERENCE

Although the adaptational frame of reference does not provide answers to all the questions raised about health and illness, it does provide a nondogmatic method of investigation. The origin of the adaptational approach used here is rooted in natural science, as will be detailed in the next chapter. Adaptation is a biological concept referring to alterations in the organism's pattern of interaction (behavior) with the environment. These altera-

tions favor survival of the organism and the species and can be
effected either within the organism (autoplastic adaptation) or
within the environment (alloplastic adaptation). The adaptational frame of reference views behavior in broader scope than
simply cause and effect, or as a means to an end. The adaptational
view considers the adaptive value of the behavior, i.e. what does it
contribute to the utility and pleasure of the organism?

In a general way, the adaptational approach is in harmony with
Freud's first theory of instincts in which he postulated that self-
preservation is the primary motivating force governing behavior.
In 1915, in an essay, "Thoughts For the Times on War and
Death," Freud wrote "To endure life remains, when all is said,
the first duty of all living beings (*Collected Papers,* 1953). It is
also in harmony with many of his ideas about the ego, the executive and integrative part of the personality. Later, in the
1920's Freud wrote *The Ego and the Id* and *The Problem of
Anxiety,* both of which focus on the organism's interaction with
the environment.

Psychiatric study of adaptation received new emphasis by Hartmann's extension of Freud's structural theory of id-ego-superego.
Hartmann (1951) emphasized the developmental aspects and
functioning of the ego independent of the id. (In Freud's structural scheme, the psychic apparatus at birth consists only of the id
—uncultured, primitive drives and impulses; the ego and superego develop over time as the child is subjected to environmental
influences.) Hartmann and others (1946) suggested that the infant has, in addition to the id, a whole range of bodily structures
and functions, which include "ego apparatuses." These ego apparatuses have a primary autonomy: they function independently in
their own right. They have evolved during the process of evolution and help the individual adapt to "the average expectable enviroment." Thus, the functioning of the ego apparatuses in such
areas as motility, attention, memory, and imagination are free of
libidinal investment, i.e. these areas are the "conflict-free sphere
of the ego."†

---

†We know now that these functions are greatly influenced by emotional mechanisms. A child's learning disability or shortened attention span may be a reflection
of emotional conflict.

Ego study was further advanced by Anna Freud (1946) in her work, *The Ego and Mechanisms of Defense* and Erik Erikson (1950) in *Childhood and Society*. Anna Freud wrote that psychic defenses in children are not limited to "the warding off of internal instinctual stimuli" but might also be concerned with dangers which have their source in the outside world. Erikson similarly broadened the original Freudian scheme to account for the development of a psychosocial identity.

As will be discussed in the next chapter, adaptation itself is limited by the range of the adaptive mechanisms present. These mechanisms extend from the most primitive reflex mechanisms (e.g. hunger) to highly complex, long-range intellectual mechanisms. In the adaptational scheme, the functioning of the mental apparatus is one aspect of adaptation to life, and thus pathology is viewed as impairment of adaptive capacity; in other words, there is significant pathology when an individual cannot do something which he ordinarily expects himself to do or which society expects him to be able to do. Pathology can stem from limitation of function in any area of life. It need not be confined to the area of sexual functioning alone.

In measuring any degree of impairment, the demands of the environment must be taken into account. A farmer can be an isolate, but a courtroom lawyer cannot. This is the essence of the adaptational approach: one takes into account the demands of the environment and the person's subjective perceptions or attitudes toward these demands. During individual psychotherapy or psychoanalysis, impairments can usually be traced back to early key relationships.

In the usual course of life, it is rare that we are tested to the outer limits of our adaptive capacity. Generally, we use only specialized aspects of our resources. People who have impairments of mental functioning tend to seek out environments which protect them from stresses that will highlight their impairments. The overly-dependent person finds a job where he can rely on others. A paranoid person who is an "injustice collector" may seek out situations which confirm or justify his paranoid feelings: in this way, he does not feel so out of place. Therefore, the question of an individual's "sickness" in a particular situation is often difficult to answer. One must examine the alternatives available to the individual. What would happen if he were placed in a different type of situation? Rarely are situations so circumspect that the individual cannot escape from them. One situation where alternatives are limited is in war; hence, traumatic neuroses during wartime are common. (Perhaps the only escape from the stresses of war is "battle fatigue." These same individuals, now patients, may have functioned well away from war, in environments of their own choosing.)

Symptoms in children are often a reflection of their parents' difficulties. Scapegoating allows one to block out problem areas by focusing attention on another individual whose behavior has been designated as sick or deviant. In the family completely dominated by a stern mother, the other members of the family may behave in such a way so as not to "upset" her.

The *cause* of the limitation of function is another matter. The adaptational frame of reference defines pathology as a limitation of function, but the etiology of this limitation of function can stem from a variety of causes. These include genetic defects, anything from Huntington's chorea to diabetes; chemical defects stemming from metabolic disease or poisons; organic disease of the brain; and neurosis or psychosis.

Another example of limitation of function is the behavior of the sociopath (psychopath). This limitation is reflected by his inability to tolerate frustration or to maintain a sustained adaptive effort. He is only minimally responsive to the emotional needs of others with whom he comes into contact and is more preoccupied with his own whims. In many ways he is similar to a child who craves relief from frustration: he needs immediate gratification and cannot think in terms of future pleasure. There is faulty development of the conscience (restraining) mechanism. Psychiatrists usually see sociopaths when they are compensated and ingratiating. Only their families, or the police, see them when they are explosive.

As children, these individuals have either been severely deprived or completely overindulged. Thus they lack a built-in set of emotional rewards which aid in stabilizing their conduct. Constant adulation or success may be necessary, and fulfillment of these cravings may be sought by any means available.

In Shakespeare's *Merchant of Venice,* Nerissa observes, "They are as sick that surfeit with too much as they that starve with nothing." So it is with the sociopath.

It should be remembered that in many circumstances the sociopath can adjust within his own limited range. For example, in veterans' hospitals there are innumerable sociopaths (and "burned-out psychopaths") who spent many a year in the Army. They did their soldiering, were looked after, and had relatively little frustration. In contrast to the soiciopath's limited range of behavior, an individual whose emotional mechanisms of adaptation are intact has a number of ways of dealing with frustrations.

As noted previously, Karen Horney (1937) felt that nonconformity signified neurotic behavior. A further clinical note on conformity needs to be added. Conformity itself often can indicate a significant impairment stemming from timidity and fear. In the adaptational approach, conformity is studied by focusing on the individual's inability to be flexible. The conformist necessarily chooses that which others choose. Thus conformity, as well as nonconformity, may denote impairment of healthy functioning in an individual. Both types of impairment are studied by noting the environment and by listening to the subjective perceptions of the individual.

In order to label a person "sick," there must be evidence that he has had the capacity to function in a more effective way but that this capacity has somehow been impaired. It is true that we all go through countless impairments of function which are a response to difficult situations, but generally these impairments are temporary.

When we attempt to talk about the *sickest* person, it is difficult to be precise. For instance, a married couple who have achieved an equilibrium may both have severe personality conflicts, but they compensate for each other's problems by inhibiting behavior which would upset the equilibrium. In Ibsen's play, *A Doll's House,* Nora appears emotionally immature and mentally retarded. She uses her irresponsibility to cover over her capacity for independence in order to protect her husband, Torvald, from having to deal with a self-respecting and assertive female. He can get along with "a little squirrel" living in a doll's house but not with an emancipated woman (cf. "protector role," p. 117).

A good illustration of equilibration in a family is found in the study on wife-beater's wives by Snell *et al.* (1964). They discovered that in many of these situations there was a pathological interaction from the outset; the husband and wife found a role relationship that, however pathological, fitted their needs. Why then did the woman decide to prefer criminal charges against her husband when the wife-beating had gone on for many years? Generally, this happened when a son in the family reached adolescence and began to protest. He would no longer stand idly by and watch the father beat up the mother.

The sickest person might be the one who has the most permanent kind of impairment, i.e. when the environment changes, the one who has the most difficulty adjusting to the new environment. Adaptive functioning is never adequately tested by any one situation.

It is apparent that an individual's distorted perceptions are in themselves a reflection of adaptive impairment, since the mind itself can be considered an adaptive instrument. Before determining the extent of impairment of functioning, one needs to know the quality of these perceptions. A Big League baseball pitcher may be knocked out of the box on a particular day. If asked about it, he might philosophically say, "It happens to everybody; it's only temporary." If his trouble continues over a period of days, his perceptions may become more imprecise, and he may begin rationalizing the situation—blaming the weather, his diet, or other things. But if he stoutly maintains that someone has put a hex on him, or is out to get him, he needs psychiatric evaluation.‡

---

‡In making a diagnosis, the psychiatrist relies more and more on knowledge of the patient's cultural background. Some psychiatrists who practice in the Appalachian Mountain region suggest that hysteria, which is common, is the "language" of that social community. When provoked or conflicted, an individual uses repression as the primary means for handling conflicts. Paranoid reactions are rare in this group; they are more the "language" of the bubbling metropolis, with projection being the main defense mechanism. This topic will be covered in Chapter VIII.

Chapter II

Adaptation in the Individual
How the Individual Copes With Stress

All creatures, to survive,
Adapt themselves to the changing conditions under which they live;
If they can grow new faculties to meet the new necessity, they thrive;
Otherwise not; the inflexible organism, however much alive
Today, is tomorrow extinct.

Edna St. Vincent Millay
Conversations at Midnight

The organism has a number of adaptive mechanisms which are necessary for its survival in an environment which is sometimes hostile, sometimes cooperative. By definition, adaptation refers to alterations that the organism makes in its patterns of interaction with the environment. Alterations may be made within the organism itself or in the environment. These alterations perpetuate survival of the organism and its species and also increase the organism's utility, performance, and pleasure. This is the keystone of the adaptational scheme.

HOMEOSTASIS

The model used for the study of adaptation in these chapters is that of the early physiologists. No one typifies this approach better than Claude Bernard, the French physiologist who lived from 1813 to 1876. Bernard started out as a vaudeville comedy writer. Later, he wrote a five act play, which was produced in Paris. A drama critic urged him to go into medicine. (One can speculate about the reason for this advice.) In any case, it was fortunate for science that he shifted to medicine. As an intern he came under the influence of the great physiologist, Magendie, and later succeeded to Magendie's professorship of physiology at the College de France. Bernard was intrigued by the natural science approach to the study of behavior. He made his greatest contribution in describing the constancy of the internal environment. This constancy, or "steady state," was labeled *homeostasis* by Bernard. He borrowed the term from chemistry. According to Bernard (1927):

> There is an arrangement in the living being, a kind of regulated activity, which must never be neglected because it is in truth the most striking characteristic of living beings. Vital phenomena possess indeed a rigorously determined physical-chemical condition, but, at the same time, they subordinate themselves and succeed one another in a pattern and according to a role which pre-exists: They repeat themselves with order, regularity, constancy, and they harmonize in such a manner as to bring about the organization and growth of the individual animal or plant.

After a distinguished career in research and after being honored academically and politically by election to the French Academy and the Senate, Bernard found himself disabled by a serious illness. He was forced into temporary retirement for several years. Out of this meditative period came the brilliant essay in 1865 entitled, *"Introduction à l'étude de la médecine experimentale."* In this work Bernard elucidated his approach to scientific experimentation: one begins with a hypothesis, then makes observations, and finally reaches conclusions. For example, an animal (or man) feels thirsty and drinks. It is hypothesized, then, that water is necessary to maintain life. What is the purpose of this response, both in the immediate situation and in terms of the long-range past of the organism? This question leads to a study of the importance of ordered responses in the organism and their regulation. In a laboratory one can observe the results of water deprivation in an animal by starving it. In the absence of water, what alternatives exist? Can one define centers in the nervous system that regulate water metabolism? From his observations, Bernard concluded first, that water was the first necessary ingredient for life; second, that temperature had to be regulated; third, that air was necessary, and so on. The same approach used to study the necessity for water can be applied to the study of any other area as well.

Bernard also anticipated studies which were to show that the boundaries between the organism and the environment were often artificially drawn. In Bernard's words:

> Life is made manifest by the action of outer stimuli on irritable living tissues which react by manifesting their special properties. The physiological conditions of life are therefore nothing but the special physico-chemical stimuli which set in action the tissues of the organism. These stimuli are found in the atmosphere or environment which the animal inhabits; but we know that the properties of the general outer atmosphere pass into the organic atmosphere in which all the physiological conditions of the outer atmosphere are found, plus a certain number of others peculiar to the inner environment.

It is apparent, then, that the distinction between "inner" and "outer" becomes artificial, and this emphasizes the need to study the organism and the environment simultaneously. Is the air in the lungs part of the organism or part of the environment? Does the term "intrapsychic" not imply that the influence of the environment has been incorporated into the subjective perceptions of an individual? (To anticipate a later chapter, the family therapist is struck by how frequently thoughts or phantasies occurring in the mind of one member of a family, occur to all the members of a family.)

One other name deserves mention here: Walter B. Cannon. Starting in 1880 and continuing throughout a long and full life, Cannon (1929; 1932) described in a number of classical works the physiological changes, or adaptations, that take place when the organism is beset with an emergency. These changes include deepening of respiration; increased heart rate; rise in arterial blood pressure; spilling of sugar into the bloodstream from the liver storehouse; shifting of blood away from the intestinal system to the heart, central nervous system, and muscles; and the secretion of adrenalin. These responses are a natural sequence to "fight or flight" phenomena: running away when the danger is overwhelming, or fighting and attacking in order to be dominant—"whichever the situation, a life or death struggle may ensue." Cannon pointed out that these responses prepare the organism for a struggle—a struggle which Cannon called a "nerve and muscle struggle." He viewed these phenomena in the light of the evolutionary history of the organism: the physiological apparatus was a recapitulation of many millenia of struggle by the organism in a hostile environment. By means of natural selection, those organisms that evolved the most effective means of facing emergencies in life survived the longest. (Of course, the evolutionary approach calls attention to differences in species, and the physiologist can observe these in the laboratory. The psychiatrist studying humans must add the data of introspection—the thoughts and phantasies communicated by a patient's free associations, for example.)

THE PSYCHODYNAMIC SYSTEM

Could the same methods of natural science used to study physiology be applied to studying the psychological aspects of behavior? (The distinction here between "psychological" and "physiological" is artificial. One could presumably explain all pyschological behavior on a neurophysiological basis. In effect, the distinction boils down to separate sets of data gathered by investigators with different training using different tools and methods.)

Three psychiatrists were preeminent in extending these natural science concepts to mental activity. They are Sandor Rado, Abram Kardiner, and David Levy. In essence, they stated that just as physiologists look into the developmental ancestral history of the organism to study the physiological apparatus and its emergency operations, so can one do the same in studying mental operations. From this theory evolved a psychodynamic system similar in many ways to the physiologic system. We look for responses of the organism to emergencies and then evolve a system for explaining the psychodynamic activities; the postulate is that behavior has a purpose in the immediate present and may have a direct relationship to an evolutionary past. For example, a fit of anger might be provoked by a noxious stimulus in the immediate environment. The organism may overreact to this stimulus even though it is not life-threatening. In its evolutionary history, the anger may have represented a response to a threatening situation, e.g. attack by an animal, and the response could have been lifesaving.

Study of the psychodynamic system is intimately connected with study of the neurological apparatus. Rado (1956) has correlated certain levels of adaptation with the hierarchical organization of the nervous system. He distinguishes (1) the hedonic, (2) the emotional, and (3) the intellectual levels of adaptation. Responses on a hedonic level, or the pain and pleasure level, may be detected in some of the lowest organisms, perhaps even in protozoa. They are the most primitive. The neurological centers for these responses are in the spinal cord, brain stem, hypothalamus, and thalamus. The organism avoids pain and tries to rid itself of it when it supervenes. At the next level of adaptation, the emotional level, responses related to fear, rage, and pleasure are primary. Distance receptors have evolved with their central connections to the limbic system. As will be recounted in detail later, the emotional level alerts the organism for action in anticipation of future events. With the development of the cerebral cortex, the organism became capable of using the intellect to govern its behavior, in addition to the pain and pleasure test, or the emotional mechanisms of anticipation.

For the sake of completeness, we may include here the reflex level: that level of adaptation which is automatic and which maintains a constant internal environment. Thus, the reflex level is concerned with automatic adjustment of the organism's internal environment (homeostasis); the hedonic level involves constant and automatic adaptational changes to alterations in the immediate external environment; the emotional level is concerned with anticipating short-range future events; the intellectual level is concerned with long-range future activity. The organism exercises voluntary control over its behavior at this level. Responses at higher levels can modify responses at lower levels.

The terms "homeostasis" and "adaptation" have been carried over into other areas. "Social homeostasis" (Chapter VIII) is an example. Homeostasis implies that there is not a fixed state, but rather a *range* of reaction within which the organism can function. When this range is exceeded, the organism must change itself or change the environment in order to return to the range of homeostatic equilibrium. In cold weather, the organism can regulate its body temperature; if the temperature gets too far out of range, however, clothes or heat are necessary to bring the temperature back to where the homeostatic mechanisms can take over and ensure the person's survival. At each level of functioning, there are specialized mechanisms of adaptation, beginning with the cellular level (see Holland and Ward, 1966). At the upper end of the spectrum, the brain may be considered a specialized organ of adaptation on the neurological level. This concept seems more satisfactory than the early psychoanalytic theory that the brain's function was mainly to minimize stimuli and quiet the organism.

Using the adaptational scheme outlined, one's attention is inevitably drawn to the interaction of the organism and its environment. Therefore, in the study of behavior, it is important to note what is *absent* as well as what is *present*. Here is where learning theory is incorporated into the understanding of the organism's responses. Faulty integration of behavior may be due to a failure to learn appropriate responses to particular stimuli. Traditionally, psychiatrists have been taught to look primarily for pathological mechanisms present in their patients. Why this focus on what is "present" rather than what is "absent"? Perhaps this is due to Freud's medical orientation and that of psychiatry in general. In his *Introductory Lectures* in 1916, Freud (1943) likens psychoanalysis to a surgical operation. Later on in these same lectures, he refers to treatment as being similar to the extirpation of a tumor. (Also, as noted in Chapter I, pathology limits the range of behavior in an individual. Just as severe emphysema limits a person's physical activity, so does severe paranoia limit psychological reactions. In both examples, limitation of adaptation stems from pathology. It is easier, and more exact, to describe pathology than it is to describe health.)

ADAPTIVE MECHANISMS

When speaking of adaptation, one automatically speaks of adaptive mechanisms; to separate the process from the mechanisms which subserve it seems artificial. Adaptation is always limited by the range and flexibility of these mechanisms. It is necessary to understand these mechanisms when they function in healthy fashion, when they malfunction, or when they are absent. A clinical description of adaptive and maladaptive functioning of the mechanisms will be given in Chapter III.

One way of viewing a society or even a culture is to hypothesize that these groups in themselves represent organized adaptation to an environment, the purpose being to promote the survival of the group. Kardiner (1939) postulated that cultures develop institutions and traditions as part of the adaptive process for survival in certain kinds of environments, as will be detailed later. In the Marquesas, there is a limited food supply; therefore, female infanticide is practiced in order to control the population and to allow the society to survive. One out of every three newborn females is destroyed.

The most obvious aspect of evolutionary adaptation is that the adaptive mechanisms ensure survival. The organism born without a desire for food or water would not exist very long. Similarly, those organisms that overate or overdrank did not survive, nor did the species that failed to reproduce. Such primitive mechanisms as hunger, satiety, and sexual drive are fairly fixed and rigid parts of the nervous system; they guarantee the organism's survival. Adaptive mechanisms have evolved through the process of natural selection, with improvements through the ages.

One cannot talk about adaptation without considering integration of behavior: each experience influences future responses (Hebb, 1959). The most crucial years for integration of behavior are the early ones. From the standpoint of social order, emotional experiences are the most crucial. The child who has experienced a cold, unloving relationship early in life anticipates repetition of this type of relationship as he grows up. Rather than expecting acceptance from his environment, he foresees frustration and rejection.

The levels of adaptation—hedonic, emotional, and intellectual —can be analogized to computer technology. The simplest model is the thermostat in the house. It is hooked to a heater and when the temperature falls below a desired level, the heater is automatically turned on. This automatic adjustment to change in the immediate environment is equivalent to the "hedonic" level.

An example of the second order of mechanism is the computer used by many manufacturing companies. An order comes in for a particular item, which the computer registers. Then, from a feedback system, it determines where this item is stored, selects the factory closest to the buyer, and then feeds these data to a mailer (or mailing machine). This is roughly analogous to the "emotional" level.

The third order of mechanism can similarly be demonstrated by this manufacturing example. Here the feedback into the system tells the computer, in addition to the above, the exact quantity of materials ordered in any given time, what the influence of weather on purchases might be, the expected quantity that will be needed for any given length of time, and so on. All of the interdependent facts are taken into account before a particular manufacturing plan is programmed. This process is equivalent to operations on the intellectual level.

With each step toward complexity, the greater the chance for malfunction. In the human, most hedonic behavior is involuntary; most behavior on the intellectual level is voluntary. The middle range, or emotional level, is semivoluntary. Before considering these three important levels of adaptation, it is necessary to discuss the most basic level of adaptation, the reflex level.

The Reflex Level

There are many built-in physiological regulatory mechanisms which have limited flexibility and which are basic to life. These include body temperature control, water and electrolyte balance, and control of blood pressure. In addition to this "sensing of the internal environment," one might also include here the cutaneous senses (pressure, pain, cold, warmth); the kinesthetic senses (body movements); and the labyrinthine senses (body position). The neurological centers for these mechanisms are mainly in the peripheral nervous system and are concerned with the automatic regulation of the organism's own internal environment. Their effects are immediate, and there is little conscious control over their operation. Often, they are felt as "biological drives."

This automatic regulation is crucial since these basic functions could not be left to the whims of the individual.*

The reflex level of adaptation is the one usually referred to when using the term "homeostasis." Breakdown of the mechanisms at this level can lead to water intoxication, anoxia, polycythemia, etc., and treatment would be medically—or physiologically—oriented.

The Hedonic Level

At the hedonic level the environment comes into play. This factor distinguishes the reflex level from the hedonic level. At this level behavior is integrated primarily on the basis of avoidance of pain and movement toward pleasure. Pain organizes behavior which attempts to rid the organism of the pain. The riddance mechanism is discussed below. Pleasure organizes behavior which attempts to incorporate the source of pleasure. Loss of pleasure leads to behavior which seeks to regain the pleasure.

At the hedonic level, there is immediate and constant response to the external environment. There may be little actual awareness of pain and pleasure sensations because they are forms of ongoing behavior; we become aware of these automatic or semi-automatic responses only when there is interference with them. The individual sitting in a chair shifts continuously and is generally unaware of crossing or uncrossing his legs unless there is interference with this activity.

The inability to experience pain can threaten the organism's survival. The writer once witnessed an episode involving a woman who had a severed nerve in her arm; she had no sensation in the limb. She delighted in reaching into a pot full of boiling water and bringing out the sweet corn, much to the amazement

---

*It should be pointed out, however, that there is some conscious control possible over basic physiological mechanisms. By controlling the rate of breathing, the heart rate can also be controlled. Many practitioners of Yoga use this knowledge to develop extensive control over their autonomic nervous system. Some are reported able to "drink" through the anal orifice by inducing reverse peristalsis. Similarly, Miller (1969) has reported that subjects could learn to control visceral and glandular responses by conditioning techniques; exactly where in the nervous system this control stems from is very much an open question.

and curiosity of her neighbors, but with severe damage to her flesh.

The awareness of pleasure may not be as necessary for survival of the organism as is the awareness of pain, but experience of pleasure enhances the organism's performance and functioning. It is the glue that binds. In everyday life, those activities which seem to be beneficial for the organism are usually accompanied by pleasurable sensation. Eating or sexual activity are examples. There is no emergency with pleasurable learning, as there may be with learning associated with avoiding pain.

The neurological center for pleasure is the septal area of the brain. Pleasure may be divided into (1) the immediate experiencing of pleasure, which tends to be on the hedonic level and, more important, (2) the memory and anticipation of pleasure, which operates more on the emotional level. The *threat* of deprivation of pleasure is often a more potent experience than is the actual experience of deprivation. A person who lived through the great economic depression of the 1930's may have experienced profound deprivation of the basic necessities of life, particularly food. Decades later, when this individual is very affluent indeed, he may still harbor the dread that someday he will lose his business and want for food. The memory of the earlier trauma is more powerful to him than is his perception of the here-and-now situation. Likewise, the anticipation of pleasure often outweighs the pleasurable experience itself.

Insofar as the riddance mechanism is concerned, there are numerous direct observations from physiology which illustrate how the organism removes noxious stimuli. When a foreign body is present in the mucous membrane of the nose, it is expelled by sneezing. Elsewhere in the body, foreign substances are encapsulated and isolated in a sheath of fibrous tissue.

Another example of the riddance mechanism at a higher level of integration was described by Air Force surgeons in Europe during World War II. Some English-based airmen who made bomb runs over Germany were subjected repeatedly to fighter plane attacks, anti-aircraft fire, and loss of buddies. On the way *back* to England, even though out of range of enemy fighters, some would end it all by diving their bombers into the Channel. The dread of repeating this experience was more than they could tolerate.

Learning on the hedonic level can be viewed in the traditional Pavlovian sense. For example, although eating is a necessary activity, the organism can condition itself not to recognize the signals for hunger. One cannot, however, get rid of the biological need for food. Proof that hedonic regulation is an important part of life in lower forms is illustrated by the fact that birds can be taught to screen targets or to pick out defective electrical parts by using a reward system—food and water. During World War II, pigeons were put into the nose cone of missiles; by pecking at an image of a target, they could accurately steer the missile to the target. This technique was perfected but never actually used in warfare. Similarly, birds have been used to spot defective drug capsules in pharmaceutical factories.

Rado (1954), who has studied the pleasure mechanisms extensively, states that pleasure is as necessary for healthy psychological functioning as are vitamins for healthy physiological functioning. It should be noted that the relief of pain is not the same as pleasure, nor is the absence of pain the equivalent of pleasure. Relief of pain leads to more comfort and freedom from anxiety, of course, and sometimes people who have had severe pain may misinterpret the relief as pleasure. In many of the television commercials, for example, the relief of the pounding pain of a headache is followed by a scene in which the individual appears ecstatically happy.

The nervous system center for the hedonic level includes parts of the spinal cord, medulla, and midbrain. An interesting speculation can be made in the light of what Freud said in a moment of jest in the 1920's. Freud stated to his colleagues, "Gentlemen, we must hurry up because a man with a hypodermic syringe is right behind us."† In other words, Freud foresaw the significance of the enormous developments that were taking place in the fields of neurochemistry and physiology, and sensed that these new discoveries would modify many of the theories concerning psycho-

---

†Rado, Personal communication.

logical illness. Today we can speculate that it is the man with the oscilloscope who is "right behind." Each month brings new discoveries in terms of understanding electrical activity of various parts of the brain, and this coupled with the knowledge of the metabolism of some of the nucleic acids, may change our physiological understanding of the nervous system.‡

The necessity for pleasurable activity is most graphically demonstrated by the soldier in combat. He must be given periodic relief from the painful stress to which he is constantly exposed in order to prevent "battle fatigue." In the submarine service, men who have been on a prolonged cruise are relieved completely of sea duty by putting a new crew aboard. The anticipation of this change is an important morale factor.

Tolerance for pain is limited. This fact is used in brainwashing. The captive is kept in a situation of unrelieved painful tension until the higher intellectual and emotional mechanisms of adaptation are exhausted. Then the individual operates primarily on a hedonic level, with very little capacity for discrimination. At this point, he can easily be taught any doctrine by Pavlovian-type conditioning. As a general rule, pleasure is the antidote to prolonged pain. The soldier with battle fatigue needs plenty of sleep, a chance to "ventilate," and the support and encouragement of those around him. Recovery is faster when the soldier is kept near his unit so that his buddies can reassure him. Eventually, his complete ensemble of adaptive mechanisms begins to work again.

What sense organs are involved at the hedonic level of integration? Hedonic mechanisms are concerned with the immediate present, with immediate pleasure, and with immediate riddance of pain. As Sherrington (1933), the neurophysiologist, has pointed out, before emotional mechanisms come into play, the

---

‡A movie made in England in 1965, *The Ipcress File,* dramatizes this theory. Men were effectively conditioned to block out certain parts of their lives by being subjected to a variety of stimuli having to do with vision, sound, and body motion. Signals to forget were introduced to the subject at a frequency matching that of periodic electrical discharges of the brain. Who knows what this might lead to in terms of therapy for nervous disorders? There is some evidence (Hare, 1968) suggesting the sociopath has aberrant electrical discharges in the cerebral cortex.

organism's "shell of its immediate future surrounds its head." Therefore, senses involved are primarily touch, perhaps taste and, to some degree, smell and hearing.

There is a tendency to minimize the importance of these short-range senses in humans, particularly taste and touch. Witness how indiscriminately food is prepared in most homes and restaurants. It is "impolite" to touch someone, even though the infant starts out in life responding primarily to touch. Although Latin American men greet each other with an *abrazo* (embrace), this is frowned upon in most Western societies. As a matter of fact, past the age of eight a male can seldom find any socially acceptable way for satisfying a need to touch or be touched until courtship or marriage. Who knows whether this custom is of significance in the wide increase in homosexuality in Western society?

What clinical disorders (cf. Maladaptive Behavior, Chapter III) are recognizable at the hedonic level of integration? When discussing psychopathology (or psychotherapy) , it is obviously impossible to distinguish maladaptive behavior only at one level of integration—reflex, hedonic, emotional, and intellectual—for each syndrome. However, in depressive reactions, in schizophrenia, and in sociopathic (psychopathic) disorders, there is marked disarray of the hedonic mechanisms. Brainwashing has already been mentioned. Drug addiction, alcoholism, and obesity are other examples. In harmony with the knowledge that hedonic mechanisms involve the organism's adjusting to its immediate external environment, treatment of the disorders noted above begins by controlling the environment which evoked the maladaptive response. After the environment is controlled and the patient stabilized, it is possible to work with other mechanisms of adaptation, i.e. the emotional and intellectual.

Treatment of a drug addict or an alcoholic must first concern itself with the disordered hedonic control. In other words, there must be some "rearrangement" of the hedonic mechanisms which will provide gratification without using drugs. As experienced clinicians have long stated, the first step in treating these people is to substitute food for the addicting substance. It is an everyday observation that a person can only stop smoking "when conditions are right." In other words, an acceptable substitute must be provided for the gratification that smoking supplies. Hopefully, it might even be the pleasure derived from knowing that one has broken the habit.

The hypothesis here concerning the depressive spell is that depression represents a total failure to cope with stress after all the other adaptive mechanisms have been utilized. The "slowing-down" or retardation that ensues protects the individual from being completely overwhelmed by stress. A depressive spell is quite a different kettle of fish from a simple discouragement or loss of self-esteem (mild reactive depression) or from a phobic or an obsessive reaction. In the depressive spell, the whole being is flooded by emergency responses; data from physiological and biochemical measurements during the depressive spell attest to this fact (Gaylin, 1968).

The most efficacious way of avoiding a progressive schizophrenic withdrawal is to take the person out of the environment that is producing the response. From the standpoint of more traditional psychotherapeutic methods, schizophrenia is treated by using "covering techniques," e.g. fostering repression of painful impulses and facilitating rationalization. Clinical experience has shown that the schizophrenic can function adequately in life provided he learns how to adjust the environment to himself and to use his intellect to control disorganizing hedonic and emotional responses. As will be noted below, this is the opposite tack from that generally used in treating neuroses. Here, the individual learns how to "adjust himself" to the demands of the environment.

Emotional Level

As has been pointed out previously, hedonic reactions are "immediate" reactions to pain and pleasure. The anticipation of pain and pleasure is a function of the emotional level. Therefore, most traditional psychotherapy, especially psychoanalysis, is much more involved with mechanisms on the emotional level than those on the hedonic level. Mechanisms of defense are emotional mechanisms: the individual has adapted to a given set of life circumstances with responses which may, in fact, be maladaptive, but they are necessary to ensure survival and, to a degree, pleasure, uility, and performance. The child brought up in a home with severely authoritarian parents may become passive, dependent, and ingratiating. In this way, he "defends" himself, since the expression of open defiance might be dangerous. (The distinction between defense mechanisms and adaptive mechanisms is noted in Chapter III.) In psychotherapy, this same individual attempts to retrace the circumstances which evoked these defensive responses. Naturally, the better the therapeutic setting is able to recreate the circumstances under which the original responses were learned, i.e. "transference," the better the chance of therapeutic success.

In standard psychiatric practice, most of the patients seen have difficulty with the emotional mechanisms of adaptation. In this category are the typical neuroses—phobias, obsessions, and so forth. The word "emotion" is derived from the Latin verb *emovere,* which means to excite, agitate, upset, or to stir up. By definition, *emotions are patterns of organized events which occur in interaction between the organism and the environment and which serve to focus attention selectively and thus to energize the organism to take action.* They serve also to communicate, the mother and her preverbal child being a prime example. Strong emotion breaks through the hedonic and intellectual levels, and this can be lifesaving. In hypnosis, the trance will be broken when strong emotion is aroused.

There needs to be a distinction between emotion and biological drive. Both involve responses in the organism, but emotion springs from interaction between the organism and its environment, biological drive from tissue needs within the organism. The biological drive is more automatic.

Learning on the Emotional Level

Learning on the emotional level consists of a sequence of reactions, all of which must be connected: sense receptors are stimulated; perception is evoked; the source of the stimulation identified; the character of the stimulation—whether dangerous or pleasurable—is clarified; and the organism is moved to a response. A soldier may be trigger-happy at first, but with seasoning in combat, he shoots only when necessary. Therefore, when an individual is faced with new decisions involving emotional mechanisms, unless danger obviously impends, these decisions will take time.

The signals that stimulate an emotional response are important in understanding the sequence. The organism learns which signals to respond to and which signals to ignore. One does not always respond to an object or situation per se but to a symbol or indication of these. Omens or intuitions are examples. The phobic patient may avoid high places, the latter symbolizing a conflicted situation to him. The lion responds to the lion tamer's whip and chair: presumably, to the lion, the prongs on the chair along with the lash of the whip represent a more powerful animal than he. He may see the whip as part of the tamer's arm and this "reach" makes the man appear awesome.

An example of faulty learning of response to signals is the following. An individual is aroused sexually by a suitable object, but instead of responding appropriately, he runs in terror. His behavior may be the result of extremely puritanical upbringing. The person cannot even allow himself an intermediate response, such as a sexual phantasy. Further, if the upbringing were sufficiently strict, he might not even be consciously aware (due to repression) of the original stimulus. The pleasurable anticipation of sexual fulfillment has been replaced by the inappropriate behavior of running in terror, a completely contradictory response.

The survival value of an emotional response that prepares the organism for action is obvious. There is probably no thought component at this automatic "preparedness" level, although there is a feeling tone which may be pleasant or unpleasant. Later, a thought component, by which the organism determines the source of pain or pleasure, comes into play. One can easily see that the emotional response to a situation and the actual behavioral response are often quite different. The obsessive patient may smilingly deny that he is angry, although the truth is otherwise.

Once the organism anticipates the future, there is movement from the level of pure emotional response to what Rado calls the level of emotional thought. (It is doubtful if one ever responds on a purely emotional basis without a thought component.) This level of emotional thought can be viewed as a transitional level between the emotional and intellectual levels of adaptation.

Freud and Emotions

Beginning with Freud, early psychoanalytic theory neglected emotions. Freud relegated the emotions to "epiphenomena"; the core of behavior was the pleasure aspect of sex, and this became Freud's focus of study. He felt that the energy of the sexual drive determined the individual's behavior. He was also concerned with "affects," which he described as the emotion of the sexual drive. Freud felt that the affect is a built-in part of the sexual instinct. However, it is apparent from Sherrington's work that emotions first appear in evolutionary development with the advent of distance receptors: eyes, ears, smell, etc. Hence, the affect may not be instinctual but may rather result from stimulation of the central nervous system by the distance receptors.

In his early work on the sexual instinct, Freud pointed out that with sexual arousal there was a drive to complete the sex act. Inadequate or incomplete discharge of this sexual impulse, as with masturbation or coitus interruptus, were said by Freud to lead to neurasthenia. There was rising tension, and if this tension were not discharged, frustration would result. Freud focused sharply on this inner tension and the subsequent urge to action, and this led him to look for energic roots of behavior, i.e. the energy of the sexual instinct. Together with most scientific workers of that period, Freud was influenced by the discoveries of the physicists. In the 1850's, physicists evolved the law of conservation of energy, or the first law of thermodynamics. This influenced Freud's formulation of the libido theory. While there is seldom disagreement with Freud's clinical observations, there are many questions raised about the libido theory as an explanation for all neurotic conflicts (see Kardiner, Karush and Ovesey, 1959). Freud originally considered rage as being central in understanding depression (*Mourning and Melancholia*), but in his later writings of the

1920's he began to question systematically the importance of other emotional responses.

Emergency Emotions and Welfare Emotions

Rado (1956) divides the emotions into emergency emotions and welfare emotions. The emergency emotions are concerned with pain and expectation of pain and include fear, rage, guilty fear, and guilty rage. The welfare emotions are concerned with pleasure and the pursuit of pleasure and include joy, love, and pride. Both sets of emotions maintain the health and security of the organism. Emergency emotion responses (involving fear or rage) are usually expressed using the large voluntary muscles. Fear impels the organism to flee; rage impels the organism to fight to eliminate the noxious stimulus. Welfare emotions involve activities more central to the nervous system, i.e. there is a desire to perpetuate or repeat pleasure, whether it be in actuality or through phantasy. In phantasy, the organism uses the intellect to conjure up memories that provide emotional gratification.

Anticipation of pleasure can bring about love toward the source of the pleasure. Anticipation of pain can lead to chronic hatred. Naturally, anticipation of pain can make a fairly ordinary activity or event appear ominous. The man who needs to go in and talk to his boss about a raise may plan his approach for weeks in advance. He listens attentively every time his boss speaks and is quite aware of his superior's moods, comings, and goings. The night before he decides to make his approach, the employee may be tense and apprehensive and envision the worst. When he finally goes in to ask for the raise, he may discover that the event itself is almost anticlimactic compared to all the preliminary build-up.

On the other hand, by having the capacity for anticipation, emotional mechanisms assist the organism in withstanding frustration by anticipating pleasure. Or, as is often stated, pleasure is the antidote for pain.

The psychiatrist, dealing primarily with emotional mechanisms of adaptation, must be particularly adept at recognizing and differentiating emotional responses. Fear may be expressed verbally as an open emotion or expressed by fearful behavior. The schizophrenic may be flooded with waves of emotions, often contrasting in polarity, e.g. fear and rage, which render him powerless to react. The physician's most sensitive instrument is his capacity to use his own internal (emotional) perception to discern the emotional state of the patient.

It is a disaster when the therapist is repeatedly unable to receive clearly-sent emotional messages from his patient. This may be due to wide differences in cultural background of the two or to the lack of emotional receptivity (psychopathology) in the therapist.

One of the goals of therapy is to help the patient work out emotional aspects of problems before they happen. In surgery, before there is an amputation of a limb, the patient needs preparatory "emotional work" prior to the operation. *Before* a woman has surgery for breast cancer, she needs to come to grips with her "image" following the procedure (Chap. V).

The Limbic System

The nervous system's center for emotional activity is primarily the limbic system (Solnitsky, 1966). It is remarkable to note how similar the cellular structure of the limbic system remains, beginning with the lower animals and progressing on up the evolutionary scale to man. Emotional responses as such are stereotyped patterns throughout many species of the animal kingdom, but these patterns can be modified by learning. (Witness the domesticated and the wild members of the same species of animals.) Sometimes the modifications that come about through learning, e.g. repressing emotional responses, are to the disadvantage of the organism. Anatomically, as one ascends the phylogenetic scale, much of the limbic system is crowded out by the neocortex. One cerebral hemisphere innervates the opposite half of the body; the limbic system is bilateral in its neuroanatomic representation. By destruction, electrical stimulation, and clinical observation, it is clear that the limbic system, both within its structure and through its connections, has much to do with receiving somatic, visual, olfactory, gustatory, and auditory impulses, and it forms a means of expressing various emotional states and moods.

Neurophysiological studies suggest that the anterior portion of the limbic system is concerned with self-preservation; the posterior portion is concerned with species preservation. Damage to the limbic system brings on memory disturbances, especially difficulty in forming new memories.

Ernst Gellhorn (1967) has summarized recent work on the hypothalamic-limbic-reticular system. This system, which plays an important role in determining behavior, produces *ergotropic effects* (arousal) and *trophotropic effects* (lethargy and sleep). These two types of reactions are normally reciprocal and interference with this reciprocity results in disturbed behavior.

The short-range senses of smell and hearing are particularly involved in the emotional responses of the organism. Contrast persons who are deaf with those who are blind. Deaf people are more attuned to intellectual experience, the blind to emotional (feeling) experience.

Hearing is an especially important modality in the newborn. Newborns respond to the rhythmic sound of heartbeat and to the vibration of the mother's chest when they are nursed or cradled. In modern society, otologists are asking whether there is "too much noise." Could this "noise" interfere with emotional communication? Ostwald (1963) points out that communication by sound is necessary for human comfort and survival. In pathology, e.g. schizophrenia, auditory hallucinations are much more common than are visual hallucinations. When aged persons lose their hearing, they tend to withdraw and become rapidly seclusive.

Smell is the sense about which poets have written since time immemorial, yet little is known about this sense. As population density increases, emphasis is being placed on the negative aspects of smell; namely, offensive body odors. (Many an evening's television is sponsored by makers of deodorants, mouthwashes, soaps, *ad nauseum.*) The body has two main types of sweat glands, the eccrine and the apocrine. The eccrine glands secrete sweat, the ordinary perspiration of exercise. The apocrine glands are active primarily during sexual arousal. The latter are located in the axillae and pelvic regions and have a distinctive odor. To many, this odor is sexually exciting. Advertisers would have us replace this normal smell (in both male and female) with an artificial perfume. In the process, we may be lessening sexual arousal. The male goat emits a powerful sexual odor during mating season, and this "sends" all the nanny goats. Allowing the billy goat in heat to remain in a pasture overnight with a herd of nanny goats will ensure that all of the females are fertilized by morning.

Concerning hunger and appetite, a generalization often made is that appetite is the pleasurable anticipation of food and is more an emotional mechanism; hunger is more a reflex or hedonic mechanism, since hunger produces painful contractions in the abdomen. One can be ravenously hungry and eat enough meat and potatoes to be completely satiated. If a tantalizing dessert is offered, the appetite is again stimulated; one can always "make room."

Much is known about the physiological concomitants that accompany emotional responses, once these are set into motion. The first is an autonomic nervous system response at the visceral level. Heart rate can increase, respiration may deepen, secretion of acid in the stomach may change, etc.—the so-called Cannon phenomena. Anger, fear, or guilt can be perceived by the individual both as feeling tone and as autonomic response. It is possible, however, to learn not to pay attention to the feeling tone via repression.

The Family and Emotions

Since emotions are to a great extent influenced by learning, the family becomes the mainstay for teaching emotional responses. Out of literally thousands of random pieces of behavior, the family selects that behavior in the child which it chooses to encourage. (The therapy group has many of the same characteristics of the family [see Chap. V].) A message is sent and is repeated until the child learns the desired response. (In our time, adults who feel impoverished emotionally may attempt to remedy this deficit by joining "sensitivity groups.")

Emotional learning (and memories) are not easily forgotten. During analysis, a woman of fifty-six recovered painful memories of fifty years ago that had been repressed. She remembered that as a child, whenever her mother wanted to demonstrate "love," she would feed her cake. In analysis, the woman became aware of the inadequacy of this expression of love on the part of her mother and began to feel anger toward her—something she had never felt before. Emotional messages in a family are usually nonverbal in character. This allows for needs to be communicated without unnecessary expenditure of energy or effort. When an outsider, or a person from a different cultural background enters a family group, both sides must learn new cues before the capacity for understanding nonverbal (emotional) communication is effected.

The Intellectual Level

In the evolutionary development of the nervous system, man alone has evolved the massive cerebral hemispheres with areas for abstract thinking and association. This intellectual capacity allows the organism to anticipate future events and mobilize itself accordingly. Thus, *the intellectual level of adaptation concerns itself with foreseeing events over a long range of time, the emotional level over a middle range, the hedonic level over a short range.* (It is interesting that narcotic drugs with a short duration of action, e.g., morphine [2 hours], are highly addictive; methadone [8 hours] is much less addictive.)

The higher centers of the nervous system exercise control over the lower centers. Man is able to use his intellect to control his emotional responses, and emotions (plus the intellect) likewise serve to protect the organism against hedonic "excesses." Hedonic responses can be regulated by controlling the environment which produces these responses. When pain impends, the situation producing the pain is avoided. Learning on the hedonic level consists mainly of Pavlovian-type conditioning, but it is important to note that this type of learning occurs only when the organism allows it to occur, or when circumstances allow it to occur. Pavlov's dogs were strapped in and had little choice about their environment.

The characteristics of the intellectual mechanisms of adaptation are long-range calculations and delay of activity, use of conscious memory and associations, dominance by one cerebral hemisphere, and use of skilled motor acts through the voluntary motor system. We think of the intellectual level of adaptation as having to do with law and order, with teaching, and with ethics. In terms of traditional psychopathology, one cannot single out specific clinical disorders which represent malfunction of the intellectual mechanisms. Even with learning disorders, one can usually demonstrate disarray of the emotional mechanisms that interfere with the capacity to learn. Although the terms "motivational" and "emotional" are often used synonymously, this usage is incorrect. Intellectual mechanisms have a motivation as well, but over a longer range; hedonic mechanisms have a motivation over a shorter range.

From biological studies, we know that it is important to follow an emotional sequence through to its natural ending. When great anger is aroused, some means of discharging this emotion or of coping with its force is necessary. When pleasure mechanisms are stimulated, we also seek to obtain full gratification of these impulses. Not so well known is the necessity of following through on intellectual impulses. An example will illustrate. A business executive is planning a new sales campaign. He awakens in the middle of the night with an idea which he analyzes thoroughly. If he wants to get back to sleep, he had best get up and make written notes or dictate his thoughts into a machine. Attempting to "remember" the idea while trying to sleep may ruin his night's rest. Patients in psychotherapy who are awakened by a dream learn to write a note about it. Then they can go back to sleep; if they try to remember it until morning, chances of sleeping peacefully are slim. The creative artist also learns to work feverishly while riding the crest of a sequence of new ideas. He can get plenty of rest when the mind is fallow.

Learning on the intellectual level consists of the ability to reason and abstract and hence falls into the realm of the educational process. The most successful intellectual learning takes place when there are no significant emotional, hedonic, or physiological barriers to the learning.§ In learning on the intellectual level, perception is primarily by gestalt, i.e. wholes. Gestalts are formed, and there is reaction to these whole images. This is in contrast to the searching for signals or omens that occurs at the emotional level; by avoiding the symbol, one avoids the whole situation. The individual who has unacceptable impulses related to sex or aggression, for example, can displace these impulses onto the street; by avoiding the street, one avoids having to deal with these unacceptable impulses. Response at the emotional level is not to a whole person but to some aspect of a person, and usually only one aspect at a time. In contrast to wholes, the individual deals with parts. On the intellectual level one can analyze the origins of be-havior rather than simply responding to the behavior itself.

The intellectual level is characterized by the ability to shift from one course of action to another. However, there are times when emotional responses overrule the intellect, such as when danger or pleasure are in the offing. At such times, the ability to consider alternatives of behavior is diminished. In psychotherapy, by listening and then questioning, the physician can support the capacity to shift to other ways of responding. The healthy person is one who retains a maximum degree of flexibility in response to stress. The process of sitting and talking with someone enhances thinking, clarifies the problem, and reduces the distorting effect of emotion. One can examine various courses of action without nec-essarily executing them. (An anlage for this activity is children's play; the child learns symbol formation and begins to "move" the outer world by moving his playthings.)

As indicated, when there are runaway emotions, the individual can learn to institute controls by using his intellect; conscious mechanisms of control can overcome aberrant emotional reac-tions. Rado (1956) always stressed that "fear begets fear." The more one runs from danger, the more one is afraid. Therefore, ex-

§It is important that psychiatrists come to grips with how people learn, especially on the level of intellectual adaptation. Psychotherapy is in the main a learning and reeducational process. Many psychiatrists have been content to work with hedonic and emotional reactions, and to let the reeducational process take care of itself. But, increasingly, attempts are being made to incorporate learning theory into an understanding of the psychotherapeutic process (Alexander, 1963).

ercising initial control over fear is paramount. It has been found that exercising rigid control over the muscles can overcome many fears. For example, restlessness and agitation can be counteracted by rigid control of posture and by sitting motionless. Sleeplessness may be overcome by rigorously lying still in bed without turning or twisting.

Wilhelm Reich (1949) recognized many years ago that character could be linked with posture. The long-suffering Siberian peasant woman wears a shawl and walks with a shuffling gait. The depressed person conveys his mood by facies and posture. Among Indian tribes, the war dance and war paint had the purpose of rousing the braves to fever pitch for battle. Some psychiatrists treat passive persons who harbor much repressed anger by encouraging them to dress in rough clothes and act in a "hostile" manner in a controlled setting. This allows them to discharge some of their bottled-up emotion, the hypothesis being that there is feedback from motor activity to sensory perception.

A clinical example which demonstrates the contrast between emotional and intellectual learning is that of the patient who "needs to be needed." This is the man who begins to wonder about his marriage if, at home, his wife does not *need* to talk over every household detail. At work, if he is not constantly "needed" by his employees or peers, he begins to wonder about his worth. Very often, physicians fall into this category. After all, to be needed is embodied in their calling. The physician working in a busy medical ward is summoned repeatedly and is thus able to satisfy this need. However, if he is shifted to the emergency ward, he is called only for emergencies. He may begin to feel anxious and depressed. His perceptions are influenced primarily by disarray of the emotional mechanisms of adaptation: he needs constant reinforcement of his sense of importance. Were he able to use his intellectual mechanisms, he would see the whole picture (gestalt): the hospital's smooth functioning depends on his being available to take care of emergencies.||

||Clinically, an exaggerated "need to be needed" often results from a child's feeling unimportant to his parents. Being left with endless babysitters, no parent at home to greet him after school, being sent away to camp and not visited—all of

Brain Structure

Intellectual functioning is concerned with learning of language, special memory associations, and discriminative motor acts. In contrast to the anatomy of the limbic system, which is the same throughout most species, the neocortex changes with evolutionary ascent, with man showing the most elaboration. For specific human functions, there are intrinsic cellular changes in that region of the brain which subserves the function. The neocortex consists of six layers, and projection systems connect the cortex with other subcortical centers. The neocortex is connected with peripheral receptors in voluntary muscles by way of the extrapyramidal and pyramidal tracts and the corpus callosum. Via these long reflex arcs, the neocortex is able to deal with the external environment and its ever-changing conditions.

In the structure of the human brain, the main sensory apparatus of the intellectual level is vision, and this modality is represented in the occipital cortex. Although other animals, particularly eagles, have better vision, the ability to discriminate and interpret visual stimuli is greater in humans. Also, in contrast to the short-range senses of touch and smell, vision is capable of much symbolization.

In the human, motor functions tend to be organized according to the laws of dominance. In persons with mixed dominance, that is, where incomplete dominance by one hemisphere extends beyond childhood maturation, there may be stuttering, or reading and writing problems. Control of muscular patterns which are related to emotional mechanisms (the limbic system) are generally represented bilaterally in the nervous system. The higher up in evolutionary development, the greater the tendency toward unilateral control. The most extensive part of the cortex is taken up by association areas which coordinate sensory and motor activity.

---

these factors can be interpreted by the child as meaning he is not important to the parents. The same is true when there is very little emotional interaction between parent and child. The "screaming mother" deserves a high mark on this score since there is no doubt about her interaction with the child (an *encounter*, in existential terms). The most self-sufficient parents often produce children who feel the most unwanted.

Because of the structure of the brain, there is the capacity of some parts of the brain to take over other parts of functioning. (This is true in muscle reeducation as well; in some muscle diseases, one muscle can replace another that has become immobilized.)

PIAGET

Any consideration of the levels of adaptation would be incomplete without including Jean Piaget's work on cognitive development in children. Beginning as a zoologist, Piaget received a doctorate while still a teen-ager. He made many empirical observations on how children learn to learn. According to Piaget (Flavell, 1963), there are several stages of cognition in the developing child and an equilibrium between these stages. What upsets the equilibrium? New learning. If this new learning can be assimilated into the child's existing schemas of knowledge without disruption, fine; if this is not possible and the new knowledge does disrupt schemas already established, the child accommodates by developing new schemas. (It is rare that the former is the case.) Piaget believes that the intelligence faculty has its own drive to function.

In Piaget's classification, there are four levels of thought process: (a) sensorimotor, (b) pre-operational, (c) concrete operations, and (d) formal operations.

In the *sensorimotor stage,* which exists approximately from birth until two years, the child responds to contact stimuli primarily by automatic patterns of response. For example, in the infant, the sucking reflex is automatic and hardly modifiable. This activity ensures survival. The child will suck on anything; the reflex pattern knows nothing about its object. With more motor activity, there is corresponding need for learning, still primarily on the motor level. There is little classification of objects except as to sizes and shapes during these early years. The sensorimotor stage roughly parallels the hedonic level of adaptation.

From two to seven, the child is in the *preoperational stage.* He no longer responds only to physical characteristics of objects but can now think in terms of symbols and meaning of stimuli. He can perform certain tasks but cannot explain these with any clarity. Put a three-year-old on a toy horse, and he will play but will have difficulty describing the play. There is limited abstract reasoning ability. Many characteristics here are reminiscent of the level of emotional mechanisms, particularly the use of symbols.

During the *concrete-operations stage,* which lasts from approximately seven to eleven years of age, the child is able to reason about concrete objects, but as yet possesses no powers of reflection, i.e. is not capable of dealing critically with his own thinking. He learns to deal more effectively with his environment by using logical rules. For example, he is able to reason accurately about the whole in relationship to its parts.

The final stage, from eleven to fifteen years of age (or eleven onward) , is that of *formal operations.* The distinguishing characteristic of this stage is the child's ability to reason deductively and to deal with hypothetical concepts. His reasoning is no longer dependent on concrete objects but is now on the abstract level. During this period he is able, for the first time, to evaluate the quality of his own thinking. These last two stages are equivalent to the intellectual level in the adaptational scheme.

More and more, it is recognized that the early years of the child's development are crucial. From birth to four years of age, the child develops one-half of all intellectual ability, and from four to eight years, another one-third. In studies of twins reared in opposite types of environments, the favorable enviroment may bring as much as a 20 point IQ difference. After the first four years, the IQ will increase approximately a half a point a year. The English psychiatrist, John Bowlby (1963), feels that the capacity for affection in children develops in the first three years. If the child is devoid of affectional response in these years, the capacity to develop affectionate behavior is severely impaired. Similarly, the capacity for assertion and self-confidence develops quite early, and both of these qualities must be nurtured in a favorable environment.

MAN ADAPTING

Perhaps the outstanding virtue of the adaptational frame of reference in studying personality and behavior is the open-ended nature of this scheme. Who knows how many adaptive mechanisms man has available and the extent to which he can adapt? In our time outstanding figures such as Einstein, Freud, and Winston Churchill come to mind. What does greatness consist of? In an article about Adlai Stevenson, Hans Morgenthau (1965) defines greatness as follows:

> It consists in man's ability to push the human potential for achievement in a particular respect to its outer limits, or beyond them if they are defined in terms of what can be expected in the ordinary course of events. Thus, we speak of great painters and great writers, great liars and great lovers, great statesmen, and great merchants, great saints and great crooks. We call them great because they have done what others may do well, indifferently or badly, with a measure of excellence that at least imitates perfection.

A striking example of man pushing himself to a seemingly impossible goal was the running of a four-minute mile in 1954 by Roger Bannister. He did what Greek athletes dreamt of doing two thousand years ago. It is worth recounting Bannister's "experiment." He regarded the four-minute mile as an "intellectual challenge," with the research project being his own body. He worked to improve the basic physiological capacities of his heart and lungs. Thus, after two years of training, he could absorb five liters of oxygen into his lungs in a minute, about twice the normal rate. His pulse rate was lowered to 50, and the cardiac output was 50 percent more efficient than usual. In his book, *The Four Minute Mile,* Bannister states, "A race like the four-minute mile required an extraordinary mental approach, a conditioning. In fact, I have never thought the physical side was all that important; it can be mastered by effort, but to create a climate of incentive in the mind—that is the real accomplishment."

For the climactic race, Bannister was paced by two other athletes who stood aside in the final lap so that Bannister could storm across the finish line. At the end of the race, he was suffering from acute lack of oxygen, had only partial consciousness, his pulse rate was 155, and he was totally unable to distinguish colors. He states, "Real pain overtook me. I felt like an exploding flashlight with no will to live; I went on existing in the most passive physical state without being quite unconscious. Blood surged from my muscles and seemed to fell me. It was as if all my limbs were caught in an ever tightening vise."

The example of fatigue of a part of the body can be used to demonstrate that the physical capacity of man may be far beyond our wildest dreams. Squeeze a rubber ball in one hand until the limb has become fatigued. (Depending on the physical condition, training, and will of the person, this might be done for five or ten minutes before fatigue sets in.) However, if an electric current is applied to the nerves innervating the muscles in the area of the brachial plexus, it is possible to continue squeezing the object even though fatigue had just previously made this impossible. Once exhaustion again sets in and it is no longer possible to squeeze the ball, one can stimulate the muscle directly with an electrode and it is possible to resume squeezing. Accordingly, fatigue has to be understood at the central (perceptual) level, the peripheral-nerve level, and the muscle-cell level.

Another example of adaptation at the level of basic biology is as follows. One of the striking things in Japan today, as contrasted to a few years ago, is the difference in size of the average Japanese adult. This difference is evident in terms of the height of the individual, in terms of muscular mass of the body, and the more ample bosoms of the girls. (A Japanese girl recently won a worldwide beauty pageant.) Japanese tailors also report that they have had to change the standard sizes of children's clothes to accommodate the growth spurt of children in each age group. In schools, furniture has had to be remodeled so that the children will be more comfortable.

Why this change in stature? It is clearly due to the Westernization of Japan. Children now sit upright in chairs and no longer squat cross-legged on mats. (This perpetual squatting produced the bandy-legged Japanese.) The dress of Japanese girls is more Western, too. They are no longer tightly bound in kimonos, which are now worn primarily for holidays or festivals. They are much freer to exercise their whole body. The major factor, however, seems to be a change in the standard Japanese diet. Prior to World War II, their diet consisted mainly of polished rice, which was deficient in vitamins, and some of the amino acids and proteins. After World War II the Japanese instituted a school lunch program which provided most children with milk and meat or wheat products.

The combination of these changes in clothing, posture and diet has allowed the Japanese to shoot up from an average 5 feet a few decades ago to the present height of 5 feet, 4 inches. It is estimated that in fifty years, the Japanese will attain the average height of 5 feet, 8 inches.

These examples of man's capacity to adapt to new circumstances forces us to look at the other side of the coin. Is the human capacity for adaptation so great that it may be somewhat of a liability? Dubos (1965) points out that the human can tolerate polluted air and water, crowded environment, ugly landscape, and a constant barrage of noise and music to such a degree that there can be a "decline in the quality of life." Although the immediate adaptation to these environmental stresses may be necessary and seemingly beneficial, the long-term effects may be pathological. Constant smog can cause pulmonary changes, perhaps even be a factor in lung cancer. Insecticides may add chemical poisons to food, the effects of which do not show up immediately. Dubos also speculates that the pressures of living in crowded, noisy and ugly areas may predispose to neurosis. Lastly, there is a necessity for harmony between man and nature, and modern life tends to put distance and obstacles in the path of this relationship.¶

If it is possible to achieve goals hitherto thought impossible on the level of basic physiology, then why not comparable achievements on the intellectual level as well? An example is the revolution going on in preschool education. Bruner (1960) describes how young children can grasp difficult ideas if the curriculum is designed to engage their natural curiosity, their intellectual initiative, and their level of interest. For instance, it has been shown conclusively that some two-year-old children can be taught to read, not by being handed books and alphabets but rather by

---

¶How many large cities have ready access to beautiful and expansive parks such as Chapultepec in Mexico City?

using their own curiosity and drive in a "responsive environment." The responsive environment here is a giant teaching machine—an electric typewriter that is computerized. When the child strikes the keys and punches out a word, a particular signal is given by the machine. The child then begins to associate these keys and signals and soon begins to read words. Similarly, in "new math," first graders can master algebra; third graders can work in geometry and hypotheses of relativity physics; and fifth graders discover set theory in mathematics.

Many of these new concepts are offshoots of a new awareness about motivation in animals as well as children. The traditional theory about motivation based on reward and punishment must now take into account the fact that human beings are born with a desire to know, to explore, to master their environment, and to achieve. The limitations on learning have been due not so much to the child's incapacity or unreadiness to deal with complex ideas, but rather with the failure of adults to present ideas in ways to capture a child's imagination and interest.

ETHOLOGY

No discussion of adaptation would be complete without reference to some of the recent findings in ethology, the study of animal behavior. Insofar as possible, studies are carried out in the organism's natural environment. The potential for understanding human adaptation and maladaptation as a result of these studies is enormous. For example, research by many ethologists has shown that most primates separated from their mothers early in infancy develop stereotyped patterns of behavior similar to those seen among humans who are mentally defective or mentally ill. The common types of stereotyped behavior, such as finger- and thumb-sucking, body-rocking, head-banging and head-rolling, occur naturally during early infancy. The same is true for such movements as eye-poking, self-biting, repeating human sounds, and repetitive hand movements. In a ward for mental defectives or chronic schizophrenics, the patients spend much of their time repeating these same stereotyped acts. The extent of the stereotyped behavior generally is related to two things: the amount of excitement an individual feels and, secondly, other alternatives of behavior available to him in the environment. In monkey studies, Berkson (1966) has concluded that the abnormal behavior manifested by the stereotyped patterns begins as normal responses in the infant. When the animal—and perhaps the same is true for the human child—does not have the opportunity to develop more mature forms of activity in his environment, then the stereotyped patterns persist, resulting in abnormal behavior. If the newborn monkey does not have a mother to clasp, he clutches a furry cloth or any object available to him; if these are denied him, he clutches and sucks himself.

This focus on ethology leads to an attempt to define instinctual behavior. It might be defined as a biological drive which is goal-directed, the organism reacting without any particular awareness of its activity. Further, this activity is not particularly modified by experience. In effect, the reaction is a universal one, representing the whole species and not a single organism. In human beings, it is probably best to talk about instinctual drives and not about instincts. (The instinct is "recognized" by the behavior.) Is there a maternal instinct? Studies in lower animals suggest that there is, because hormone injections can stimulate maternal desires. In human beings, there must be some mutual interlocking mechanism that ties the mother and child together. The survival value of such a mechanism is obvious. Bowlby feels that this is demonstrable in terms of the signal the child sends the mother and the mother's response to this signal.

The study of imprinting and critical periods of development in both lower animals and humans points to the fact that there may be an instinctual "train" with which an individual is born. In his pioneering work on the ego and adaptation, Hartmann (1951) suggests that an individual has an average "expectable" social environment to which his resources are geared. This same expectable environment may be necessary to release the orderly sequence of the instinctual train with which an individual is born. Imprinting refers to the object fixation which occurs in the early developmental life of the organism. For imprinting to take place, the object must have a certain color, must be moving, and must be supplied at the critical time in the development of the organism. The classic example are the geese who imprinted the experimenter, Lorenz (1952), and followed him around indiscriminately, ignoring their real mother. Experiments also suggest that the time at which the capacity for imprinting ends corresponds to the time when fear is first aroused in the organism. Perhaps the organism is automatically responsive during the earlier state, almost as if it were hypnotized, but once the capacity for emotional arousal is present, the spell is broken and the capacity for imprinting lost.

We have not yet been able to understand imprinting in the human, but it may be that the first six months of life are most critical. What is learned during this period influences subsequent learning. Each age period has its own special adaptations in a progressive pattern of adjustment. Because of man's slower development, he may be the most imprintable of all the species. The sensitive parent knows how important body contact is for the infant. Perhaps more body contact between mother and infant during the first six months, even during sleep, may facilitate the growth and development which follows imprinting at the various critical periods. In other words, the "train" must be kept on the track. When learning by imprinting is not possible, the infant tries to make up for the deficit by the traditional associative learning technique. If this still is not possible, then there may be faulty development in adaptation, and this may be a factor in mental illness.

In their unique research with monkeys, the Harlows (1965) found two conditions necessary for the orderly development of intellectual and affectional capacity: proper mothering and peer play. The infant monkey deprived of adequate maternal and peer contact is left with a deficit insofar as the development of later sexual and parental behavior is concerned. The severity of the defect is related to the time at which the social isolation began and the period over which it was sustained. It is not hard to make parallel observations in children raised in institutions without adequate parenting or emotional nurturance. The "affect hunger" in these children is overwhelming; psychotherapy for affect-hungry patients is often a matter of substitute mothering.

Does man have an innate instinct for aggressive behavior? The answer to this question is speculative, but there is no doubt about man's *capacity* for aggressive behavior. Presumably, this capacity is part of his genetic endowment, and when utilized for self-protection or pursuit of realistic and socially-acceptable goals, it is constructive. However, some biologists (Ardrey, 1966; Lorenz, 1966) argue that man is unique in the primate world because he alone has a destructive instinct. In their view, murder and wars are therefore an expectable end product of this genetic predisposition. Wild animals seem to have mechanisms which allow control of aggression. Two wolves may be locked in a fierce battle and one emerge victorious. As he is about to kill the other, the defeated wolf bares his neck and the victor stops immediately. This is the animal's way of surrendering.

Man does not seem to have this built-in capacity for restraint. Therefore, one can speculate that wild beasts have evolved this method of signaling each other because other restraining mechanisms (e.g. conscience) have not been developed. Most animals kill for food or out of fear. The human being has highly-developed cerebral hemispheres which other animals do not have and thus can have premeditated thoughts of killing. One of the problems confronting society is to provide an outlet for handling aggression in the individual and to channel the aggression in socially acceptable ways.

One other concept from ethology now being applied to humans is that of territoriality: a home range or an area to which the animal always returns. Different kinds of animals—fishes, lizards, birds, and mammals—may actively defend a part of their total range, especially during the breeding season.

Allee and Schmidt (1951) identify the following characteristics of territoriality: territorial habit generally produces a more uniform occupancy of habitation; it limits the breeding population and hence controls population size; it furnishes partial protection of helpless young; where well-developed in territorial birds, it provides a reserve of unmated males and females; with larger territories it tends to insure an adequate supply of nearby food; it limits the spread of disease and parasites; it aids in the avoidance of predators because of the close proximity of the given species; and lastly, and apparently for psychological reasons, there is increased vigor of defense by the occupant and decreased vigor of attack by the intruder of the same species.

The concept of territoriality was applied to human problems during the 1950's when social scientists began studying territories of adolescent groups and gangs, housing problems, and patterns of social interaction (Ardrey, 1966). More recently, this concept has been applied to the study of behavior of schizophrenic patients. In some psychotic wards, it is found that intrusion on a patient's "territory" can lead either to withdrawal or an outburst of aggression. The patients who are most verbal and socially aggressive do not seem to be in need of establishing ownership of a spot. The least verbal and most socially nonaggressive patients tend to withdraw to secluded spots.

In contemporary life, the educational, social and welfare needs of the inhabitants of the "inner city" are far different from those of rural or suburban dwellers; how significant is the study of territoriality for provision of these needs? The population explosion being what it is, will territories have to be allocated in such a way as to try to reduce conflict?

Chapter III

Pathological (Maladaptive) Behavior
Psychotherapy for Maladaptive Behavior

The writer once stopped at a roadside nightclub. In the parking area a baby was crying furiously in one of the parked cars, which was completely locked. When this was mentioned to the headwaiter inside, he replied quite reassuringly, "Oh, that's the baby of the couple who are the entertainers here. Don't worry, he'll fall asleep in a few minutes. He cries himself to sleep every night."

To reconstruct the situation, one can assume that (1) the child had perceived some discomfort and (2) had begun crying and writhing; the purpose of the crying and writhing was (3) to send a message and (4) to obtain a response from someone in the environment. This behavior could be called instinctual, or as preferred here, an adaptive sequence. The behavior enhances the chances for the infant's survival. (This specific behavior may also be the anlage for the adult's reaching out for emotional contact.) If there is no response to the message despite its being sent repetitively, there may be some breakdown in the adaptive machinery: the more frustration the child feels, the more undifferentiated his screaming becomes. In other words, the correlation between the child's discomfort and his signaling behavior becomes less and less precise. In time, he may begin sucking his thumb and may become withdrawn or apathetic. (In an older child, there might also be a reparative phantasy in which there is some kind of illusory gratification.) The frustrated child may also begin to suck on a block or chew a blanket which can provide the illusion that he is receiving oral satisfaction. This is a sign of deterioration in perception and is the beginning of maladaptive behavior.

51

ADAPTIVE MECHANISMS

What is an adaptive mechanism and how does it work? What causes it to malfunction?

By definition, an adaptive mechanism is a biologic sequence built into the organism for the purpose of survival and self-realization. The mechanism may reflect genetic inheritance directly or may reflect the genetic potential with which the organism is endowed. The mechanisms range from simple reflexes to complex patterns of behavior. The knee jerk is an example of a simple adaptive mechanism which readily demonstrates fixed genetic inheritance. Similarly, the sequence of a hungry child crying out to be fed is an adaptive mechanism. In much of nature, adaptive mechanisms link the organism to its environment. A crying child arouses an adult. The higher up one goes in the evolutionary scale, the more complex are the emotional and intellectual levels of behavior and the more difficult it is to describe the adaptive mechanisms precisely. The knee jerk is easily described, but a more complex act, such as self-assertion, is not so readily defined. In the latter, the genetic potential must be actualized by learning. The type of environment—whether favorable or unfavorable—determines the degree of success of actualization. To assert himself, an individual must first be aroused, perhaps experience some autonomic nervous system response, appraise the situation, and decide on a course of action. His overt behavior comes after this mental activity. This sequence is all part of the adaptive mechanism of self-assertion; whether there are several mechanisms here or a single one is debatable.

How is an adaptive sequence altered? An individual attempting to repress feelings of anger, or pushed to the point where ordinarily there should be an angry response, might spontaneously say that he cannot feel anything, certainly not anger. Repression has done its work. Yet this same person may have frightening dreams following such an episode. Or, instead of responding with anger to a situation where this emotion is appropriate, he may respond with fear. These responses represent an alteration of the ordinary adaptive sequence and here again the *defense mechanism* of repression is seen in operation; feelings of anger are pushed out of conscious awareness into the unconscious. Hence, a distinction can be made between a defense mechanism and an adaptive mechanism, even though both are important in the organism's functioning and survival. The defense mechanism is utilized to reduce anxiety or tension and usually involves some compromise or loss of function.

To summarize, an adaptive sequence begins with the perception of stress, discomfort, or an emergency. This sets in operation machinery which, in the child, results in the sending of a signal, such as a cry, which calls for a response from the environment. If there is no response, he will keep sending the signal, and after repeated frustration, he will gradually bring other behavior into play. This behavior may include writhing, substituting a blanket or doll for an individual, rocking back and forth, or seeking comfort by other body movement. (Perhaps this is due to activation of other nervous system centers in the limbic system or in the reticular formation, both of which seem able to initiate a generalized response to relieve frustration.) If the frustration continues, the child may become apathetic. It should be noted that at some point in the above sequence, one can see both healthy and unhealthy behavior operating simultaneously. The signaling and looking for comfort constitute continuing healthy behavior. The unhealthy behavior is the beginning apathy which comes with the change in perception of the environment. During the time that both healthy (adaptive) behavior and unhealthy (maladaptive) behavior coexist, the sequence is readily reversed by appropriate response: moving the child to a more favorable environment, where someone will respond to his needs.

How long can the frustration continue before there is permanent impairment? The answer is speculative. Minimal biological confirmation is a very potent reinforcer of an adaptive sequence, many times more potent than is frustration leading to a maladaptive response. Harlow (1965) has shown this vividly in monkey experiments. He showed that only twenty minutes a day of peer play is enough for the animal to become socialized. The other twenty-three hours and forty minutes can be spent in isolation! In the human infant one can measure the degree of impairment of the mechanism by seeing its long-term effects. What happens when the infant is placed in a situation in which someone does respond? If the infant cringes, one may assume that he perceives the environment to be hostile rather than comforting. Not only has the mechanism become impaired, but the infant may be in worse shape than before the maladaptive response: he can no longer respond even tentatively in a "positive" way. (Volunteers who work with abandoned children face this problem every day. The closer they get to a child, the more likely he is to lash out at them verbally and physically.) In order to understand fully an adaptive sequence, the individual must be studied in relation to his environment. A child must be studied with his family. How do they respond to his messages? Is he left to sweat out problems on his own or is quick and immediate help available? In some families children are left to cry it out. In others, children are taught never to show anger. In still other families, children are taught always to plead for a response. This interaction may be instituted at a very primitive level, typified by Pavlovian-type conditioning, and may be carried to the highest intellectual level.

To use the level of physiological adaptation—that which was described by Walter B. Cannon (1932) under the rubric "homeostasis"—we note that wide ranges in blood pressure, heart rate, salt concentration, clotting time, and so forth, are possible. However, if the organism has been pushed beyond its capacity to adapt by utilizing its homeostatic mechanisms, i.e. exhaustion and beyond, there is physiologic decompensation with collapse.

In a sense, the adaptive mechanisms that we describe as "psychological" work similarly. A child can absorb stress up to a point. (The younger the child, the less stress he can absorb.) If the stress continues unabated, the child may respond by becoming withdrawn or by having a temper tantrum. The apathetic child is usually one who has been under severe stress for a long time and is "psychologically exhausted." In some of his studies on the natives in Alor, Kardiner (1945) has shown that much of their difficulty in functioning as adults can be traced to their inability as children to integrate certain adaptive mechanisms because they were constantly in situations of dire emergency. Learning was therefore impeded.

The adaptive capacity of the individual cannot, of course, be measured in only one dimension. The adaptive equipment of any individual is a broad-ranged capacity for adjustment, and this can be sampled only by a wide inventory of reactions and responses to stress. In taking a psychiatric history, the tradition is to measure the here-and-now life performance of an individual in at least three areas: the sexual, the social, and the vocational. Limitations or inflexibility of response will generally show up in these areas.

As has been noted previously, adaptational study of an individual's behavior always draws attention to what is *absent* in an ensemble of responses, as well as to what is *present*. One cannot make a judgment about a patient's response without knowledge of the stresses he is under. Therefore, systematic understanding of adaptive responses is necessary before one can study maladaptive responses. Benjamin Rush recognized this fact in the phenomenon of denial of illness. In studying a yellow fever epidemic in 1793, he wrote:

> Upon first visiting a patient, answers to questions were calculated to convince the physician that the patient's disease was not the malignant yellow fever, prevailing in epidemic proportions at the time. I did not for many weeks meet even 12 patients who acknowledged that they had any other indisposition than a common cold, or a slight remitting or intermitting fever. I was particularly struck with this self-deception in persons who had nursed relations who had died with the disease and who had been exposed to it in neighborhoods where it had prevailed for days and even weeks with great mortality (Rush, 1805, pp. 95–96.

He said afterwards, "Perhaps it would be proper to rank self-deception, with respect to the nature and danger of the disease, among the instances of derangement of the mind." In other words, reasonable anxiety in the presence of sickness is normal.

ADAPTIVE MECHANISMS AND MATURATIONAL LEVELS

An adaptive sequence can be temporarily disorganized when the environmental response does not follow the established pattern. An example is that of a person becoming angry; if the other person quickly admits he is at fault or turns the other cheek, the angry person may temporarily be "disorganized." It is hard to argue with a telephone operator; she is trained to be "nice" and to apologize, no matter what.

This same finding is true for maladaptive sequences as well; in the obsessional patient continually concerned with fighting and rebelliousness, the therapist can save him a lot of time and energy by saying that he, the therapist, is not there to fight, or "Look, I'm on your side." The value of this approach is that the patient may become aware of the deviant nature of his emotional patterns. He has been conditioned from early childhood to anticipate a battle and acts accordingly throughout his life. He has unwittingly cast the therapist into an authoritarian role and fights against submitting to domination.

What is the relationship between the adaptational classification —reflex, hedonic, emotional, and intellectual levels of integration —and the Freudian-structured classification of the id, ego, and superego? At this time, the answer must be speculative. Dr. Richard S. Ward,* who is both a child psychiatrist and a psychoanalyst, suggests that the id, ego, and superego represent dynamic forces or clusters that center about the emotional mechanisms of adaptation. The id is a fairly organized structure and has within it the memories of pleasure experiences; the ego consists of organized memories of reality functioning; the superego, organized memories of punishment and restrictions. The structural model of id-ego-superego is incomplete, he suggests, for at a deeper level is a physiological level which is not perceptible to us. It is probably related to the reflex level of evolutionary adaptation. The conflict-free sphere of the ego is, in the main, synonymous with the intellectual mechanisms of adaptation.

The complexity of the adaptive mechanisms varies with the stages of development and maturation of the nervous system. The infant at birth is primarily a reflex and hedonic being, with most of his activity geared directly to survival. It is interesting that the only nerves fully myelinated at birth serve the mouth, and this is essential for survival; the infant who is not prone to suck at birth is at a distinct disadvantage.

---

*Personal communication, 1970.

The developmental periods can be separated into (a) dependency, (b) assertivity, and (c) socialization.

In the period of dependency adaptation, the infant starts at a level of complete helplessness, where all must be done for him by those in the environment. Gradually, there is increasing independence. Every child must go through the experience of having his dependency needs satisfied in order to develop trust and emotional relatedness to others. Some pathologic responses in children who are not allowed appropriate dependency have been alluded to above. The period of dependency adaptation varies widely in different species, man having the longest time period in terms of needing biological care by others. It goes without saying that in times of stress, or when an individual feels he has lost mastery in a situation, he may fall back to the dependency level of adaptation and yearn for someone to care for him (Karush and Ovesey, 1961). Chronic yearning for care typifies the passive-dependent personality disorder.†

In the period of assertivity, the child begins to do for himself using his own developing resources. The first assertive (aggressive) act the mother is generally aware of is the feeding infant biting at the nipple. Commonly, however, assertivity is looked upon as beginning at eighteen to twenty-four months, the age at which

---

†A primordial period of development in the infant has also been postulated by Ferenczi (1950) and Rado (1956), in particular. This period coincides with the infant's first thought picture of himself, namely, that he is an omnipotent being: this is the stage of "primary omnipotence." All that is done for him is ordered by him, since he sees himself as having infinite power. As the child begins to realize that not only is he not omnipotent but essentially helpless, he delegates the omnipotence to those around him, usually his parents ("delegated omnipotence"). As time goes on, reality testing occupies the child more and more, and eventually he comes to grips with his real circumstances in life. Rado feels that the phantasy of omnipotence is never completely relinquished, however, and that it remains a primary craving throughout life. There is a quaint Old Testament story which bears on this. How were the prophets of old able to explain a person who lived in Egypt dreaming about being in China? They postulated that the infant lies *in utero* in the form of a tablet with open pages, and while still in the womb, the angel of the Lord takes him throughout the length and breadth of the world. Just before the gates of light open (birth), an angel taps the infant on the upper lip and causes him to forget all he has seen. (This tap is supposedly the origin of the frenum on the upper lip.)

maturation of the nervous system allows for more control of the large muscles. Then the child can throw classic temper tantrums, since he is able to use his arms and legs. Maturation at all the periods of development is generally enhanced by some frustration in the environment. The child must learn how to cope with his frustrations. At the same time that the child uses the large muscles of the arms and legs more freely, he may be undergoing toilet training. He experiences the latter as an interference with his pleasure, and thus the beginnings of the period of assertivity are replete with battles between mother and child, particularly with regard to toilet training. Ask any mother about the "terrible two's."

Socialization of the child begins in infancy, also, and society entrusts this function primarily to the family. He must learn how to get along with others and must learn the range of socially-acceptable behavior. (This is detailed in Chapter IV.) These developmental periods follow the biological curve of development. Much of the behavior noted in the periods of dependency, assertivity, and socialization can also be described utilizing libido theory. The three periods correspond roughly to the oral, anal-sadistic, and genital stages of libidinal development.‡

ADAPTIVE BEHAVIOR, MALADAPTIVE BEHAVIOR AND CHILD REARING

Different cultures approach the problem of child rearing in different ways and, accordingly, a different personality results. In the Sioux Indian, the tendency is to respond only occasionally to the crying child in order to make him hardened and insensitive to pain. In other cultures, response to children is primarily at times when they are frustrated, deprived, or in discomfort. In certain segments of our own culture, there is the tendency to overanticipate the child's needs, that is, not to allow him to experience the full emotional retinue of perceiving discomfort and calling for assistance. In the latter case the child may be all the more disturbed because his adaptive mechanisms have never had a chance to de-

---

‡No attempt is made here to contrast or evaluate the two frames of reference. The reader is referred to Kardiner, Karush, and Ovesey (1959) .

velop in full. All in all, one can see how an entirely different character can be produced, depending on the response of the parents to the child's needs. This response is a product both of the personalities of the parents and the dictates of the culture.

In the first year and a half of life, there is ever-increasing accuracy of messages sent between child and mother. Both learn a great deal about each other and how they respond to stress. The response, however, can be titrated, depending on what behavior the parents want to reinforce in the child. If they wish to produce a Spartan-type individual who will become almost entirely self-reliant and will seldom call out for help, they respond minimally; if they want to produce someone completely dependent, they respond maximally.

The growing child exhibits literally thousands of pieces of random behavior. Parents can reinforce any particular kind of behavior simply by licensing it, or similarly, they can condition a child to repress certain responses, for example, anger. The extent of repression may be such that it alters the response entirely, if family circumstances so dictate. In psychodynamic investigation, this alteration is often apparent in individuals who have sexual pathology. Usually, the individual exposed to a normal sexual stimulus exhibits a typical adaptive sequence: there is a feeling of arousal, a reflex response, and an intellectual awareness of what is happening. The individual conditioned to repress any kind of sexual arousal may exhibit a maladaptive sequence; he may experience discomfort when exposed to the sexual stimulus. A psychic operation changes that which ordinarily would be a sexual response to a perception of external danger.

After two or two and a half years of age, the child begins to respond to stress with more precise emotional mechanisms. In his classic film of a child hospitalized for medical treatment, Bowlby has shown that there is progressive withdrawal in the child. After a day's separation, the mother had only slight difficulty in making contact with the child. The next day, it was a little harder. After several days' separation, it was very difficult to elicit the child's response.§ The child is using his emotional mechanisms of adaptation, which are more complex than those in the infant—there is anticipation of the separation, with subsequent anger and withdrawal. Complete abandonment may bring the child to a point where he can no longer respond even minimally to stimulation from the environment. René Spitz (1945) documented this fact in his study of affect-hungry children in orphanages.

As the child grows older, he learns to send messages which have even greater specificity. Thus, with a young child of three or four, it becomes important to respond quite accurately to messages whenever possible. Child developmentists stress that this is not a good time for joking; the child who needs to have a bowel movement does not appreciate his parent's saying that first the child's temperature needs to be taken.

ADAPTIVE BEHAVIOR, MALADAPTIVE BEHAVIOR AND CULTURAL FACTORS

How does one measure stress in a situation? In some instances it is possible to find the origin and the extent of the stress; in other situations it is impossible. The individual faced by a wild charging animal is in a dangerously stressful situation, as most observers would agree. However, in the business world where competition is keen, there would be wide disagreement as to the definition of stress. The measurement of stress, therefore, is primarily dependent on the individual's subjective perception of a situation. The element of subjective perception is emphasized because the psychotic individual may have distorted perceptions. Further, as Cantril (1957) has pointed out, ". . . what we perceive is . . . in large part our own creation and depends on the assumptions we bring to the particular occasion. We seem to give meaning and order to sensory impingement in terms of our own needs and purposes, and this selection is actively creative."

§Anything that significantly decreases the interaction between parents and dependent children evokes some feeling of guilt in the parents. Putting a child in a hospital for organic illness is a case in point. Also, the parents feel guilty that they were not "better parents." Placement of a child in a psychiatric hospital would naturally arouse the most guilt in parents.

Freud's writings about cultural institutions are limited to a few essays, "Totem and Taboo" and *Civilization and Its Discontents,* in particular. Freud used the idea of primal parricide to explain the internalized guilt that plagued individuals. This guilt made them conform to certain cultural standards. Similarly, Freud postulated a universal oedipal complex, with the attendant guilt that arose from the unacceptable sexual (and aggressive) strivings. The energy of these unacceptable drives was "sublimated" and channeled into "acceptable" behavior. The force behind certain cultural institutions, then, is the inhibition of the unacceptable drives and the sublimation of their energies.

It was the difficulty in demonstrating the theory of primal parricide and the concept of the universal oedipal complex that led Kardiner (1945) and others to seek alternate explanations for the origin of cultural institutions. In some instances, conflicts in an individual may well be a manifestation of an ocdipal conflict, but by using the postulate of the universal oedipal complex as the tool of observation, one is limited in the findings that are possible. They began to look at the problems different societies faced in adapting to their physical environment. This led to the hypothesis that the adaptational problems which a given society faces produce cultural institutions. Kardiner defines a culture as a collection of institutions devised to enhance the survival of man and the species. These institutions also serve to enhance the growth of the individual, serve to relieve tensions and, in short, are the methods by which society perpetuates itself. In an area where there is very little food, female infanticide can hold down the population. In this particular society, mothers may loathe to see their female infants killed, but they have no choice because the practice has been institutionalized. Therefore, a cultural institution can be at variance with an individual's own desires or needs and thus can create conflicts in the individual.

The differences in adaptation or needs for survival in various cultures are vast. Some societies lack warriors and have great difficulty in defending themselves against onslaught by enemy tribes. Others have difficulty in obtaining food because of climate; only part of the land can be used for cultivation. As noted above, one of the ways of dealing with a limited food supply is to control the population, and female infanticide is an effective institution. Similarly, most societies recognize that sexual drive is a force that can be destructive or create difficulties within a society and therefore needs regulation. A farmer going off to till his fields will not be very proficient in his work if he is constantly worrying that his wife may be seduced by other men.

The private property owner is more at ease if he knows that no one can stake a claim to his property while he is away. In the days of the gold rushes, a prospector had to be on his claim at all times in order to protect it. Therefore, laws protecting private property evolved. (Many economists feel a developing nation must accumulate enough capital resources of its own if it is not to become an aggressor nation.) Similarly, when a small group of people own most of the property, they invoke rules to safeguard this property. In many royal families, there is inbreeding to protect and preserve private property.

Private property may also include wives. In those cultures where wives are considered private property, the greatest amount of sexual restriction or inhibition is imposed.|| In Eastern lands where traditionally women belong to the reigning monarch, the rigid sexual restrictions may have been a factor in widespread homosexuality and pederasty. Now, in the 1970's, women are taking off their veils and appearing in public; sexual restriction is less as women become freer.¶ The Italian family avidly protects the pur-

---

||In Granada, Spain, stands the magnificient Alhambra, residence of the Moorish sultans for many centuries. In one of the rooms there is a center fount. Into this fount fell the heads of 32 male members of the Abencerrajes family. One of these men had seen the Queen without her veil in place, and the Sultan wanted to be certain he got rid of the man whom he felt to be a threat.

¶In *The New York Times,* January 30, 1966, there is an article from Libya describing the remarkable circumstances of a teen-age girl appearing unveiled on a television program. In reply to a question about her future, she stated that she hoped to become prime minister of the country. This is a far cry from the fact that, traditionally, a Libyan girl generally went "behind the veil" when she reached puberty and was not seen by any man except those in the immediate family until unveiled on her wedding night. She continued to wear the veil after marriage. Frequently these girls were married at age 12 or 13 to men selected by their families. They had little opportunity for schooling or education. When professional schools, such as nursing, opened for women, they had trouble recruiting students. With the

ity of a daughter. She is a valuable commodity in terms of making a suitable marriage and gaining status or property. Accordingly, this asset must be safeguarded, and if a man molests such a girl, he must be ready to marry her; if not, he may be assassinated. In Western societies, with concern for private property (inheritance rights) and concern for women's personal integrity, masturbation has generally been interdicted. This interdiction could control sexual impulses from the very beginning, and a general sexual inhibition results. This preserves monogamous union and prevents out-of-wedlock births.

What happens when there is an inhibition? Usually, the inhibition begins as a form of adaptation to insure survival. In succeeding generations, this inhibition often overshoots the mark and becomes a liability. Once the adaptational need for institutions has passed, they may remain as traditions. Often, these traditions are seen as sentimental links to the past.**

The prohibition against masturbation illustrates the effect of inhibition on a child. He does not understand why there is an inhibition and he may rebel against this arbitrary demand for compliance. This rebellion creates a conflict. As the child goes through the sequence of inhibition, conflict, and rebellion, there is a fall in his self-esteem and self-confidence. In response to this, he may try to find a powerful figure on whom he can be magically dependent. Accompanying all of this, there can be a change in his perception in that the world is seen as being full of danger rather than pleasure.

The woman who is sexually crippled may fear an attack by a snake. She may fear not only the masculine organ or its symbol, but the man himself, because he possesses a "hurtful object." Further, the sense of danger is increased the longer the inhibition

---

advent of modern communications and affluence (Libya has vast oil resources), noted change has taken place, but not without difficulty. In the article, stories were told of Liban women who married "modern-minded young men" and abandoned their veils. However, their fathers threatened to disown them unless they took up the veil again.

**Not so the physiological. Sickling of red blood cells has an adaptive value in Africa since it makes these cells less hospitable to the malarial parasite. In the United States, sickling represents a decided impairment to healthy function.

continues. Such a woman having severe sexual inhibitions may then rationalize this inhibition as stemming from a fear of men. The original inhibition, i.e. sexual interdiction, is thus transformed to a fear of an object. The adaptive mechanism has been altered and now there is a maladaptive sequence.

Those societies with the greatest overpopulation must exercise the greatest control of aggression. Thus, in India, even aggression toward animals is not allowed. When the controls are removed, aggression may burst out openly and in exaggerated fashion. The surest way of inhibiting aggression in children is to make the child completely obedient to the parent, allowing no assertion. The child is then made to feel guilty about any aggressive urges, even those which arise naturally in day-to-day dealings with the parents or with others.†† As the child begins to inhibit his impulses, he will perceive his inhibitions as fear of the powerful authority of the parent. It follows, then, that the child may attempt to ingratiate himself constantly, simply out of fear of authority. The individual in whom the greatest amount of repression has taken place will endow figures in his environment with the most awesome power. There has been a change in the individual's perception of the environment. He is now functioning with only part of his resources; the others are impounded. It is like having an automobile that can run only in first gear. While this is useful for going up steep hills, on the open highway it is a liability. This is maladaptive behavior in pure form.

The assertion (or aggression) which the individual has been forced to inhibit is projected outward and the individual feels himself vulnerable. A patient in analysis undergoing a change from passivity to assertivity will often give a clue to this change by

---

†† In authoritarian training, one encourages an aggressive outburst in a child and then proceeds to inhibit his assertion. It then becomes not just a simple inhibition but provoked aggression followed by reinhibition. Each time the child attempts to assert himself, guilt arises because of this attempt, and gradually the child's will is broken. It goes beyond simple obedience. It binds the repression and produces hostility against the authority. But since the hostility cannot be acted upon, greater repression and loss of self-esteem occur. This is the pattern that the obsessional person goes through over and over again: the desire to rebel, inhibition of the desire, followed by repression and guilt.

having a dream in which he is attacked by two or three figures. The individual has begun to feel the desire for independence, but because of the defects in his own personality resources and his own perception of himself as a weakling, he has to repress this desire. He projects the potential aggression onto others; hence the fear of attack from the outside.

CULTURAL INHIBITIONS AND PSYCHOTHERAPY

Kardiner (1939) pointed out that when the inhibited individual begins to understand his pattern of behavior, then he can begin to change the projective system, the projective system being the *result,* not the *cause,* of the individual's attempt to adapt to stresses in the environment. This led Kardiner to evolve his concept of "the basic personality" in which he used the individual's projective system to understand how the individual had attempted to adapt to stress in the past.‡‡

An understanding of how inhibitions work becomes crucial in psychotherapy. The individual who has been brought up to be extremely dependent will have deflated self-esteem and deflated self-confidence. He perceives his self-image as one of weakness and dependency. Assertive activity has been inhibited. Eventually, he rationalizes his inability to be assertive as being due to the weakness and dependency. But his low self-image results from the inhibition of self-assertion; the weakness and dependency is a *result* and not a *cause* of this inhibition. The deflated self-esteem is caused by a failure to take action. In psychotherapy, it is useful to begin with an appraisal of the individual's here-and-now functioning and then retrace the origins of his inhibitions.

Inhibitions usually begin in childhood, since the child has limited freedom to choose his response to parental demands. Since dependency needs are so basic, the child will fulfill almost any condition and inhibit almost any activity the parent demands in order to insure the necessary care and nurture. Why do some

---

‡‡ In analyzing phantasies in folklore, Kardiner (1945) hypothesized that certain phantasies and myths were a clue to the circumstances or conditions of adaptation in the individual's background. If a particular culture were short of water, there might be various myths about water either being scarce or in bountiful supply.

children rebel and others do not? There are many factors: the constitution of the child, his ordinal position, and the degree of protection from others in the family who may (or may not) support his rebellion. The goal of psychotherapy must be to change the individual's behavior, because maladaptive sequences reinforce an image of weakness and inadequacy. Action changes feeling. It is not possible to "understand" problems and solve them without action. Nothing ventured, nothing gained. This is the clinical basis for the old but wise therapeutic dictum: when you have an obsessional patient in treatment, always try to get him to complete an act, no matter how insignificant, despite all of his obsessional rumination and doubting. This will start the curve in the other direction—toward more self-assertion, more self-esteem, more self-confidence, less dependency, and toward a more realistic image of oneself from the "inside" rather than a projected feeling of power emanating from the "outside." This form of learning is crucial in psychotherapy; the patient must understand that the origin of his symptoms is bound up in the inhibition.

An individual must be willing to take a chance, to take independent action. He must accept the possibility of defeat but recognize full well the concomitant possibility of success.

The psychiatrist must be fully aware of the relationship between lack of action and emotional consequences. Emotions are forces within the individual which serve to alert him and precipitate action. When a stimulus triggers an emotional response, but it is not followed through, some abortive means will usually be found for expressing the impulse, and the form of expression may be maladaptive. If an individual is apprehensive about a particular situation, common sense dictates that he prepare himself and decide the best time and the best means of facing this situation, and then go ahead. Action brings about relief of emotional tension; stress hanging over an individual's head creates tension. Thus, when emotional growth is related to action, one always experiences a number of successes and failures. Perpetual success can be as harmful to the individual's growth as is perpetual failure. The developing child must experience some frustrations as well as some successes in his developmental years.

Chapter IV

Family Equilibrium (Homeostasis)
How Families Operate in Health and in Conflict

HISTORICAL ORIGINS OF FAMILY LIFE

How did family life begin, and why has the institution endured? Although volumes have been written about the origin of the family, it must be conceded that these theories are all purely speculative. The only safe assumption is that it is a very old practice for a man and woman, or several men and women, to live together and rear their offspring. Family life existed long before homo sapiens appeared on earth. In the anthropoid apes, there are many similarities to the human family: mate selection, rearing of offspring by both mates, and some role definition—the male is the protector and the female is the nurturer. But, as Burgess and Locke point out, there is one great difference: "In any given ape species, family life is much the same, whereas with man family behavior varies greatly from place to place" (1960, p. 5). The reason for this difference lies in the fact that the animal family is largely biological or "instinctual" in nature, its function being to perpetuate the species, while in man, out of this same common biological instinct, an institution has evolved. Since all institutions are influenced by culture, and because there have been and still are many different cultures, there are many forms of the family.

In ancient society, the structure of the family was of the extended type. Several generations lived together as a single household. In this type of family, the father was usually a patriarch who had complete control over family members. Sons, though married and having children of their own, continued to live in their father's household where all were in complete subjection to the patriarchal figure. Patriarchal family life was characteristic of the

Greek, Roman, and Hebrew families. In the Greek tragedies there are precise descriptions of the family as a clan or unit. If the sin of Hubris (pride) was committed by the father, the sons could suffer for this sin. The same was true of the ancient Hebrew family. In the Inca Empire of South America (c. 700-1400), if the father committed a punishable crime, he and his whole family were put to death.

Genesis (29:15–30) describes the practice of "selling one's daughter" into marriage. Laban required Jacob to work seven years before he was given one of Laban's daughters in marriage.

Far from being a thing of the past, the large patriarchal family is the family organization of a majority of the human race today. Fathers still arrange suitable mates for their children.

The Old Testament also gives one of the first descriptions of a girl marrying and renouncing ties to her family of origin and forming a new family with her husband's relatives. Ruth chose to remain with her husband's mother after his death.

14 Then they lifted up their voices and wept again; and Orpah kissed her mother-in-law, but Ruth clung to her.

15 And she said, See, your sister-in-law has gone back to her people and to her gods; return after your sister-in-law.

16 But Ruth said, Entreat me not to leave you or to return from following you; for where you go I will go, and where you lodge I will lodge; your people shall be my people, and your God my God;

17 where you die I will die, and there will I be buried. May the Lord do so to me and more also if even death parts me from you.

18 And when Naomi saw that she was determined to go with her, she said no more.

Ruth 1:14-18

The development of skills required by crafts in medieval times made the large patriarchal family inefficient. "Specialists" were needed; thus the extended family became a smaller unit, consisting generally of husband, wife, children, and perhaps one or more relatives. In these feudal societies, the male head of the family still ruled with absolute authority. Marriages were arranged by parents. Children were considered chattels and were entirely at the mercy of their fathers.

Several other factors, aside from the development of crafts, made for contraction of the family unit into this smaller organization. The development of gunpowder and firearms gave a degree of protection that had not existed before. Prior to this, if the family group was not big enough to have several swords ready to fend off marauding bands, they would perish; there was safety in numbers. The progressive development of law and order was also an important element in affording protection. The development of better housing and plumbing facilities also allowed for contraction of the family unit. (In many old European castles, one can still see the common sleeping rooms and common bathrooms.)

With the Industrial Revolution came new independence for young people. In the United States a young man no longer had to depend on his father for food and shelter but could go out and get a factory job, or obtain free land, thereby gaining the right to choose a mate and set up his own household. The extended family living under the same roof eventually became the exception rather than the rule in Western civilization. The extension of democratic principles, with emphasis on individual freedom, further paved the way for the breakdown of the extended, patriarchal family and the emergence of the democratic type family of today.

DEFINITION OF A FAMILY

What is a useful definition of a family? Whenever one attempts to define a family in psychological terms, the sociologist throws a monkey wrench into this attempt by pointing out that such a definition pertains to a particular group that is being studied. An Irish working man often has a warmer feeling toward his co-workers than he does toward his blood family. For our purposes here, it is best to consider a family as an organization or a social institution in which there are certain "family feelings or family behavior": sharing of goals and identity, concern for provision of certain physical and emotional needs of its members, and patterns of response which do not require the individual to be constantly on guard. Or, put another way, a family is a group of two or more people who call themselves a family and who significantly affect one another. The family is a group with continuity—a past, a present, and a future.

In clinical practice, it is useful to ask the members, Who is your family? Frequently, the answer includes an uncle, an aunt, a clergyman, a dog, or anyone else. In this way, they will also disclose who is *not* considered a member of the group. A child may consider certain people to be members of the family who are not considered by the parents—or even the family therapist—as family members. One technical aspect of treating a family is relevant here: the family may leave one member out when they come for treatment. This person is often the "sickest" (Sonne, Speck, and Jungreis, 1962) and is excluded for this very reason. Or, the absent individual's symptoms may reflect family conflict, and he has been designated the scapegoat for the family pathology. For treatment purposes, a family can be defined as all those who consider themselves a family, who live close enough to affect each other significantly, and who are available for family treatment.*

Aside from the natural family, many other units assume the characteristics of a family. The employer is often a "father" to his regular employees; the office supervisor may be a type of "mother." An employer and his secretary have a kind of family relationship. She is privy to many opinions that could never be voiced in public. Analyst and analysand have a kind of "marriage." As will be stressed later in this chapter, an ancestor may be considered a viable part of the family and can be used to impose restraints on the family, e.g. an alcoholic ancestor may "remind" the members not to drink.

An easy way to determine whether or not a person is a member of a viable family is to observe him with other members of the group. Do non-self-conscious or habitual patterns exist? Do members let their hair down with one another? On initial meeting, two strangers "calibrate" each other. With time, they find a pat-

---

*Bowen *et al.* (1959) feel that family therapy can be done with only one member of the family present. Psychotherapy is oriented toward family interaction rather than one individual's subjective phantasies.

tern of interaction, and calibration is no longer necessary. Similarly, with members of a family, there is a great deal of communication which takes place without any conscious effort. When a stranger arrives in the home, the pattern is broken and self-consciousness is again notable: there is a new set of expectancies. People who reach a significant level of emotional intimacy can convey feelings indirectly. This is the optimum in family behavior. Disturbed families do not have this freedom or ease of relatedness (Lidz, Cornelison, Fleck, and Terry, 1957). The family is the primary vehicle by which the child tests out emotional reactions. Learning to reach emotional equilibrium in the family augurs well for the child's being able to repeat the pattern elsewhere in life. The "family romance," in which the youngsters go through a flirtation with the parent of the opposite sex and a subsequent feeling of rivalry with the parent of the same sex, is almost a *sine qua non* for successful dating and courtship. As more and more cultural institutions disappear, such as neighborhood centers and clubs, more than ever the burden of teaching emotional relatedness falls on the family.

There is often a tendency to measure family interaction on the basis of number of verbalizations. For example, sociological surveys are conducted to determine the amount of interaction between people, judged by the number of words passed between them. Or, both parents and their children may be observed for an hour and the number of verbal interchanges tabulated. Psychiatric clinical experience shows that these are not valid observations, because there are many subliminal interchanges. The more cohesive the family, the more nonverbal its messages. The most graphic example is a family interview in which the wife, by the faintest flicker of expression in her face or eyes, gives the husband or children permission to speak.

Many of these nonverbal messages are being codified by students of linguistics and kinesics (Birdwhistell, 1963). The pitch and loudness of the voice, the set of the forehead, clearing the throat, the frequency and depth of respiration, all are forms of communication. These are *paralanguage* phenomena and can be studied as they correspond to, or are independent of, the spoken word. The psychoanalyst has a unique opportunity to observe these phenomena. It is sometimes necessary for him to see a patient whom he analyzed five or ten years ago. Despite the fact that years have passed without contact, the interview has the character of one following a session of a few days ago. There are many well-developed channels of communication between the two individuals, and these are not easily forgotten.

FAMILY TASKS, FUNCTIONS AND ROLES

By its nature, the family fulfills many functions for itself as a unit and for its individual members. Each generation, as well as each member, has different needs and is assigned different tasks in the family organization. These tasks are apportioned among various members and, as a result, the whole is far greater than the sum of the parts. Perhaps the major function of the parental generation is to educate the child generation, both by actual instruction and by serving as models. Parents who avoid this role— perhaps by trying to relive their own lives vicariously through the children or by forcing the children into constant leadership roles —create problems for the children. As one family therapist stated, "One of the hardest jobs is to kick the parents out of the children's bed." The parents not only teach the child language but perceptions and defensive patterns as well. This fact is reflected clinically, since in intimate family relationships, the thoughts and reactions of one member regarding the family probably occur to every other member. Therefore, each member's response to the behavior of another family member should be predictable.

There is great similarity in the way a family apportions role functions and in the way society parcels out functions. There are people to enforce laws, to teach school, to practice medicine, and to fight fires. The presence of these specialists allows the rest of the group to concentrate on their own tasks, but in an emergency, each specialist is backstopped by the population at large. In the family, there is the "breadwinner," the "family healer," the "rebel," or perhaps the "jester." If the "jester" leaves home, this role may be taken up by another member of the family, or split

between several members.† There are performance roles—breadwinner, homemaker, chauffeur, gardener—and emotional roles—
leader, nurturer, protector, arbitrator, sexpot, and so forth. Naturally, the fewer people there are to fulfill these roles, the more is
demanded of each member. These roles are schematized in the
following clock diagrams.

PERFORMANCE ("Instrumental")   EMOTIONAL ("Expressive")

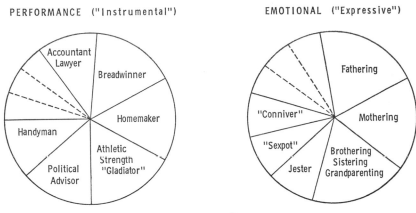

FIGURE I

Sociologists have long divided family functions into "expressive" and "instrumental," terms that parallel "emotional" and
"performance." Any member of the family can satisfactorily fulfill
any of the roles in either category unless he or she is uncomfortable in the role. A man who feels himself truly masculine will have
no emotional problem in cooking a meal or diapering a baby; a
woman who is sure of her femininity has no trouble calling the
plumber or taking the car for repair. (A fuller description of the
emotional role is found in Chapter V.)

At the most basic level, the family takes care of the physical
needs of its members: food, clothing, shelter, protection against
danger, provision for bodily repairs after fatigue or illness, and
provision for reproduction. In primitive societies, provision of

---

†In this sense, the family is like a theatrical repertory company. There are many
roles to be fulfilled and these roles are assigned according to the personality and
capacity of each member. If one "actor" falls ill, another doubles up and fills his
role.

these basic needs may be the dominant concern of all family members. Nomads often spend the entire day foraging for food. In Western society, more of these needs are taken for granted, although there still may be family conflict over who does the cooking, who takes the child to the doctor, and so on.

Next in importance would be provision of affectional needs. It has been amply demonstrated that the child who feels loved contracts fewer physical illnesses, learns quicker and, in general, has an easier time growing up. The affectional needs continue throughout life. Parents or grandparents who feel temporarily defeated need as much tender loving care as does a child.

Although more and more of the functions traditionally belonging to the family, such as medical care, education, and job training, are being absorbed by other agencies of society, the family still remains primary in providing affectional needs for its members. When more group living prevailed, this need was shared by a number of people. In immigrant neighborhoods, children were looked after by the entire neighborhood. If a child wandered away from home, there was always someone to look after him and to make sure he was returned home safely.

During the civil rights riots in Chicago and in the Watts area of Los Angeles, the woeful lack of social control was very much in evidence. People not generally inclined toward criminal activity turned into looters and risked being shot in order to steal a lamp or some article of clothing from a store. This lack of control can in part be attributed to the fact that the neighborhood, as such, is lost and also the extended family that went with it. At one time, children were so well-known to others in the neighborhood that if the parents were not around to discipline a child who showed lack of social control, others would "correct" the child.

This writer is located near one of the largest aerospace centers in the United States. Families move here continually, since job opportunities are plentiful for skilled professionals or semiskilled individuals with technical abilities. Their intent in moving is to gain economic security. Thus they hurriedly build houses and the main goal is to succeed financially. But the nagging question is, What type of men will these individuals be in ten or fifteen years? They have no real roots in the community, little in common with one another, and have very little identity apart from their job and the money it brings. The incidence of alcoholism, infidelity, depression, and divorce is far greater than in the population that has roots in the community.

Child Rearing

One of the facts of life in an affluent society is that more child care is left to maids, baby-sitters, or other parent-surrogates. (Working mothers have always had to find substitutes, but in earlier times these were usually family members.) What happens if the mother and the surrogate-mother differ widely when it comes to child-rearing practices? Generally, the child recognizes the mother as being the seat of power, but it is worth paying attention to the phenomenon of surrogate parents.

As noted previously, the growing child exhibits thousands of pieces of behavior and the parent chooses to license and reinforce behavior which conforms to the socially-desired image. Thus, it becomes important to look at the parents' behavior in order to understand much of the child's behavior. An obsessive mother will "transmit" these values to her child; to please her, he may emulate her behavior and also become obsessively preoccupied with details in life. The hysterical woman given to ingratiation and expression of phantasies will encourage similar behavior in her child. This is not a one-to-one correlation, because no situation involving the mother and child can be considered a closed relationship; one must consider the interaction with the other parent, siblings, parent-surrogates, and peers. In the extended family, there was a neutralizing effect by virtue of having many other family members around the house. But in the more vertical family of today, the child is more and more exclusively under the influence of the mother.

From pediatrics comes specific clinical evidence of the effects of emotional deprivation in children (Powell *et al.*, 1967). These children have symptoms reminiscent of idiopathic hypopituitarism: retarded growth, poor social and intellectual responses, and frequent bizarre behavior patterns. Removal of these deprived children to a hospital or a foster home effects a startling change. One boy of eleven grew 1.2 inches per month in the hospital. There was also a change to more appropriate eating habits and less bizarre behavior.

In describing family functions, one must remember that affectional and emotional needs vary with age and psychosocial development. The five-year-old needs an entirely different type of demonstrativeness than does a ten-year-old. The affection that a child receives from his mother is far different from that received from his father or grown sister.

A third task of the family is socialization of its members. Society makes the family responsible for the first sixteen or eighteen years of the child's life. In the earliest phases of life, the child learns by mimicking and then by "identifying" with his parents. Discipline and education about himself, his body, his peers, his family, and his community follow. Age role also needs to be taught. Similarly, there should be adequate preparation of the individual for his biological role. Freud was able to show an amazed world that the first several years in a child's life are crucial.

Stoller (1968) has shown that the first two years are the key years for learning sexual gender role; presumably, parents make little boys out of infant boys, little girls out of infant girls, and can even "make" little boys out of infant girls.

From the family, the child also learns social values. By definition, a value is a belief or custom in the family that is defended when it is challenged. Society entrusts the family with the task of instilling values in the individual, values which will not cause continual conflict between the individual and his society.

Of what use are family ethics or family values? They make life much easier, i.e. the process of adaptation to challenge or stress is enhanced. Ethics and values define boundaries for the family members in the same way that laws or customs define boundaries for acceptable conduct in society-at-large. Because of family values, a person does not have to stop and ponder his response to every event in life. When two cars approach an intersection, custom (in this case, traffic laws) dictates who goes first. The drivers do not have to wait for messages from each other. No matter how severe the argument a couple is having, if there is a dinner that includes spouses at the man's place of business, both put aside the argument to attend. The argument may be important, but the long-term effects of the particular social engagement are more significant.

The family must also teach children about the different standards society asks in delegating responsibility to various groups. The professional man, the physician, the lawyer, the architect—those in whom people confide and to whom they entrust their lives and fortunes—is held much more accountable for ethical behavior than is the farmer or longshoreman. Further, there is a difference in the type of contact society has with a particular group: the milkman does not enter the home and therefore is judged by different standards than the exterminator who has freedom to enter a home and look into every corner.

Further tasks of the family are to foster the creative growth of each member, whether it be encouragement in school, encouragement on the job, or the ability to "retire" to a new career. The family is also the main bulwark for supporting the individual's self-esteem and self-identity. One of the needs of a growing child, at times, is a feeling of "exclusive possession" of a parent. Marriage partners also have this need periodically. The family is the best vehicle for providing fulfillment of these needs.

Another function of the human family is care of the aged, which is subject to wide variation. The necessity for creating an environment where the young could be dependent was always recognized; otherwise, the group would not survive. In most primitive tribes, there was little concern for the aged until it was recognized that they were the repositories of knowledge which could otherwise be gained only through trial and error. Thus the aged came to be viewed somewhat as a natural resource and were protected and cared for. In contemporary times, books, films, and myriad ways of accumulating information have diminished the role of elders as reservoirs of knowledge. Other reasons for protecting the aged must therefore be sought. The Fifth Commandment enjoins us to honor our father and mother. (This may have evolved empirically; in those societies in which there was honor and reverence for older people, there was more harmony.) Today, the presence of grandparents in a home provides a child with visible evidence of his stream of history; he knows not only who he is but where he came from.

In discussing socialization of children, one must consider the socializing agent and the child who is being "socialized." Typically, behavior excused in a child of two or three is viewed as rebellion in an older child. Bed-wetting in a child of four may be imputed to be rebellion against parental authority. How does this imputing behavior come about? Probably through one's own past experience and learning. We teach what we ourselves have been taught.

There is no doubt that the child's behavior *must* elicit some response from the parent—whether it be approval or rejection—in order for the youngster to learn what is expected of him. Some of the most inhibited and guilt-ridden adults come from homes in which the parents intervened little, if at all, in what the child did. Therefore, the child had to concoct in his phantasy what the parents might do if they were angry, if they were fearful, or if they were joyful. Unfortunately, the phantasy usually overshoots the mark, particularly on the side of the emergency emotions, and the fearful, guilt-ridden character emerges.

One of the characteristics of a young child's play is the periodic interruption of his activity in order to "touch base." He runs back to the parent for a brief touch contact and then continues his play. As the child grows, a word or glance from the parent becomes sufficient. The surfeited child is free to give vent to his inquisitive or creative urges; he is no longer craving satisfaction of basic emotional needs and can use his resources for other activities. Mahler (1952) has written in detail about the separation-individuation phase in the developing child. She traces the early symbiotic relationship between mother and child and shows how gradually the child begins to separate himself as a physical being and as an entity from the parent.

During this separation, there is need for some intermittent control, and this may be satisfied by a look, a gesture, or a touch from the parent. This brings into question the practice of sending young children away to boarding or military schools. In such an impersonal atmosphere, can the child "touch base" as readily as he can in the highly personal atmosphere at home? (An unforgettable tale of a child placed in a boarding school is provided by George Orwell [1953].)

Here, then, is one of the major advantages of the family: the opportunities for emotional surfeiting are greatest within the family setting. Later on, as the child becomes more peer-oriented, the family allows for modulation between individual needs and group needs. In some societies, children are thrust into all-day play with other children, which may be detrimental to individual growth; on the other hand, the child who is reared alone does not have an opportunity to learn social relationships ("transactions").

Roles and Division of Labor in a Family

In contemporary society, the necessity for differentiating roles into male and female is not so great as in past generations. There is no vital need for the physical strength man once possessed as a huntsman, except in athletics or war. Male and female tasks now overlap. The female role in the past was one of omnipresent concern for the needs of the family. Thus the saying, "A woman's work is never done!" aptly described this role. On the other hand, the man in this same society performed those functions which involved maximum expenditure of effort over a short period of time, such as hunting. After this burst of work, the man relaxed or slept until he was ready to resume his tasks again.

Division of labor is influenced by the fact that people have different motivations and different emotional perceptions of their roles. The person who can suppress pain is better suited for work involving physical risk; the more sensitive person is more responsive to the needs of children. In the human species, with a prolonged dependency period for children, it is necessary that someone be available for continuous care of the children. When the female must play both roles (mother and father), or when the male must play both roles, probably both suffer. The woman (or man) who must be both father and mother cannot adequately pay attention to the long-term needs of the child.

In addition to cultural factors, the question of neurotic fixation in roles must be considered. A family functions best when there is capacity for shift in roles as necessitated by life or when there is an emotional desire for shift, as in play or phantasy. When inflexibility prevents any shift in role, neurotic fixation exists. In some families, there is an agreement that the wife never inhibits or corrects her husband's role as a "man"; all decisions and matters requiring self-assertion are the province of the male. This family is then at a sharp disadvantage if the woman, because of adverse circumstances, is required to become the assertive member of the family. In lower-class Southern Negro families, the female could always work as a domestic, whereas the male often had a hard time finding employment. Hence, the female typically became the more serious, responsible adult in the family, the male more "romantic" and whimsical. This apparent polarization of males and females into roles generally associated with the opposite gender comes about because of both cultural and personality factors.

In order to understand how a family functions to fulfill its operations, several dimensions need to be appraised. The observer can make an objective evaluation during an interview. Second, the family can make a subjective appraisal of how they feel they are functioning in day-to-day activities. Third, one has to view the family's functioning from the community standpoint and note whether the family operations are performed in a way that is in harmony with the standards of the community. Last, one might ask the family if their present functioning is in keeping with their desired or wished-for level. Have they fulfilled their aspirations, at least in part?

An individual in a stressful situation may respond by invoking any of several defense mechanisms: he may deny any difficulty, become fearful and flee, become enraged and combative, or begin blaming others for his discomfort. As adaptive flexibility becomes constricted, more and more defensive behavior can be noted. There are parallel findings in troubled families. Such a family may stoutly deny they have any problems and insist that everything is going well. Frequently, the family with the most inflexibility presents itself as having the most consensus and harmony.

When problems arise, such as the child's school phobia described in Chapter VI, the family sees this as a separate problem, entirely divorced from any difficulties within the family. (In the school phobia case, the parents insisted that everything would be all right if only the boy would go to school.) The capacity for a family to see the problems of one member as related to the entire family varies, of course, with the degree of flexibility in the family, the homeostatic functions served by the symptom, and with the family's capacity for psychological insight.

Cultural and social factors in mental illness have been discussed in Chapter III. Myers and Roberts (1959) studied fifty patients from two social classes. Their first group represented 21 percent of the greater New Haven community in Connecticut; all were high school graduates and predominantly white-collar workers (Class 3). The other group was made up of economically-depressed individuals (Class 5); 18 percent were not regularly employed and when employed did unskilled work—they had only grammar school education. In general, the study showed that those families which were most disorganized and which had the least supportive relationship with parents, siblings, and the community tended to produce patients with the most disorganized personalities and most severe pathological forms of behavior. The Class 5 families were generally isolated from community institutions, mothers generally worked, and fathers were quite brutal; in this group patients were more often diagnosed as schizophrenic. In the Class 3 group, families were much more organized: the mother was the dominant parent, and patients tended to be diagnosed as psychoneurotic. Some emphasis is placed on the fact that in Class 3 families there was an upward mobility, which may in itself have been a cohesive factor.

New Roles

The family is the primary agency for preparing its members for new roles in life—particularly the emotional aspect of these roles. It is well-known that conflict between the prior role for which an individual has been prepared and the current role expectation may lead to disorganization of the personality. The linotype operator who is phased out because of changeover to automated printing machines may have trouble adjusting to a bench in a watch factory. In bridging this gap, the family is nuclear. In our technological society, many conflicts arise because the demands for adapting to changes in social organization are rapid and intense. These conflicts are evident at many levels. The working mother, the father who has to travel, the fierce competition among adolescents which does not allow them an opportunity to develop their creative resources, the fact that the individual must often commit himself to a course of training at a tender age instead of having a chance to explore many fields of endeavor—all of these are part of the social demand on the individual.

How does the family prepare each individual member for social change? First and foremost, this preparation begins in child-rearing practices, as has been stressed in the chapter on individual adaptation. Then, in childhood and adolescence, it is fostered by the family's openness to new experience. In those families in which there is exclusive concern for tradition and preservation of the past without proper regard for the present, there is little opportunity for exploration or a chance to tempt one's curiosity and initiative.

This tendency to cling to past ideas and methods is often what differentiates technologically-oriented societies from more rural or preliterate societies. In many areas of the world today, the plow and the yoke are used because fathers and grandfathers used this method of harvest, and any attempt at change is met with great resistance. Those individuals who do attempt change are often victims of scapegoating by those who want to retain the *status quo.*

In the discussion of individual adaptation, the various levels were defined as follows: the hedonic level is concerned with the direct experiencing of pleasure; the emotional level is tied to the anticipation of pleasure; and the intellectual level is concerned with expansion into group activity. The emotional level is the kingpin of family living. People are more concerned with the anticipation of pleasure than they are with the actual pleasure experience. The cohesive family, as contrasted with the split family, is much more concerned with the setting in which food is prepared, the way it is served, and the taste of the food. In the family in which there is emotional involvement and concern, the members may even feel a loss if one of the group is absent at mealtime. (In airline travel, the major difference between many first-class meals and tourist meals is not in the food itself, but the way in which it is served. In first class, a lovely hostess passes out white, starched napkins and then offers food from silver serving pieces; in tourist class, a single tray with napkin, silverware, and food is plunked down in front of each passenger and that is that.)

WHEN STRESS SUPERVENES

In terms of adaptation to stress, the family that has lived a hand-to-mouth existence has more difficulty than the family that is more or less intact. In the former, members tend to be preoccupied with self, and there is little chance for any emotional interaction.

When a family is faced with a crisis, the event is usually experienced first by the necessity for some change in role function. If the event is one for which the family is prepared, it may not be felt as a severe crisis. In frontier days, the family was organized along fairly rigid structural lines. They tilled the soil, cared for the livestock, harvested the crops, and baked the bread. During an Indian attack, there were ascribed roles for each family member. The father was the commander and handled the rifle. The wife had the task of loading the rifles and handing them to her husband. The eldest son might be the lookout and the youngest son the messenger. Thus, even so dire an emergency as an Indian attack might be handled without much loss of family equilibrium. The family had a prepared plan of adaptation or mobilization. The crisis could be felt in a physical sense, but the organizational plan took care of the emotional components of the crisis. This crisis brought forth family executive action, a "family ego-functioning," to borrow a term from individual psychology. It was a stressful situation but did not make for an emotional crisis.

If the father were wounded, however, the eldest son would have to take over command of the family, and this would necessitate a sharp role change. This, then, might constitute an emotional crisis. The eldest son must decide how the battle should be fought, whether to send the brother for help, or whether he thinks they can fight it out alone. Thus, the crisis revolves around change; the father has been wounded, so there must be a redefinition of roles, both on the performance (instrumental) level and on the emotional (expressive) level. The father may offer some battle advice, but still the eldest boy must decide what to do. There has been a change in the relationship between the mother and the eldest son in that she now has to look to him as head of the family. The youngest son must now view his brother as leader and put aside any feelings of sibling rivalry. (The effects of emotional role change are detailed in the next chapter.)

The crisis described above took place during an emergency. Not all family crises occur during emergencies but rather where changes in roles impend. Take the matter of stealing apples. A boy from a prominent family in a well-to-do suburb who is arrested for stealing apples brings shame and humiliation upon his family. The boy from the slums who steals apples might be seen as a "plucky kid." No role change is involved for the slum child, while there may be for the well-to-do youngster. Thus, the same event elicits contrasting responses: in one family a crisis situation results because of unexpected change in role; in the other family there is little reaction. One has to view an event in two dimensions—at times the emotional significance of the event itself will be more important; at times practical consequences of the event will have more impact. A family breadwinner losing his job may be experienced as a tragedy because of loss of income. In another family this same event is experienced primarily as a profound humiliation.

Recently, much has been written about short-term "crisis intervention" in families, the major intent being to define the family stress and to return the family to premorbid functioning (Langsley *et al.*, 1968) .

Family Homeostasis

The best functioning family is the one that maintains anxiety and conflict within tolerable limits. Or, if there is loss of family equilibrium, the healthy family can right itself. To characterize this phenomenon, the concept of "homeostasis" has been borrowed from physiology and was first applied to family study by Jackson (1957). How this concept evolved from the work of Claude Bernard has already been reviewed in Chapter II. Some writers are replacing the term "homeostasis" as it applies to the psychological aspects of individual and family living, with "homeo-dynamic equilibrium," the purpose being to indicate that there is not just a static equilibrium, but a balance between the past homeostatic forces and new ongoing experiences (I. Galdston, 1959). There is a need for growth as well as adjustment, or adaptation, suitable to the changing conditions of life.

The word "homeostasis" has undergone a considerable broadening since it was introduced by Bernard a century ago to indicate the steady state of the body chemistry and body physiology. Bernard described in great detail the mechanisms by which the body was able to maintain internal constancy by an interplay of dynamic forces. Family homeostasis represents the means by which a family maintains an internal equilibrium, so that it is able to fulfill its family tasks and allow for growth of the individual members. There is also the term "social homeostasis," an eponym for societal order which allows for health and growth of the total membership of that group.

As has been emphasized in the opening chapters, the concept of homeostasis refers to a range of functioning in which the organism—in this case, a family—can operate so that it is able to cope with stresses and yet fulfill all of its necessary functions. The simplest way of explaining homeostatic mechanisms is to use an analogy from physical medicine. Suppose a knee is injured. The part may be splinted in a number of ways: by hobbling around and favoring it, by using a crutch, by bandaging, or by applying a plaster cast. A new way of getting around is found, temporarily giving the injured part a chance to heal. If a plaster cast is used and is left on too long, however, some of the muscles may atrophy and permanent disability results (Fig. II). The pain is gone, but there is loss of function. With atrophy, the individual is in worse shape than when the knee was first injured.

AN INJURED PART   CAN BE SPLINTED TO FOSTER HEALING BY

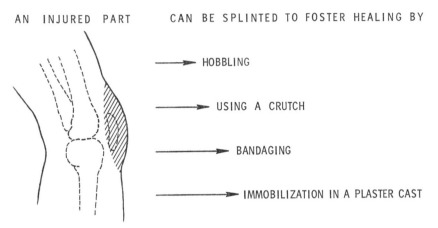

→ HOBBLING

→ USING A CRUTCH

→ BANDAGING

→ IMMOBILIZATION IN A PLASTER CAST

FIGURE II

The family, too, finds ways of dealing with stress until there can be resolution and a return of equilibrium. Some capacity for functioning may be sacrificed in order to control a conflict. Like the plaster cast, though, splinting can result in permanent loss of function, and this state of affairs is characterized by some as being equivalent to a *family defense:* there has been a change in "structure." Therefore, when such a family is confronted by a new stress, their functioning will be even more impaired than before. The family in which the members have withdrawn emotionally from one another will be in bad straits when they are forced to function as one unit. Thus the concept of a family defense implies that the homeostatic mechanisms have been extended to the point where a permanent change has taken place in role relationships or in family functioning. *The homeostatic mechanisms range from complete reversibility to complete irreversibility, and appraisal of the status of these mechanisms is the major focus of family diagnosis by the psychiatrist.*

To summarize, there are a group of homeostatic mechanisms

which serve to maintain the equilibrium within the family by splinting out areas of dysfunction. These mechanisms can cross the line and become inflexible or stereotyped, resulting in permanent disablement. With decompensation in any biological system, whether it be heart failure or failure in human interaction, more and more homeostatic mechanisms are brought into play to help the system keep going. However, the point of no return can be reached.

The family therapist opens up these areas of splinting and attempts to prevent fixidity or permanent atrophy of functioning. In essence, this may be what is fostered in the great emphasis today on "communication." By talking and confrontation, the family itself can open up these areas.

There are ways of maintaining homeostasis at a lower level of integration in which equilibrium or fulfillment of functions is not lost and after which there is a return to normal functioning. On the family interactional level, temporary withdrawal of affect can allow a conflict to "heal." The equilibrium is maintained but at a lower level and with some loss of functioning. *Homeostatic mechanisms,* as described in this chapter, tend to be temporary in nature; *defense mechanisms* imply pathology with more permanent, rather than temporary, loss of function. The crucial test is whether or not the mechanism remains open-ended. Can there be resolution of the conflict and reestablishment of full family functioning?

In a somewhat similar vein, Krober (1963) and Haan (1963) have written extensively about the coping functions of the individual's ego mechanisms. They differentiate between coping ego-behavior, which is flexible, involves choice, is oriented to reality, and operates in accordance with the necessities of the individual, versus defensive ego behavior, which is rigid, compelled, pushed from the past, distorting of the present situation, and usually involves magical thinking. These writers describe the ego mechanisms as inborn potentialities for behavior and subject to ontogenetic development.

Weinstock (1967) has also approached this problem by attempting to trace the longitudinal development of "defense and coping mechanisms" in the individual. The grossly immature child uses the parents as models and copies primitive behavioral mechanisms such as denial, regression, and doubting. As the child grows and his cognitive faculties develop, he is better able to confront conflict and control his impulses by utilizing more sophisticated and open-ended mechanisms. Thus, it is important to understand the child's level of cognitive functioning at the time significant family conflicts occur. The similarity here to Piaget's formulations (Chap. II) is obvious.

A Family Conflict

Family conflicts abound in daily life. For instance, there is an argument about whether the family should go to a movie. Some members want to go, others do not. There is a brief argument, some flurry of accusation, sulkiness on the part of one family member, and perhaps someone going off to his room. There is an awareness on the part of all, however, that this is not a permanent impairment. By the next morning, things are back to their usual state and the family has righted itself from the temporary upset.

Suppose, however, there is a conflict which involves a more disturbing element: a teen-age boy wants to go off with some friends for the weekend to see their football team play in another city. This is the first time that such a trip has been suggested, and when the subject is brought up, the mother immediately says "no" because she is afraid that her son may get involved in some kind of antisocial behavior, anything from drinking to sexual escapades. The father has mixed feelings about the idea. On the one hand, he shares some of his wife's fears, but he feels his son needs this opportunity to associate with his peers and to explore new vistas of life. The younger sibling immediately raises an objection because he feels this is a privilege to which the older boy is not entitled. A family argument takes place for the next hour or so. It can end when the father decides to join the mother and firmly says "no," assuring his son that in time he will be able to go on such trips and perhaps offering some substitute excursion. Or, the conflict can be resolved if the mother says the boy can go under certain conditions, such as his being properly chaperoned. (If the boy is allowed to go on the trip, some role change on the part of each family member is necessary, for the event heralds the fact that there is now another adult around the house.) If, however, there is no agreement on what course to pursue, and the conflict continues for many days, the family may use any of the following homeostatic mechanisms to control the conflict. (It should be remembered—as will be stressed later—that these are *temporary* mechanisms and are analogous to the splinting that takes place when a body part is injured.)

Family Homeostatic Mechanisms

Scapegoating

In the example used above, the child who brought up the subject of the trip may be labeled a rebel by the family members. He is the "cause" of all the trouble in the family. This labeling serves to control the conflict and reduce the parents' anxiety about restricting the boy. This mechanism works temporarily, but there is no growth toward resolution. If similar conflicts arise, chances are that the boy will more and more become the "rebel."

In studying scapegoating patterns in the family, one needs to know something about the circumstances of the parents' own primary homes of origin. A woman who feels herself deformed in any way—physically or emotionally—may "blame" her children for this deformity. Very often she unconsciously picks out the child born at a particularly stressful time in her life or a child with physical characteristics which unconsciously remind her of someone in her past. This child becomes the family scapegoat. Families are sometimes seen in which the oldest child has been marked for this role almost from the word "go." Investigation may reveal that the child was born during a period of great parental upheaval. One parent may feel that he or she would never have stayed in the marriage except for the birth of this child.‡ If a

---

‡Figures are hard to come by, but it is estimated that at the present time (early 1970's), as many as one third of the brides who walk to the altar are pregnant. A child born of such a marriage may be marked for scapegoating if there is marital discord. The couple may think, "If it weren't for him, we would not have married."

second child is born, the latter can become the desired and adored one (Vogel and Bell, 1960).

Scapegoating is often a mechanism used in the authoritarian family. In this family, the members are ruled by an unbending and intolerant parent. Although the family resents the authority and would like to neutralize it or rebel against it, they feel helpless to do so. When one member finally does rebel, even in some childish or immature way, the other members may label him as the rebel, the fool, the black sheep or, as used here, the scapegoat. The other family members can project onto this scapegoated individual all of the rebellious impulses they themselves harbor. At the same time, they punish him for his rebellion. It is fairly certain that the member who is scapegoated will maintain himself in this role as rebel, and the rest of the members can be counted on to keep punishing him. The trouble with the scapegoating mechanism is that there is never any resolution of the basic problem— the authoritarian nature of the family constellation. Scapegoating has lessened the tension, but it has blocked the way to solution of family problems. In general, the family says of the scapegoat, "He is different from me." It is only at the rare moment of insight that an individual says, "He is the same as me," and then there is growth.§

It is not unusual for one member of a family to "offer" himself as the scapegoat or sacrificial lamb in time of family conflict. During a family argument, the mother may end the disagreement by stating with finality, "It's all my fault, I have a headache." The other members can remark to themselves, "She's cranky today." By using this simple technique, the mother ends a bitter discussion, knowing that things will be better. On the other hand, she may make this statement in order to choke off discussion of a topic that stirs unbearable anxiety within herself, an entirely different motivation. Investigation may show that she utilizes this

---

§This concept has been extended to explain the biological basis of prejudice. When unacceptable impulses arise in an individual, they are projected onto a "feared stranger." The latter is generally a member of a minority group. From the standpoint of social evolution, the drawback of this mechanism is the fact that the stranger must be "kept in his place"—don't touch him, eat with him, etc. (West, 1967).

mechanism repeatedly. Unless the woman understands the underlying cause of her anxiety, resolution of certain conflicts in the family may be interfered with.

It is often found that a child who is picked for the role of scapegoat in the family can, at other times, be projected into the role as healer for the family wounds, or protector of a parent.

Following is a clinical example of scapegoating.

A youth of eighteen was admitted to a psychiatric ward late one spring because he had threatened suicide. He had been in psychotherapy and had done well for a time, but then became depressed and was beset by fears that he would do away with himself.The boy was initially seen alone. He was quite obese, no dieting routine ever having been of help. He had had asthma and eczema as a child and was consequently babied by his mother. He described his home as one of constant turmoil. His father drank heavily and had an explosive temper. They lived in an apartment which was much too small for them. Hovering over the family were a great-aunt and great-uncle, who periodically gave the family money. The boy stated that his father had been considered a rare memory expert as a child, but as he grew up he seemed to lose his talent. He had drifted from job to job in adult life, never achieving a stable work situation. Thus the family was always under economic pressure and was beholden to the extended family for support. As an adolescent, the youth (our patient) always had trouble keeping friends. When a friendship was going well, "something" would always happen to dissolve it. The most satisfying time in his life was a year spent at a small liberal arts college in the Midwest. He tended to be a "maternal" figure—fellow students came to him with their problems, and he was the carrier of gossip from one group to another, all of which gained him popularity. Although academically he did excellent work, the faculty were disturbed by his "immature behavior" and suggested he leave before the year was out "to have a chance to mature" and also to seek psychiatric treatment.

While he was in the psychiatric hospital, the boy and his family were seen together. There were three other children in this family, a boy of sixteen, a sister fifteen, and a boy twelve. The patient sat in the center of the family group between the two younger children. The father and mother sat together at one end with the great-aunt and at the other end sat the sixteen-year-old. When the therapist asked the family what the problem was, the answers were diverse and unclear. The father stated the boy was "nervous"; the mother stated that she felt terribly guilty because she had not known how depressed the boy was; the aunt stated the whole trouble was that the boy had stayed at home instead of coming to live with her. The mother countered by saying that the problem was that the youth would never "take hold in life," was lackadaisical and immature, and that it did not matter where he lived.

The therapist tried to explore the relationship between husband and wife, but this proved to be impossible since the aunt kept interceding. The aunt had always felt responsible for her niece because the latter's mother had died when the girl was fourteen. The aunt had tried to guide and direct her niece, and had met with varied success. Occasionally the niece would listen; more often, she would not. The aunt sat like Queen Victoria with arms and legs folded tightly. At one point the therapist decided to excuse her, stating that he saw she was "uncomfortable." She left the room fuming, and it was later reported by the social worker that she was extremely bitter. (The therapist had done this on purpose: better that she vent some of her spleen toward him than allow the family to founder during the interview because of her overbearing presence.)

The mother and father were still deeply tied to their own families of origin. They depended on them for money and for guidance. In effect, their own children had many sets of parents. Although the woman kept using the phrase, "let's face it," it was clear from the discussion that this couple had never faced life directly. When she used this phrase, her husband's face and neck flushed with anger, and he sat back in his chair, kicking one leg with vengeance. When the therapist noted this behavior, the woman said sharply that her husband refused to face the fact that he was not making a proper living and was not providing sufficiently for his family. The apartment was too small, food and clothes were scarce. The best the man could do was to respond with some chagrin that he recently had found a job and felt it might work out. Further, he insisted that they would sometimes have to "take" from the parents, and there was "no sense in getting disturbed about it."

At one point in the interview, the wife attacked the husband, pointing her finger at him. He, in turn, immediately began attacking his son. Later in the interview, the father was asked what he thought was wrong with the boy. He stated that his son had never been able to face life and that he had always been worried about him because of this fact. There was a constant series of battles between the father and the boy. Generally, the mother would intervene on the side of the boy and would "protect" and baby him. She stated that when she heard a few weeks previous that the boy was sick and needed hospitalization, she suddenly felt that she wanted to cradle him to her bosom as she had always done. When the examiner pointed out that she still tried to baby him, she flushed with embarrassment and replied, "Yes, but I just can't help it." During the session the younger children volunteered little. Occasionally, the eighteen-year-old would bring them into the conversation by focusing on the hope that things would be better for them. However, it was disclosed that he periodically attacked them viciously, and once when he was uncontrollably angry, he even attempted to choke his younger sister.

It was apparent during the interview that the father and mother had never faced up to their responsibilities as adults. The mother had made an attempt to deal with some of her own difficulties, as well as those of the family, during a brief period of psychotherapy at a mental health clinic; when the father was invited to attend, he refused. Since the present interview was for purposes of disposition as well as diagnosis, the examiner told the father that we would not join the wife in "pointing the finger at him." He flushed. The therapist suggested that a lot of fingers had been pointed in this family to find scapegoats and that they would need help to change this system.

The father then talked about the fact that he was exploited as a child by his own father. Although he had been put on exhibition frequently and had made a great deal of money, none was ever given to him. His expectation in life, then, was that he would be exploited, and this was pointed out to him. Further, the shoe was now on the other foot; he was exploiting others.

In summary, the oldest boy was a convenient scapegoat for the parental inadequacies. They were not able to face up to life, but it was easier to decry this behavior in the son. Just as a family rebel usually stays in that role, here, too, the eighteen-year-old boy was filling the bill. Also, scapegoaters are prone to be vindictive: some inhibited parents want their children to become even more inhibited than they themselves are. If they are not free to assert themselves, then why should their children be! This eighteen-year-old learned early in life to curb attempts at being assertive.

In our time, with more mental health facilities available, problem children are very frequently referred for psychological testing or psychiatric examination. Once this has been done, and the parents have paid seventy-five dollars for the evaluation, the child who might well have been a scapegoat for family conflicts is now more than ever fixed in that role. It becomes necessary, then, for the professional to structure his testing in such a way that the family is part of the procedure.

Formation of Defensive Alliances or Coalitions

In the situation described previously under "A Family Conflict," let us suppose that the father joins with the boy and says that he can go on the weekend trip, even though the mother demurs. An open debate follows in which the father and son are on one side, the mother and younger sibling on the other. These alliances may then extend into other areas: the father and son may go off hiking together or the mother and the younger sibling may go off on a shopping spree. There is a type of "splitting" among various members of the family. As noted previously, this alliance-formation occurs temporarily in most families when one member comes to the support of another during an argument, but generally it withers away. It is a routine part of family life. However, *permanent* defensive alliances seriously impair the adaptive function of the family. Such an instance is demonstrated by the following clinical vignette.

John S. was a nineteen-year-old student who was referred to a psychiatrist by his parents for treatment of homosexuality. They sent him to the therapist "in order that something be done about the homosexuality." The family had known of the boy's homosexuality for two years, but only lately had they become uncomfortable about it. They boy himself stated that he was not concerned, that he participated actively in homosexual activity, and enoyed this way of life. When asked whether there were any problems he did want help with, he admitted that he was easily influenced by his homosexual friends to behave in a immature, prankish manner. This behavior included such things as staying out all night, driving wildly and noisily in a rented car, and calling up strangers in the middle of the night. John stated he was willing to talk about how to improve his social relationships but had no desire to do anything about the homosexuality. John gave all of the above information readily and was invited to come in again, this time with his family. The latter group consisted of the father and mother and a large German Shepherd. The dog lay protectively at the mother's side during the interview.

The father owned several farms outside a small cotton town where he was the municipal judge and one of the town's leading citizens. The wife and son joined in to testify as to the father's business success and civic importance. He was a massive man, well over six feet tall, wore horn-rimmed glasses, and his hair was slicked back with a patent leather look. He spoke in sonorous tones and dropped names of

United States Senators whom he felt free to call when he needed them. The wife, on the other hand, seemed quiet and reticent and stated that all she cared about was having peace in the family. She had been brought up in a home with a tyrannical and overbearing father and had seen enough "fussing" in her life.

During the interview, it became evident that the husband carried on extramarital activities both in the town and on business trips. The wife hinted that she knew about these but stated that what he did away from home was "his business." Nevertheless, the barbs she tossed at him were clearly indicative of the hostility she felt toward him. When the psychiatrist questioned the husband further about his personal life, he was evasive and resorted to talking about all of his accomplishments and about his many important acquaintances. He did state, however, that in his own home his mother had worn the pants. When the relationship between John and his father was brought up again, the older man went back to talking about his own achievements. He undermined the boy's attempts at assertion.

It was apparent that the father felt inadequate in his masculine role and could tolerate no challenge to his position. Accordingly, any attempt toward masculinity on the part of the boy was thwarted, and toward this aim, the father was abetted by his wife. She kept the boy close to home and raised him in a rather "sissyish" fashion. The family had been troubled when he reached the age to begin social contacts with girls, yet made no move toward dating any of the girls in town.

The hypothesis in the case was that the boy's homosexuality reflected the family's inability to tolerate any masculinity other than the father's. In this endeavor, there was a coalition between the two spouses: the father was unable to withstand competition because of his own sense of inadequacy; the mother feared that any show of masculinity would again result in her being dominated and humiliated. She therefore managed to tie the boy to her apron strings. When he took a job as a camp counselor at seventeen, he called home every night and wrote her long letters. When he went off to prep school, the mother stayed with him a few days "to help him get adjusted." (It is interesting that the public image this family presented was that of a close-knit group in which the father was strong and dominant.) From a therapeutic standpoint, the only hope was to help the boy withstand the pathogenic influence of his family until he was able to leave home and be on his own. It was not clinically feasible to attempt an alteration of the parents' adjustment to life.

Withdrawal of Affect

Here the family handles its problems by ceasing emotional communication with each other, and conflicts remain unresolved. Using the family problem cited previously in which the conflict centered around the teen-age boy's desire to go off on a weekend trip, let us say the father sullenly refuses to give in, as does the mother, and gradually the family members become cold and distant. They go through the motions of family functioning, but there is no meaningful emotional contact among them. Families who routinely control a conflict by withdrawal of affect become mechanized, rigid families, often like military organizations. In such a family, all the children may go "through" the mother in order to talk to the father, or vice-versa. There is a chain of command, of which the family may be almost totally unaware. Sometimes the members attempt to make affective contacts outside the family, the father in his business and the mother at clubs. The children find emotional contacts with peers and parents of peers.

In marriages in which affective (emotional) contact between the mates is withdrawn, both can look for substitutes. However, the infant or young child has no such opportunity because of his age. Also, in families where parents are still completely "tied" to their own parents, i.e. where they are still excessively dependent on them for acceptance and emotional gratification, the second-generation offspring will be shortchanged by the lack of emotional interaction with their parents. In our time, this same situation is often duplicated by an artifact of psychotherapy and therefore raises a pertinent question: Should both parents of young children be in intensive individual psychotherapy or psychoanalysis at the same time? From the standpoint of the children, probably not. Much of the matrix of emotional interaction between parent and child is based on the projection of certain expectations and unresolved needs from the parent's past onto the child.|| To

----

||Rather gruesome validation of this fact comes from study of battered children. A man who fractured his nine-month-old son's skull said, "He thinks he's boss, trying to run things, but I showed him who's in charge around here." The father's own father was an alcoholic who beat and tyrannized him in his childhood (R. Galdston, 1965).

these messages, the child reacts, and from them, he learns a range of emotional signals and responses. In these "transference" aspects of the relationship, the parent projects different "pieces" of his own personality onto the child. (One is struck by the number of languages in which the colloquialism "little father" or "little mother" is used by the parent to address a child.) These elements make for intense emotional interaction between parent and child. The nature of these emotional interactions changes as both parent and child move through various developmental sequences. But the developing child needs the intensity of the whole range of emotional responses in order to develop the capacity to deal in all of these areas as he matures.

If both parents are being psychoanalyzed at the same time, each is involved emotionally with someone outside the family; each can resolve "transferences" with the aid of a therapist. However, this tends to muffle emotional responses within the family, and young children may suffer. If only one parent is in therapy, the other is then available to fill some of the void.

The writer was once asked to evaluate a family of four in which each parent had been in analysis for over five years. The older child—a girl of nine—had been seeing a psychologist for three years; the younger child—a boy of seven—had been seeing a social worker for two years. Four people were thus being seen by four different therapists. It is not necessary to recite the individual symptoms here, but beyond the family's ability to communicate factual material to each other, there was literally no interaction on an emotional level.

In some families, no show of emotion is tolerated. Emotionality may signify loss of control or giving in to unacceptable impulses. In such a family, the child learns to suppress emotionality.

A young physician came for psychiatric consultation because of a peptic ulcer. He was always under great tension, and in his practice was so conscientious that he never took a day off except when he was ill. He took his patients' problems home with him and slept fitfully when he had a troublesome case. His concern was not so much with their medical problems as with their personal problems. He himself recognized that his emotional involvement with patients was excessive.

The man then related that he was the only boy in a family in which there were two older girls. Both his parents worked and had little time for the family except to lecture them about success. His father, who had been orphaned as a child, worked for a steamship company. Early home life was similar to a military camp; the father said little except to enforce discipline by lecturing. Neither the father nor the mother could tolerate anything "emotional." Contacts outside the family were discouraged. The boy had received all A's in school, was a varsity athlete, and had scholarships through college and medical school, but there was never a word of praise or indication of approval of the son's success on the part of the parents, particularly the father. When he began his medical practice, the parents asked only how many patients he was seeing each day, wanting to know if he were "keeping busy." Eventually his father began badgering him to do some work for the steamship line. He did not want or need this extra involvement because he was already too busy, but at his father's insistence he took on the extra work; after that, it was getting a travel pass which would allow him free travel. When he finally obtained the pass, the father showed the free pass to all of his associates. To the father, this was more important than the boy's medical degree or other awards. The son had no self-esteem and constantly sought approval from everyone, particularly his patients. They satisfied the hunger which carried over from early life.¶

In the rigid family that is bent on controlling affect, there is little opportunity for relief of conflict by humor or nonsense. Healthy families know that within the confines of the family there are certain freedoms not available elsewhere. In a family setting, one does not have to keep one's guard up, and even a bit of foolishness and irrationality is allowed. Such a transient and nonstereotyped reaction is the following:

A man pressured and harried by business, worried about meeting payrolls and other debts, may suddenly announce to his wife somtime in late autumn that they "will not celebrate any holidays at the end of the year." If the wife is aware of her husband's emotional state at the moment, she can pass this off lightly, or she can smile and say that perhaps they had better think about it an-

¶Such children have trouble deciding if a job is well done. After all, they have been exposed only to the theme that what was done was not good enough. There was no range of comparison between a job very well done, fairly done, and poorly done. In adult life they seek constant appraisal from those around them as to the quality of their work; this incessant need often brings rejection and alienation.

other day. Trouble arises when the woman sees this as a serious and permanent decision, and is not flexible enough to apply a measure of lightheartedness to the situation.

Designation of One Member As Family Healer

In this homeostatic mechanism, one member of the family is designated as "umpire" or "healer" and contacts the dissenting parties to arrange a truce or reconciliation. Frequently, it is a grandparent or some person in the extended family regarded as the "wise one," or it may be someone who reminds the family of a person in the past who fell into this role. At times, someone outside the family, such as the family doctor, may be brought in for this purpose. Koos (1950) found that while the family healer was usually a member of the immediate family or the extended family, occasionally it was the druggist or storekeeper. In some families, the family healer is designated the "white sheep"; the scapegoat is the "black sheep."

In treating families, the therapist learns to use the role of family healer to involve a recalcitrant family member in therapy. A person in treatment may insist that the spouse or parent absolutely refuses to be involved, even though the therapist sends repeated invitations. If this resistant member is approached on the basis of "helping the patient," it is doubtful that he will refuse to participate, since very few people can resist the offer of "helping." This fact of life is used effectively in a number of ways. The typical Alcoholics Anonymous member "helps" his fellow alcoholics, as does the member of Synanon, the group that is active among drug addicts. The colostomy or laryngectomy patient may benefit enormously by talking to someone who has already had the operation.

In a remarkable little study done in a concentration camp, Selma Fraiberg (1962) found the helper role important. Despite the awesome and terrible circumstances people were forced to live under in these camps, when they could help someone worse off than they, it gave them a feeling of genuine satisfaction. Writing about brainwashing in concentration camps, she points out that the Nazis did not let prisoners help one another, and this was a powerful weapon in dehumanization.** Often, a prisoner was beaten to a pulp and left in everyone's view. No one was allowed to minister to the ravaged person. She describes what happened in one instance when she was allowed to help an old woman carry a pail of water to the shower. The woman had had both her arms broken by the Nazis, and Fraiberg describes her great feelings of elation at being able to help this woman.

What seems to be involved in all these instances is that the person in the helper role is enhanced as much as, or more than, the person who is being helped. By helping others, there may be an increase in self-esteem or enhancement of a feeling of self-worth. To some people, this represents fulfilling The Golden Rule. At the deepest level, there is some gratification of primordial feelings of omnipotence.††

In the area of social interaction, there is an interesting report by Wittenberg (1948) in which he describes the formation of a neighborhood block committee to help other deprived people living there. One of the persons participating was a woman who had been on public assistance and who had severe personality difficulties. Her involvement in helping others led to a marked positive change in her own personality. This principle is useful in school situations as well. When sixth-grade slow readers are asked to help third-grade slow readers, the older ones seem to benefit even more than the younger ones. Thus it is wise to avoid letting *only* "gifted" children read to or help younger or less-gifted children. After all, the child of average or less than average ability probably has a deeper need for enhancement of self-esteem than the gifted child. What better way to accomplish this than putting him in the role of helping or "teaching" someone else?

**One cannot speak of dehumanization in contemporary times without noting the effects of "television wars," i.e. everyday action on the battlefield filmed for nightly television viewing in the home. After watching hundreds of such telecasts, the average viewer begins to make little distinction between men dying on the battlefield and similar scenes in Western movies showing mass killing. Dehumanization has been complete.

††Emergency room physicians sometimes use this knowledge of the helper role when a patient dies as the result of an accident; the physician may suggest to the family that the fatally-injured person's kidneys or other organs be made available for transplant. In this way, a family may find "meaning" in the needless death.

A variant of the family healer is the designation of one family member as "protector" of another within the family constellation. The protector has the capacity to "take it." The following clinical vignette is illustrative.

Larry, age seventeen, was brought by his mother for psychiatric evaluation. She had been badgering the school about his poor grades. The guidance counselor told her that the school was not alarmed, that in time they felt the boy would "come around." Larry was extremely intelligent and very talented musically. He played half a dozen instruments ranging from piano to oboe. Because of his musical talents, he was accepted by a summer music institute at a university, a highly-coveted recognition. In addition, he worked after school to buy records and also to buy himself a motorcycle. He had a number of girlfriends but had never "gone steady." At the initial interview, the mother talked first about Larry's school problems then shifted the conversation to his struggles with his father. She described her husband as a martinet who demanded total compliance to authority. However, his means of enforcing this compliance were unique. He would send a verbal message to one member of the family by another member—there was a younger brother, a quiet, passive boy—or else he might leave a note asking for a change of behavior. This was tantamount to an order from "on high." If this did not work, he would then launch into a tirade against the two boys in the family, stating that, if possible, he would like to confine them on bread and water. (The father had been a sea captain.) The father steadfastly refused to come to the interview, despite all personal appeals by the therapist.

After the detailed history was obtained about the boy's school troubles, his behavior at home, and the struggles with his father, the psychiatrist asked the mother if there were any marital problems. She responded with, "Boy, are there!" emphatically punctuating her answer by rolling her head and eyes in a backward, circular motion. When asked if there had been any separations, she stated that she had thought about it but had never done so because of the children. Also, in her family there was a cultural interdiction against divorce. Each time she began discussing her marital problems, she wound up talking about Larry and his problems.

Larry then brought up the possibility of going off to a high school for musically-gifted children during the next school year. The mother stated she thought this would be very good, but she did not know if he could "adjust." He felt confident, but the mother insisted that they needed more time to think about it: he had only recently brought up this idea. Further, she said she had heard that it is best not to separate families. The examiner stated that since Larry was seventeen, seemed to have some eagerness about trying this new school, and since it would open up many opportunities in music for him, perhaps it would be beneficial. The mother then countered that they could not afford it, but presently it came out that Larry could probably get a music scholarship. Again she went back to the issue of whether he could get along: after all, he had never learned to be obedient to his father so how could he take discipline away from home? She was soon off once again, expounding her son's problems. However, this time when she talked about his rebelliousness and baiting of his father, a triumphant smile crossed her face.

It soon became evident that the mother was using the boy as a weapon, having him fight the battles with the father, since she could never do so. The son was, in effect, the mother's "protector." Family problems interfered with his doing his best work at school, but because the school officials recognized this fact, they were not alarmed by his academic performance. In many other areas, the boy did quite well. The primary reason behind his being brought for psychiatric evaluation was the mother's awareness that he would soon leave home, leaving her "exposed" to her husband's tirades. Perhaps the psychiatrist could label the boy "sick" and thus keep him at home.‡‡

In our time we are seeing a relatively new phenomenon—legal divorces of many middle-class couples who are in their fifties and sixties. No doubt some of this is a reflection of greater affluence; more of the middle class can now afford divorce financially, which only the upper class could afford decades ago. But on closer inspection, these "20-year fractures" are often seen to follow a significant change in the life situation, such as a parent-in-law dying, transfer of the husband for business reasons to a new locale, or the last child leaving home (Messer, 1969a). Any of these events tend to throw a couple more on their own and may open up latent conflicts. These conflicts might have been neutralized in the previous environment, but the neutralizing factor is no longer present.

___

‡‡One of the most frequent crises in a family is the one which occurs when an adolescent is about to leave home. This event may force the parents to interact more directly rather than via an adolescent. There may also be a phantasy, as in this case, that one parent is helplessly "exposed" to the other. In clinical practice, April and May seem to be the months for a barrage of telephone calls from families in crisis. It may be that the awareness of the impending departure hits home then.

Loosening the Family Unit

Here the family members deal with conflicts by finding emotional satisfaction in contacts with people outside the family. Home is a hotel where all the tenants are on good terms. A son may spend most of his time with peers, staying out until all hours. Similarly, the mother and father may find substitutes for family activities in friends or clubs. In effect, each member finds a "new family" for himself. The difference between this mechanism and the mechanism of withdrawal of affect is that here the family members are on good terms when they are in contact with each other.

Discharge of Tension by Repetitive Fighting

To cope with everyday tensions and frustrations, "blowing your top" brings some relief. Who does not rant about traffic jams or the undependability of automobile mechanics? The wise family learns not to make a federal case out of a minor incident or temporary disagreement. The child who threatens to run away from home may not appreciate a long intellectual inquest at the time of the particular outburst.

In some families, however, tensions are discharged by verbal abuse or physical battles which occur with regularity. Loud complaints, curses, or accusations are hurled which ordinarily might not be said. ("You really know how a person feels when he gets angry.") These fights do succeed in draining off tension and hostility and allow for emotional harmony among the family members. The theme of the fight may be repetitive, and almost any area of conflict can be poured into the mold of this particular theme. In one family it was "moving." The husband had a fine business opportunity far away from the family's home. He insisted they move. The wife had been reluctant to leave the area where her parents lived, and this became a common theme in family arguments. During a treatment session, when a conflict about their children arose, the man said to his wife, "All right, I know we should never have moved. Let's go through the song and dance and get it over with."

This mechanism of fighting is often seen in the marriage in which one member has never had a satisfying dependency relationship. A child who has been abandoned is a good example. There is always some resentment over the abandonment, as well as the expectation that nurturant needs will never be fulfilled. When such an individual moves toward a close and trusting relationship, the old fears and angers are stirred up; the anxiety generated can be discharged by fighting. The cat-and-dog marriage (or "gruesome-twosome") is common.

"Resignation" or Compromise

Here the members give up their needs for assertion, affection, or emotional expression. In a family with an obsessive father who rules with an iron fist, the mother and children may compromise any assertive demands or desires for emotional freedom in order to keep peace and harmony in the family. This then becomes a frozen family.

Compromises in a family are sometimes quite blatant, as when one partner gives up all need for sexual satisfaction to accommodate the other's sexual inhibitions. However, compromises can be more subtle, especially when linked with a consensus that all is well in the family except for "one little thing."

> Mr. and Mrs. C. had been married for twelve years. They were referred for consultation because of "bickering." Mr. C. was a trial lawyer who gave up a successful practice to become Executive Director of a large service organization. His wife, a former legal secretary, had encouraged him in this move because it meant "security." The couple had two children, ten and eight, and the woman had gone back to work, since the children were in school most of the day. The "bickering" had to do with Mr. C.'s complaints that his wife did not share her feelings with him, was always too busy to listen to him, did not "encourage" him, and avoided him sexually. Mrs. C. countered that he wanted "too much" and that she could not possibly satisfy all of his needs. During the interview, the subject of the job change came up repeatedly. Mr. C. confessed that he was extremely unhappy in his work because he felt like a clerk to a very dynamic president. He was allowed to make no decisions of substance and had to be "on call" at all times. Periodically, he considered leaving the job and reopening a

law office, but his wife always reminded him of the security and prestige of his present position.

Mrs. C. was one of four children, three daughters and a younger son. Her mother was the "strong" parent. Mrs. C. stated she felt uncomfortable with "strong men" and remarked that she had been more comfortable with her husband since he left trial work; previously, he had always seemed "too aggressive."

Mr. and Mrs. C. had suppressed their feelings of frustration in their overriding concern for "security." Mr. C. surrendered his masculine prerogatives for independence and assertivity in order to neutralize his wife's inability to tolerate the challenge of a "strong man." Toward the end of the interview, he stated that he had recently become sexually impotent. It was pointed out to him that his sexual impotence was a reflection of the impotence he felt as a man. This remark stirred a thought that outraged him even further: no longer did he think of himself simply as a clerk in the organization but as a "feminine" person to a very "masculine" president.

The Family Myth

This mechanism overlaps some of the other homeostatic mechanisms. Some families handle conflict by invoking a stated belief much in the same way that folklore is used to overcome certain anxieties. A child can control some of his inner fears by projecting these fears onto an outside boogeyman. In a family in which there is a struggle between parents and children, the family myth may become, "Children are seen but not heard." This tack dispenses with conflicts that may arise, such as the parents' feeling that the emotional push of creative or demanding children is too much; it resolves the conflict and, as a matter of fact, nips it in the bud before it really begins. The myth is part of the family identity and as such goes unchallenged (Ferreira, 1967).

The following clinical vignette is recounted to illustrate how a myth comes to be established in a family.

A family was interviewed at length, during which time it was learned that a myth existed to the effect that if anyone drank, he might become an alcoholic. Investigation revealed that indeed one of the relatives—a distant uncle—had been a chronic alcoholic and had brought great shame upon the family. His behavior was far out of line with the idealized behavior of this family. The concern generated by this aspect of the family history created anxiety, which was controlled by the family myth—if anyone drinks, he becomes an alcoholic.

Who enforced the myth? In this particular family, it was the mother. She was allowed to control the behavior of all the family members, the husband usually acceding to her authority. However, he did not go along with the alcohol myth and, further, there was evidence that he resented this myth governing the family's conduct. The matter came to a head when their adolescent boy was beginning to go out with his friends; some of the boys sneaked a can of beer or a glass of wine occasionally. The woman handled this problem by invoking the family myth, and a head-on conflict resulted. The boy was attempting to assert himself in typical adolescent fashion but had to deal with the values he had learned in his family. The anxiety generated in the boy by this conflict might have been handled by his becoming passive and retreating from these activities; but, as often happens in adolescent rebellion, he lashed out against the mother's authority. In this instance the boy was being covertly supported by his father and so continued on the latter course.

Gehrke and Kirschenbaum (1967) suggest that myths are nuclear in "family survival." For example, in their "Repressive Family," the myth in the family is that open and impulsive expression of emotion will bring about loss of love or abandonment. Consequently, children become immobilized by this inhibition toward expression of fear and rage. In their "Suicidal Family," no family member can function alone. Consequently, the myth is that the family cannot survive if any member leaves it. These survival myths are contrasted with "Reality Survival Concepts": all the members of the family are involved in a system that is oriented toward growth and creativity. The myths protect the family from recognition of certain impulses, but they inhibit the growth and differentiation of the family's functioning.§§

"Reaction Formation"

Often one sees a family in which there is an "over-harmony" or

§§In the play, *Who's Afraid of Virginia Woolf?* the central characters are a middle-aged couple who concern themselves constantly with the health of their mythical son. By so doing, the husband does not have to face his own inadequacy and impotence; the wife need not deal with the fact that she has lived her life in the shadow of an authoritarian and self-centered father. Once the myth becomes known to another couple, the system begins to change. Truth gradually becomes separated from illusion.

an "over-togetherness" based on the fact that a breakup is impending. The model here is the psychic defense mechanism of reaction formation: traumatic ideas are repressed and transformed into opposites. Thus, the overly hostile individual has a perpetual smile. Families which insist to the therapist that there is harmony everywhere may be living in a house of cards. Sometimes a clue to the fragility is the constriction in range of function, despite their high good humor. In healthy families, along with humor and a consensus that all is well, goes expansivity and creativity, rather than limitation or constriction. Thus, if one examines a family with limited adaptive resources, they may assure the therapist that everything is fine despite the fact that they are precariously compensated. On the other hand, the family with good adaptive resources can readily describe their conflicts and anxieties. (The teacher who is secure with a pupil can both praise and scold the child with ease; the teacher who is frozen emotionally can do neither comfortably but does both to extreme.)

In some families in which there is a consensus that "all is well," an injunction can exist against anyone expressing negative feelings. When the family encounters feelings of depression or resentment, instead of being able to express these feelings directly (and perhaps to counterbalance them with a positive expression), the family experiences great tension. This area of expression has been closed off for them. The family therapist must explore such an injunction to find its source. It might stem from the pathology of one member: perhaps it is a reflection of the mother's personality. Family members learn never to talk about things that will "upset mother," and the extension of this is never to talk about these subjects at all. Such a family is in disequilibrium because they are all buffaloed by one individual's needs. The woman's husband may know that it is sheer misery when she is upset, and he imposes the same burden on the children: never mention anything unpleasant because it will "upset mother."

In some authoritarian families, the child may be made to feel guilty over anything he receives. He has little chance to mature in such a family; he always remains somewhat brittle. Learning is impeded because free and open interchange is not allowed.

A family had a very wealthy great-uncle. He was retired and getting on in years, and the parents made it quite clear to the children that they anticipated an inheritance some day. Accordingly, the mother sacrificed everything to make the uncle happy, even though underneath she resented it bitterly and the children were well aware of this. Therefore, the family value was always to be subservient and to placate the uncle. The children were expected to be grateful to the mother for denying her own needs to cater to the uncle. This situation put an inordinate stress on freedom within the family and impeded the ability of the children to learn a total ensemble of emotional responses. Beneath the facade of subservience and gratitude, resentment smoldered.

Chapter V

Emotional Role

People, people who need people, are the luckiest people
in the world.
We're children needing other children,
and yet letting our grown-up pride hide all the need
inside,
acting more like children than children.
Lovers are very special people,
they're the luckiest people in the world.
With one person, one very special person, a feeling
deep in your soul says: you were half, now you're whole.
No more hunger and thirst,
but first be a person who needs people.
People who need people are the luckiest people in the
world.

From Funny Girl, the story of Fanny Brice.

A family man whose wife becomes incapacitated and who has to take over many of her duties in caring for the household may *perform* this role admirably. But how does he feel inwardly about this situation? Is he comfortable in what might be described as a "feminine" role? Does he resent being cast into this new *social* role and does he feel tense in this role? Even though he does the work that is necessary, does he detest it?

How a person feels emotionally toward a given performance role or social role in life is often as important, or perhaps more important at times, than his actual performance in that role.

In the previous chapter, the necessity for members of the family to assume roles in order to fulfill the various family functions was stressed. Someone must be the breadwinner, someone must care for the young children, and someone must fulfill the needs for intimacy and warmth. These functions are shared by all, and the greatest flexibility for role sharing exists in the healthiest families. What is seldom stressed is the emotional response of an individual to a role he must fulfill. The aim of this chapter is to emphasize the emotional component of performance roles.

The function of emotions in alerting the organism and signaling other organisms has been covered in Chapter II. "Emotional role," as the term is used here, refers to an individual's emotional response to a given performance role or social role. Many an individual performs competently in his job yet dreads going to work each morning.

Change in performance role often precipitates an emotional crisis. For example, in wartime, when there is a shortage of officers, military selection boards make on-the-spot promotions of enlisted men, usually chief petty officers in the Navy and sergeants in the Army. While the promotion to officer rank seems to be a fine recognition for the man, this new role may create havoc in his own emotional economy. After many years in the service, he is quite capable of performing any job he is assigned, since he knows the service inside and out. But the emotional demands of a highly responsible position—the place where the buck stops and cannot be passed on—may be too much for him. The tension may be reflected in a number of ways: his behavior may become rigid and stereotyped; he may resort to alcohol in order to relieve tension; or, as happens all too frequently, he may become a psychiatric casualty.

SOCIAL ROLE AND SICK ROLE

By and large, the study of the concept of role has been mainly the province of the sociologist. Parsons and Bales (1955) define role as a goal-directed pattern of acts a person may carry out in a social group. These acts are tailored by the cultural process. A person achieves a particular status in society, and there is an expected pattern of behavior that goes along with this status—his *social role*. Further, status can be broken down into *achieved* status, which is the result of what one does with one's life or *how* he behaves, and *ascribed* status, which is a *consequence of birth*. Achieved status derives from education, occupation and marriage. Ascribed status is the result of age, sex, race, religious or ethnic background. Each person—whether it be a physician, a teacher, a group therapist, a bank president, or a bank clerk—is expected to conform to the prescribed mode of behavior relative to his position. A person is often labeled mentally ill when his behavior is widely deviant from that expected in his particular social role. Also, each of these statuses, with their related expectancies, varies from culture to culture.*

Every person has several roles which he fulfills: one at work, one at home, one at Sunday school, one at the PTA, and so on. Parsons has also defined the "sick role." By definition, being in a sick role exempts a person from certain ordinary obligations, whether it be going to work, going to school, or behaving exactly according to the expectations of society. The "sick role" allows wide latitude of symptoms, anything from a sore throat to emotional upset. Being in the sick role does not automatically mean, however, that there is direct progression to the patient role. A person may recover from his "sickness" spontaneously or he may recover by having something done for him. Before one becomes a patient, one must be defined as such, and the "definer" can be the individual himself, his family, or the community. A person who develops a severe headache, takes several aspirins, and goes home to bed has put himself in the sick role; but unless he seeks the help or advice of someone regarding the pain, he does not automatically proceed to the patient role. There are those instances when an individual exploits his position in the sick role to become a patient, thereby obtaining safety or gratification by this maneuver, as, for example, the individual who avoids military service or who maintains himself on compensation payments from an insurance company.

With the concept of "sick role," the sociologist moves closer to

---

*Society is reluctant to allow some of its members to escape from their social—in this case, professional—role. The physician is always "on call": he is expected to answer any medical questions, whether he be in his office, on a hunting trip, or at a softball game. The clergyman is expected to be ready to provide spiritual comfort to others, no matter what his own personal needs may be (see Emotional Role Sets). The inability to escape from a particular social role may constitute an enormous drain on an individual. No wonder a vacation is "getting away from it all."

psychiatry and psychodynamics. The sociologist is talking about emotional attitudes toward sickness. As noted, little attention has been paid to emotional attitude toward social roles and, actually, the study of emotional attitudes toward sickness is a fairly recent undertaking. Sociologists are certainly not competent to deal with these emotional factors and, for some reason, psychiatrists have avoided this area. In part, this may stem from the fact that Freud tended to neglect emotions in his early writings. Guilt and shame are mentioned in various papers, but except for dealing with rage in the paper on depression in 1917 ("Mourning and Melancholia"), emotions are not central in his theory building until 1926 (*The Problem of Anxiety*). In Freud's view, behavior was based on the vicissitudes of the instincts. Emotions were secondary, or epi-phenomena, to instinctual drives.

EMOTIONAL INFLUENCE ON ROLE

We tend to label psychiatric illness as emotional disorder, as noted in Chapter II. This is inexact, for psychiatric illness may be related to disorders of the hedonic (pain-pleasure) level of integration. In the family or small group, emotions are used constantly for communication. As defined in Chapter II, emotions are patterns of organized events occurring in interaction of organism and environment that serve to alert the organism and to elicit a response. Since the family and the small group are the mainstays for emotional communication, emotional role is learned primarily from family experience. (The innate constitution of the child is also a factor in his learning an emotional role. The low-voltage or passive child will respond quite differently to the emotional demands of his family than will the hyperactive child.) The developing child experiments with various roles by mimicking the parents, by involving himself in stories and phantasies and, later, by identification with his elders. He will eventually find the role in which he is emotionally comfortable, i.e. the role in which he experiences the least amount of anxiety. The more the parents pressure the child to respond in a particular way, the more likely it is that he will learn only one role and be uncomfortable in other roles; an athletic champion may also become a social misfit.

The same holds true for learning perception and expression of emotional feelings. The child with a severely authoritarian parent typically responds by cowering and must, therefore, resort to phantasy to satisfy his needs for assertion. In later life, he may be a passive, ingratiating homosexual; or, in direct reaction to his family experience, he may become a perpetual rebel.

Each emotion has a feeling tone, such as pleasantness or unpleasantness, and generates some response in the autonomic nervous system, e.g. "butterflies in the stomach." There is also a skeletal muscle response—the large muscles are prepared for fight or flight.

We tend to think of emotions in two groups: emergency emotions, such as fear and anger, and welfare emotions, such as love and joy. Emotions are natural tools of communication in most higher species of the animal kingdom. A herd of deer is grazing peacefully when suddenly the buck, who is always hyperalert to any strange or threatening noise, detects something. Up go his head and antlers. If his head and antlers do not come down in a moment, an alert is communicated to the doe, and in an instant the entire herd is dashing off.

The same sequence in communications exists between mother and child or brother and sister, but it is not so graphic. A mother's anxiety is easily communicated to her child. When a child asks about "sensitive" areas, the parents' emotional response can communicate to the child that this is something not to be discussed. In our time, these areas usually concern sex or anger, and if parents forcibly and consciously rule out emotional responsiveness to anger or sexual arousal, the child learns to repress or suppress ordinary emotional responses.

Apart from the family, the child's next most important source for learning emotional response is his peer group. One child's fear of thunder is readily communicated to a sibling or to a playmate. When there are animals around the home, a child can learn a great deal about emotions. The freedom of a dog to go around barking or sniffing indiscriminately is quite a lesson to a growing child. In children's peer groups, there is a great deal of emotional experimentation in play activity. Here, they explore every nuance of dominance, submission, equality, and partnership. One child is the pirate and the other the captive; one the cowboy and the other the Indian; one plays Bonnie and another plays Clyde. The wise parent takes time to affirm the child's emotional experiences. This is as important as affirming his physical development. (The young child who takes his first step or two alone is praised and encouraged for his physical adeptness, a necessity for growth in self-confidence and self-esteem.) It is a good idea for parents to set aside an appropriate time, such as the end of a day, for the child to review his emotional experiences. If there have been clear emotional experiences such as joy, pride, or anger, it is useful for the child to recount these experiences to the parents. In so doing, he conjures up the feeling once again and integrates this feeling with the event. In this way, parents help affirm emotional growth. (By the same token, parents may retard growth in emotional areas. A mother who arrogates all feminine "beauty" in the family to herself may spawn a daughter who spends a long time in the tomboy phase. The girl may never learn to dress or groom herself as an attractive woman.)

One of the drawbacks of suburban living is the commuting father. He leaves home early and comes home late, and therefore his children see little of him. For such children, the home is, in effect, a matriarchy. The young girl has less opportunity for a "family romance"; the young boy views his mother as an all-powerful figure in the home.

Little attention has been paid to affirmation of "physical role" in the developing child. For instance, the way an infant is bounced by his father is quite different from the way he is bounced by his mother. The man encourages the child to use certain muscles. Often, these are the muscles that are equated with male strength; similarly, the father encourages certain facial expressions in his son, while the mother often encourages the opposite ones. The father may teach his son to throw a ball from the side, as does a major league baseball pitcher; the mother may teach throwing the ball from the shoulder, or she may teach the boy to throw underhand. At a Little League football game, the players exhort each other by slapping their teammates' buttocks.

How does a boy learn to differentiate this spurring gesture from a sensuous gesture? Probably by roughhousing with father and peers, the young child learns the actual limits of his physical strength: he need not relegate this to his phantasy.

These matters have been studied only sparsely, but one wonders if the absent working father has not shortchanged his son in terms of "physical" affirmation. The same parallel about physical affirmation may hold true with regard to mother and daughter, but in our society, unless the mother works full-time, the little girl fares better. Her exposure to the mother is greater and she learns the feminine role more readily.

One other aspect of emotional growth should be mentioned. It can roughly be said that every stage in life has built into it preparation for the next stage of life. The infant is preparing himself for childhood, the child for early adolescence, the pubescent for late adolescence, the teen-ager for courtship and marriage. Society allows experimentation in each area for the succeeding one, usually without penalty. Thus, emotional affirmation in the developing individual is exceedingly important as he moves through the various developmental phases. Emotional decisions take time, except when life or death is involved, and we can probably deal with only one emotion of major calibre at a time. (The schizophrenic person, flooded by many contrasting emotions simultaneously, demonstrates the disorganization which can result from such a state.) The parents of a teen-ager can furnish ample evidence about the time required by this particular group to make decisions. Also, it is worth stressing that the mature adult has within himself a "piece" of childhood and a "piece" of adolescence. The delights of these early periods are too precious simply to cast aside, and the healthy adult can readily "play" as a child or adolescent in appropriate circumstances.

EMOTIONAL ROLE SETS

Just as emotions are polarized in opposites, e.g. love and hate, fear and rage, so too can emotional roles be described in "role sets," to borrow a term from new math. These role sets range from the very obvious to the very covert. In three of the structured helper relationships—patient-doctor, client-lawyer, parishioner-clergyman—the role performance of each individual is clearly demarcated. In these relationships, the person who seeks help is allowed certain emotional "excesses" by the helper without fearing censure. The competent physician can "take" a patient's hysterical outburst without much trauma to either; the lawyer can "take" his client's screaming at him in the anteroom of the court. In other words, one is the "giver" and one is the "taker."

These polarities exist elsewhere. The wise banker tries to show the prospective depositor that he can "trust" the banker with his money. The airline tries to tell the traveler, "in an emotional way," that all clouds except "cloud nine" will be avoided. In these examples, someone needs reassurance and someone does the reassuring. Or, one person does the waiting while another is waited upon. Milton's phrase, "They also serve who only stand and wait," captures this theme well.

Emotional role complementarities often come out in play. A man and woman approach a doorway in a public building. Just as they come abreast of it, the lady stops while the man bustles around to hold the door open and allows her to pass through. She is perfectly capable of opening the door for herself, but in this little drama, she has said to him, "I am the receptive one, you are the forceful one."† This same kind of emotional role play goes on during much of family life: in language, in physical action and, of course, it is rampant during healthy sexual activity.

It is important to exercise this capacity for voluntary emotional role play. In this sense it is no different from exercising one's muscles. The healthy family is the one in which there is continual opportunity to exercise these capacities voluntarily; its members are able to shift roles with ease. In effect, the family members, particularly the children, are experimenting with the emotional aspects of future roles. Where there is rigidity and inflexibility in emo-

---

†It stands to reason that in any situation where action is based on physical disability, there is a completely different type of relationship. In this example, if the woman is paralyzed from polio, the man will open the door for her out of necessity. Here the aspects of role complementarity stressed above do not exist.

tional role, conflict may develop. As with individual pathology, the more inflexible and stereotyped the family roles or family interaction, the more likelihood of pathology. Take the situation in which a woman always acts "helpless" by tacit agreement between herself and her husband. The emotional-role relationship, therefore, is that under all conditions she acts helpless while he is a tower of strength. The husband continually denies his doubts about his own assertive capacity. The wife, on the other hand, accepts the role of the protected one, and consciously denies any capacity to assert herself. In this role stereotypy, each is busy denying some unconscious element in his or her own personality, and the marriage becomes inflexible. In the healthier complementarity, each partner is more resilient and can, at times, take the other role as his own. Thus, sometimes a person is the protected one; at other times he or she is the protector.

The same holds true in sexual activity. Healthy sex is characterized by variation in mood or anatomical position. One partner may want the other partner to gratify "unusual" desires in phantasy or in play. The man may wish his partner to play the role of a prostitute or seductress during foreplay, or the female may wish to feel powerless, wanting her partner playfully to "torture" and to "rape" her.‡ When there is rigidity and lack of capacity for variation, trouble may result.

A great fetish was once made of who was "active" and who was "passive" in sexual activity. These labels are, of course, artificial. The human being is capable of playing whatever role he wishes; sometimes he wants to experience a role in actuality, sometimes vicariously. The person who is always forced into one role may feel at a disadvantage and may harbor some resentment.

Human beings need someone around in order to accomplish "emotional work" effectively. The average individual who is unsure about what he wants to do can play out one role against the

---

‡In sadomasochistic sexual play, there is "punishment" inflicted before the actual sex act. In this way, long-standing guilt feelings about sexual participation are relieved, i.e. atonement has been accomplished beforehand. With willing mates, this "play" may be part of a standard pattern; with unwilling mates or with severe physical pain inflicted, this may constitute psychopathology and/or criminality.

other: he plays one role while someone else plays the other role. The psychotherapeutic relationship is, of course, a prime example of role complementarity. The patient can unconsciously project the physician into any role. In psychoanalysis, in particular, we are discovering that a degree of flexibility in some areas—such as the number of weekly appointments and vacations—is useful for the patient's growth. Rigid insistence on five or six visits a week may tend to stultify the patient in a "dependent" role, i.e. he puts off making decisions on his own since he will be seeing his analyst in a matter of hours.

Role playing occurs in groups as well. The family which has a long history of being together needs less time and work for apportioning various roles. The better the members know each other, the more capable they are of recognizing each other's emotional needs. The husband can be a king or a ruffian, the wife a Cassandra or a Sadie Hawkins. Emotional signals indicate what fulfillment is needed, both in actuality and in phantasy. A husband may decide to bring his wife breakfast in bed out of an awareness that she is suffering from emotional hunger. She momentarily needs to be in the role of being cared for, rather than the one who gives care.

One person can play out both parts of an emotional role complementarity; he or she can nurture someone and then vicariously experience that care through phantasy. This capacity to experience roles vicariously sustains us in periods of frustration. (It is also a very marketable commodity, as Hollywood knows.) In the complementarity of roles, it is often apparent that one-half of the emotional role is part of a much larger gestalt; one cannot very well be a woman, or be very feminine, without having a male partner to play out the masculine side of the gestalt. In other words, an emotional role does not operate in isolation but is a complemental or reciprocal *part* of a given role set. Emotional life is geared to interaction. Each part of a role has within it certain elements which elicit an answering response from the environment.

FAMILIES AND EMOTIONAL ROLE

Experimenting with various physical and emotional components of roles is the hallmark of family living. The wise father knows that it is sometimes best to let his son "win" over him. Think for a moment of the exhilaration a boy feels when he is able to "defeat" his father, whether in swimming or wrestling, at chess or in a debate. Often, a good prescription for a passive child is to encourage the boy to "beat up" the older man. In the family where the father is a severe authoritarian, the mother may be so intimidated that she, too, discourages attempts at masculine assertion on the part of a son. In Chapter IV, the instance of a homosexual boy whose father could not tolerate any challenge to his masculine role was cited. Thus, the son never had a chance to "play out" a masculine role with a key figure in his life—his father. Clinically, one sees many homosexuals who are completely passive and seem never to allow an "assertive thought" to enter their minds. Perhaps this observation was the basis for the older classification of homosexuals as *passive* and *active obligatory* homosexuals.

With regard to female homosexuality, there is often a suggestion that the feminine role was denied the young girl by her mother. The girl may then identify herself with the mother's femininity—"identification with the aggressor"—but she is not allowed to experiment with all possible roles in the family constellation because the mother cannot tolerate this experimentation. It stirs unbearable anxiety in the older woman.

A child completely dominated by his parents or older siblings never has the opportunity to be "master." He therefore has little chance to feel the emotion that goes along with a position of authority. When he is with a younger child, he may become a tyrant and completely dominate the younger child. Often, this happens in a children's camp. Older children usually dominate younger ones, but when the younger child is with even younger children, the domination is passed on with a vengeance.

In studying the life cycles of individuals, one finds that age role, always significant, becomes accentuated on particular birthdays. A man who reaches fifty may become impatient and depressed over what he feels he has not accomplished. He often has a sense of urgency about getting things done. In his turmoil (or "crisis"), the support of the family is essential. Clinically, one of the hazards of the fifty-year-old man becoming a new father is that he may be short-tempered and impatient with his growing child; he projects onto the child the same feeling he has toward himself: there is much to do and so little time remaining.

There was once a legend that having children was a remedy for a troubled marriage. Supposedly, the presence of a child would force the two parties to join in the child-rearing task and thus new roles would be apportioned; some semblance of cooperation would begin. When a married couple are stereotyped and inflexible in their role behavior, having a child may only make matters worse, and one can only feel sympathy for the child.

The Only Child Syndrome

It has been stressed that the healthiest families are those in which there is the greatest freedom in role interchange. This exchange can take place in actuality or in phantasy. Any member of a family can seek illusory or vicarious gratification from the other members. Thus, the poverty-stricken parent can say to himself (as Mr. Doolittle sings in *My Fair Lady*) that someday his children will be wealthy and will take care of him, as it was once hoped the original parents would do.

What happens in those families with only one child? Too often, psychiatrists have focused their attention solely on what this child gets from his parents and its advantages. A boy child is "Lord of the Manor"; a girl is "Queen of the May." Both parents vie for the only child's attention. The emphasis in the study of only children has been largely "child-oriented." This probably results from the observations of what happens to an older child when a younger sibling is born. The older child usually is resentful of the loss of attention and other advantages he has had. The only child has been described as being jealous and unable to share, particularly when it comes to sharing people with other people. They are "mamma's children" who supposedly lack the independence and self-confidence that make the average child a fairly good competitor among his peers.

There are certainly advantages for the parents of an only child. They have less financial strain. They are less tied down and do not have to go through six or seven years of having a "diaper child." They are spared the wear and tear of dealing with sibling rivalry.

But what about the other side? Supposing one views this same situation with a "parent-orientation"—What will the child do for me? These questions have led to the identification of the "only-child" syndrome (Messer, 1968) which has the following characteristics:

The only child seems older, more serious than his peers.

Often, this stems from the fact that the only child has never been allowed to be a child in the real sense of the word. The mature adult has within his personality a "piece" of childhood and a "piece" of adolescence, as well as a preponderance of maturity. But as an adult, the only child seems to have an overweighting of maturity. As a rule, he has never learned how to play as a child. He was overexposed to adults and underexposed to children. The only child is at a decided disadvantage with children who grow up in the rough-and-tumble atmosphere of larger families. Thus he prefers to be with older people whom he knows how to manipulate. He can ingratiate himself with adults, but his tactics do not work with children.

Being an only child deprives one of allies against sharply overbearing parents. Franklin D. Roosevelt was an only child. Who can forget the pictures of the indomitable and square-jawed Sara Delano Roosevelt? Or the shy and frightened young Franklin entering Groton? He did not bloom until late in life.

Countless girls who are only children have been thrust into the role of confidante to their mothers. This is especially true in unhappy marriages in which the mother has no one else to turn to for comfort. The daughter is placed in a maternal role; she often advises the mother about marital problems, financial worries, and family difficulties. These young confidantes are forced into the role of adults before they have had a chance to be children.

The only child tends to have a heightened sense of responsibility.

Because human beings are able to gratify emotional needs vicariously, children are the logical targets for fulfilling many of their parents' frustrated ambitions and needs. Most parents feel that a child gives them a second chance at life. They want their children to have what they themselves never had or to succeed where they failed. In a larger family, these yearnings and aspirations can be parceled out among a number of children, but when there is only one child, he cannot help but sense that his parents have all their eggs in one basket.

> A husband complained that his wife was a perfectionist, that she tried to do too much and was always tired and cross. She worried constantly about him and their children. If anything went wrong in his business or the children's school life, she felt responsible. In addition, she felt guilty over the fact that she was unable to look after her parents and grandmother who lived in another city.
>
> The wife revealed in the course of therapy that she had felt responsible almost from the day she was born. She was an only child born to upward-striving, middle-class parents. The standards her parents set for her were literally staggering. She was expected to excel in school and in her social life. At the same time she was expected to fill all her parents' needs for companionship.
>
> In her own marriage, she was attempting to fill the same kind of role. She carried the weight of the world on her shoulders and seldom felt she had the right or time to enjoy herself. Her overdeveloped sense of responsibility and her feelings of guilt when things were not perfect were the natural results of her upbringing.

The only child is often an inveterate peacemaker.

He is more likely to be involved in his parents' conflicts. Often, it is he who must maintain the harmony and preserve equilibrium in the household. Because the burden of settling parental disputes falls squarely on his shoulders, he learns the role of peacemaker or referee quite early in life.

> A man described his profound depression on leaving his office at the end of the day with an argument between two employees unsettled. He felt a personal obligation to mediate any strife or misunderstand-

ing. He was the only child of parents who bickered incessantly. They had forced their son to take sides in their arguments.

An only child feels he will not measure up.

The family unit can be likened to a repertory company: all the roles have to be filled by whoever is available (Chapter IV). There are performance roles—breadwinner, homemaker, chauffeur, gardener—and emotional roles—leader, nurturer, protector, arbitrator, sexpot. Naturally, the fewer people there are to fulfill these roles, the more is demanded of each member. The only child may be forced prematurely in life to assume roles for which he is ill-equipped. He may become deft at performing adult tasks, but his own inner perception of his capacity in these roles is uncertain.

Only children often have special problems when they become parents.

A mother may see in her firstborn daughter the sister she longed for as a child; a father may see his son as a longed-for brother. This situation could be a happy one, but there is an element of danger—rivalry. As an only child, the parent was the center of attention. Now, as a parent, he or she must share the limelight and the spouse's attention with a rival. The situation may become critical when the child reaches adolescence. A mother may see her daughter as a threat and even, perhaps unconsciously, compete with her. She may never help the girl to dress attractively, for instance. A father may never allow his son to engage in masculine pursuits, as these are perceived as threatening to his own role.§

The Banker's Son Who Became an Embezzler

The capacity of the human being to project "pieces of his emotional life" onto those around him is a crucial factor in family diagnosis and family treatment. It therefore becomes necessary to see the entire membership of a family in order to understand

§This is not to say that only children do not develop into wholesome and well-adjusted individuals. Firstborn and only children rank high on any roster of outstanding leaders, creative artists and scientists. Sir Isaac Newton, Franklin Delano Roosevelt, Emile Zola, Herbert Spencer, Rilke (the great German writer), and many of the American astronauts are examples.

these projections. When one part of an emotional conflict in a parent is projected onto a child, the therapist is able to see the effect of this projection. In the classic study by Johnson and Szurek (1952), they point out that adolescents frequently act out parents' unconscious conflicts. A parent, upon hearing that his child had caused half the Police Department to spend hours in pursuit of the youngster, noted with some pride, "He sure did a bang-up job of that, didn't he?" The hypothesis here is that the parent has projected some part of an emotional conflict onto this particular child, and the child has fulfilled the parent's instructions. This sequence of acting-out probably happens more often in life than is recognized—between student and teacher, for example, and even psychoanalyst and patient. The following vignette is an example of a son "playing out" one part of a parent's own conflicts.

A twenty-year-old part-time college student had been in trouble with the law several times. His most serious and recent offense was embezzlement of funds from his employer. He had been referred to the therapist by a judge, who stated that the boy never seemed to "learn his lesson." He repeatedly was involved in "deals"—some in the gray area between legality and illegality, some downright illegal. When the boy was seen by the psychiatrist, he readily admitted all of the details of his lawbreaking but stated that he was not worried about his latest escapade, because his father would "get him off." When he was asked how he could be so certain of this, he stated that he "just knew." A further recounting of the facts up to this time bore him out; the father had paid literally thousands of dollars to get him out of scrapes.

The boy was invited to bring his father for a subsequent visit, and the older man came willingly. The father was an intensely serious man with a furrowed brow and rimless spectacles. The first part of the interview was given over to a recitation of his frustration and exasperation with the boy's behavior. He confessed that it was bitterly shameful for him—a bank official—to have his son involved in financial chicanery.

The psychiatrist encouraged the father to talk about his own life, and he did so without hesitation. He came from a family that was always on the brink of financial disaster. His own father was a skilled artisan who took pride in his work but was inept at managing his finances. People always owed him money. His mother supplemented the family income by cooking for others. Both parents preached the necessity of working hard to make a living, saying that someday their family would be in better straits. The parents also taught their children to be independent and fiercely honest. (There was one other child, a girl, who was now married and living in a distant city.) The boy worked his way through school and college, studied accounting, and then began working in a bank "while I looked around for something to get into." His career at the bank was very successful, and he was promoted regularly.

This man was known as a pillar of integrity in his community. For instance, when there were adjudication proceedings involving money by two competing firms or individuals, he was often consulted: it was known that he would "wrestle" with the problem and come up with the most reasonable answer possible. The son attested to his father's reputation.

During the interview, the father alluded to his own financial situation, stating that he was well-off but could have been much wealthier if he had wanted to "bend a little." When the therapist asked for details, the father described many occasions when he was in a position to use his knowledge of current business transactions for his own benefit. For instance, he might evaluate a certain land tract for commercial development; there was open land nearby for sale; should he buy it and realize a substantial profit? He described how he would grapple with this temptation at home but would never do anything that might in any way hint of his being a financial opportunist.

As he was relating these episodes of temptation, the son became quite animated, reminding his father that, "Yes, but Mr. X. certainly did," Mr. X. being a colleague of the father. The son went on to tell how he always urged his father to take advantage of these situations, but the older man could do no more than toy with the idea. The father stated that although his friends could allow themselves to cut corners, he could not. While the father was relating these episodes, the son nodded, smiled, or squeezed the fingers of one hand in the palm of the other hand.

In this situation, the son had been responding to the father's internal struggle over what was allowable and what was nonallowable behavior, what was honest and what was dishonest. Further, the father's envy of those who could "bend" enough to capitalize on a financial opportunity was apparent. Therefore, in his behavior, the son was "living out" a part of life that was denied the older man, the part which was wished for but was denied him by conscience.

This struggle was an active one in the father's mind, and the son became an active participant in playing out one of the various sides of this emotional struggle. (A further hypothesis is that there were also unconscious messages from the father urging the son to participate in the shady activities.)

This clinical vignette, along with the type of case described by Johnson and Szurek (1952), offers an explanation of some cases of sociopathic (psychopathic) behavior. Ruth Eissler describes a case in which a mother became acutely depressed whenever her son's delinquency improved under therapy. She concludes, "The aggressive and asocial behavior of the love object thus served three functions: (1) The object satisfied her own inacceptable impulses by carrying them out in reality. (2) She secured a masochistic gratification which served as a punishment and relief of her guilt feelings. (3) She could use son or husband as a scapegoat, pointing at them as the criminals and thus reassuring herself of her own innocence. As soon as the love object no longer served this triad, the conflict which had been carried into the external world, by proxy so to speak, again became internalized and shattered an equilibrium which had been based on the continuous reassurance furnished by the misbehavior of an ambivalently loved male object. In the patient, on the other hand, the loss of his mother's love stirred up unbearable anxiety which consequently made him again gratify her unconscious needs in order to regain the security of her love" (Eissler, 1949, p. 293).

In storytelling we see this same phenomenon: the projection of "pieces" of one's emotional life. The author parcels out certain parts of an emotional constellation to various characters within the play or story. These characters are rarely well-rounded individuals; they are "part-people," each fulfilling a particular part of the author's emotional life, i.e. emotional projection. A human being is too complicated emotionally to tell an all-encompassing story using only one individual. Each character in a story is an abstraction of a certain facet of the author's personality. A number of analyses of this phenomenon have been done with the writing of Shakespeare, Goethe, and Joseph Conrad. The cowardly servant in a story portrays one characteristic of a writer's personality, just as does the buffoon. How much easier this is than trying to resolve a conflict by a tortured monologue! Hamlet's "to be or not to be" is a case in point.||

||One of the most welcome participants in the writer's clinical seminars on family treatment has been the Professor of Dramatic Arts. What family theme has not

Some of the most naked and brutal examples of "playing out" certain life roles occurred in concentration camps. One bizarre torture practiced by the Nazis was to force several sons to hold their father against a wall, while another son was forced to stab the father to death in the heart. How could such a revolting sequence enter the mind of a human being, much less be carried out? The answer perhaps lies in the fact that because of the complete breakdown of restraints, the Germans were able to play out in reality some of the phantasies related to events in their own childhood: How might a son feel toward a brutal, "Prussian-type father," for example? In the concentration camp, there were no ethical or social restraints on the guards, restraints that ordinarily inhibit people from bestial or sociopathic acts. Ordinarily, we make a distinction between asocial or bestial phantasies and acting out these phantasies in life. However, when someone gets "jazzed up" by the activities of the group, phantasies can be converted into action. Control of behavior from within has been lost. (Another speculation about the Nazis: there was no guilt. Having committed every conceivable sin or depravity, there was no reason to inhibit themselves since they were "damned" anyway.)

One of the advantages—and pleasures—of emotional role relationships is the reassurance which partners can gain from playful confession of anxieties. In an area of mild difficulty, such as a husband's anxiety about some phase of his job, he can seek and gain reassurance from his wife. This exchange spares him the effort of going through the mental work and anguish of playing out the pros and cons of the situation. The one who is the "responder" in the complementary situation usually senses that his partner is not in dire distress, but is experimenting with different facets of a situation. If an individual senses that his playful confessions and testing are making the responder too anxious, he can retreat, saying, "I can handle this by myself." There are endless combina-

been covered somewhere in great literature? In teaching students family dynamics, a useful technique is to have them observe the family interview, then dismiss the family and have each family role portrayed by a student. Arthur Miller (1956) has written on this topic. The play, *Six Characters in Search of An Author* (Pirandello, 1922) might be retitled "Six Characters in Search of a Family Therapist."

tions or permutations of this situation. Actual panic in a situation restricts the ability to "play out" complementary responses because of the pressure to react.

Learning Emotional Roles

How does a man who works on the assembly line in a factory become "emotionally qualified" to become a foreman, that is, how does he learn the emotional aspects of this role? How does the vice-president of a company prepare himself to be president? How does a young man prepare himself to be head of the family if the father is disabled? Again, in all of these instances, as with most instances of change in role, there should be a chance for experimentation *before* the event, rather than "on-the-job" training. The military situation in which chief petty officers are suddenly made lieutenants has already been cited. Some men can handle the job performance-wise, but cannot tolerate the emotional demands of the job.

> A regional salesman was promoted to sales manager of a large company and transferred to their headquarters in a metropolis. This man's son was in psychoanalysis at the time. He described the stark change in his father when this transfer took place. From a happy-go-lucky man, he changed into a tyrant. He hounded all of those around him unmercifully. This behavior was an index of his own anxiety and difficulties with the new job. Although he had ample training and practical experience, the emotional demands of running a large organization were such that he could respond only by becoming inflexible and rigid. He demanded the same degree of perfection from those around him that he did of himself. In analysis, the son described the hell that took place in his relationship with his father, who demanded perfection from his son as well.

Aboard a naval ship preparing for battle, there are General Quarters Drills. In these drills, every conceivable emergency is played out. What happens if the captain is killed? What happens if the executive officer is disabled? What happens if a particular gun crew is knocked out? What happens if one part of the ship is damaged and is flooded? In other words, built into the organizational structure is a plan for any type of future emergency. In

General Quarters Drills, the men are given a chance to work out some of the performance and emotional aspects of other roles before the emergencies supervene.

If the captain of a ship continually browbeats and humiliates the executive officer, the latter will have difficulty in assuming the role of captain, should this become necessary. He has constantly been humiliated and is filled with resentment; he has had no "emotional time" to work out aspects of the role of captain. Being captain is synonymous with being in an undesirable role. The same is true in corporations. If the president or chairman of the board vilifies the man who is to be his successor, the transition to the number one spot will be an arduous one.

The concept of emotional response to a new role can be extended to such areas as politics and economics. In terms of political maneuverability, anticipating how an opponent will react to a certain pronouncement can be of inestimable value during a campaign. Louis Howe, the amanuensis for Franklin D. Roosevelt, had a genius for predicting the reactions of potential foes.

In the realm of economics, there is a phenomenon which takes place in a growing economy: some people derive wealth without ever lifting a finger. They are not born wealthy, but become wealthy "by accident." For example, in almost every suburban area of this country are individuals who have owned marginal land used mainly for hunting or occasional grazing. A superhighway is then built near the tract of land. Overnight, a man may find himself fabulously wealthy because he has received thousands of dollars per acre for land which he originally might have bought for $50.00 per acre. How does he explain to himself his new-found wealth? He has not worked for it, he was not born to it, he made no real negotiations for it, but rather it came to him like manna from heaven. Emotionally, he may feel uneasy about his right to this wealth and consequently may have phantasies in which someone takes it away from him. As a reaction to this phantasy, such a man may rigidly fight any change in the *status quo*, whether social, political, or economic. (In the movie, *It Should Happen to You?* the central character played by Judy Holliday became a celebrity overnight by renting billboards on which she posted her name. Later, when she became famous, she was most uncomfortable with her unearned success.)

There is also the "young wife syndrome." A young woman consults a psychiatrist because of feelings of depression and worthlessness. These complaints are in contrast to her apparent lot in life; she is married to a rising young executive, lives in a spacious suburban home, has two fine children, and two cars in the garage. The root of her symptom is an underlying guilt—"What did I do to deserve all of this success?" The situation can even be intensified if the woman has moved from a lower social class to a higher social class and thus has surpassed her own parents in social and economic status.

One of the most striking examples of the need to experiment with emotional attitudes toward a given role can be seen in the study of the Vice Presidents who have succeeded to the office of President of the United States. What are the emotional preparations for this high office? In practice, there is usually no actual advance training or preparation for the role of President. There is only on-the-job training. Some preparation is possible when a man actually seeks the office of President; he plays out in his phantasies many of the performance and emotional aspects of this role. Thus, when a policy is announced, or when an appointment is made by an incumbent President, the would-be President can say to himself, "If I were President, I would never do that," etc. In other words, just as in courtship a couple does some of the "emotional work" of marriage before the event, so a man actively seeking the office of President does some of this "emotional work" long before his nomination or election. In our society, the press also plays a part in the emotional preparation by questioning the aspiring candidate at press conferences.

There have been eight successions of Vice-Presidents to the Presidency. These successors were John Tyler, Millard Fillmore, Andrew Johnson, Chester Arthur, Theodore Roosevelt, Calvin Coolidge, Harry Truman, and Lyndon Johnson. A review of their performance in office suggests that those Vice-Presidents who actively sought the higher office made more effective Presidents than those who had not campaigned.¶

In the family, the attributes of masculinity and femininity are taught in their most elementary sense by members of the same sex: parents serve first as models and then as teachers. Mother teaches daughter how to groom herself, how to flirt, or how to bake a cherry pie. But in terms of *responding* to flirtation, only a man can fill this role. Likewise, the father can teach his son all of the attributes of manliness, but only someone who is feminine can respond to his masculinity. Clinical experience has shown that the "sissy" can best be encouraged toward "manliness" by a feminine mother, not by an aggressive one. The phrase, "If I were a boy, I would do so-and-so," often uttered by an exasperated mother to encourage her son to be more assertive, is usually self-defeating. The fact that femininity affirms masculinity is well-portrayed in movies about gangsters and mobsters. The rival gang leaders are generally shown with one or two buxom blondes draped around their necks. These mobsters must be ready night or day for a fight to the finish with their adversaries, and the voluptuous females enhance their image as aggressive fighters. The converse is also true. The "masculine" woman often rules a wild west town and cuts all the men down with her bullwhip. One day, however, a real he-man comes to town, and as she swings her whip he catches it and pulls her to the ground. Thereafter, she is transformed into a "feminine" person. In the play, *The Rainmaker* (Nash, 1955), Lizzie talks about her poor luck in finding a man. She feels she is "not much of a woman." When her family tries to reassure her that she is a desirable woman, she insists that this is not true because no one has ever been a "man" to her.

The extent to which an emotional relationship can "expand"

¶In the framing of the Constitution, the Founding Fathers envisioned the Vice-President as being equally qualified for the Presidency. Each Elector would cast two ballots without making a distinction as to which man would be in which office; the one receiving the higher number of votes was elected President, and the one receiving the second highest was Vice-President. This was changed in 1804 by the Twelfth Amendment which provided for separate ballots for the two offices. The amendment was necessary to make certain that men of the same political party were elected.

varies in terms of the adequacy of the individuals, their freedom and openness with each other, and also with the emotional health of the relationship. The healthier the relationship, the more expansive; the more constrictive, the less possibility there is of playing out or testing certain emotional roles. One of the facts of life in our time is that as we tend to lose contact with the extended family—aunts, uncles, grandparents, other kinfolk—there tend to be fewer opportunities to play out different roles with various types of personalities.**

RATIONAL ROLE AND EMOTIONAL ROLE

In our society, people generally understand the rational aspect of role performance, but they do not always understand the emotional nature of roles or the consequences of role interchange. Or, they may feel the consequences, but not know what to do about them. One of the tasks of family therapy is to help the family predict what may happen with shifts in rational and emotional role. If the husband gets up at night and diapers the newborn child, some provision must be made to reestablish the emotional integrity of his masculine role, if that is necessary. (In most families it is.) The man tending to the newborn understands rationally the need for helping his wife, but he may at the same time be angry and bitter. Meanwhile, his wife feels guilty and depressed over his reaction to this situation. Often, that is as far as the perception goes, and a stalemate develops unless there is further understanding on both their parts.

There are countless clinical examples demonstrating the differences between one's rational role and one's emotional role. The

---

**One can speculate about the consequences of lack of role interchange in the upper-class British family. Traditionally, children go off to school at an early age. Thus young boys have little chance to form relationships with girls in their developmental years. This lack of experience with women is reflected later in marriage. A typical upper-class British gentleman seldom talks business or finance with his wife; these topics are reserved for the club, as are other intimate conversations. To what degree, then, are various members of the club projected into the more "feminine" role, there being no women around to take the passive role? (Upper-class British families have had some recent notoriety in terms of vice scandals and homosexuality.)

ultra-physical "he-man" may be a homosexual; the beautiful artist's model may feel inwardly that she is an "ugly duckling."

In any discussion of the emotional role of the male homosexual,
the striking change in the behavior of women in contemporary
times must be noted. It is not at all unusual for a girl to describe
her avid pursuit of a man: calling him up, inviting him out, even
suggesting openly to him that they engage in sexual activity.
(One young lady described her satisfaction in "putting a man to
bed.") If the man has difficulty perceiving himself emotionally in
a masculine role, he may retreat and become passive. Traditionally, in our society the male is indoctrinated into the masculine
sexual role at a slower pace. There might be some fondling or
manual manipulation of genitals, but usually with a girl more inhibited than he. Great anxiety can be stirred in the uncertain
male if the female "aggressively" demands adult sexual performance. This girl herself may have some conflict about her role: she
may demand sexual performance from the male but, at the same
time, unconsciously try to make certain that he fails in his masculine role; she is primarily a competitor, not a lover.

In other words, as there is more blatant heterosexuality and
more overt demand placed on men for masculine performance,
those who are uncertain in their masculine role can either pre-
tend to be supermen or, as is more likely, retreat into passivity or
homosexuality. This factor may be highly significant in the great
increase in the incidence of male homosexuality in our time.

A patient in psychoanalysis who is undergoing change from passivity to assertivity needs much support in this monumental role
shift. Although the change is mainly in self-perception, it is reflected in his behavior as well. In practical terms, this is frequently the case when one member of a married couple is being
analyzed. If a man changes from a passive to an assertive de-
meanor, the equilibrium in the marriage is upset because the
wife is at a loss to deal with the change in behavior. As a consequence, she may need psychotherapy for herself (see Chap. VIII,
The Ping-Pong Couple).

A change in the emotional role of an individual must, of course, take place when he is ready for such a change. If he, or those around him, are not prepared for the new role, the change is surrounded by suspicion and defeat instead of optimism and encouragement. There is an interesting illustration of emotional role adaptation in the movie, *The Journey,* based on a novel by Anatol Litvak. This movie describes an episode during the Russian occupation of Hungary in the 1950's. The Russian commander finds that he is in charge of a group of foreign travelers. Among them is a lovely English lady. He falls in love with her. The Russian is accustomed to dealing only with military routine and matters of life or death and is not ready for the role of lover. He is completely confused and ungainly. At the end of the movie, there is the improbable scene of the Russian sacrificing his life to allow this woman and her lover to escape. Such a shift in behavior in so short a time would be unlikely.

The family therapist must help members of a conflicted family recognize the importance of role change and role interchange in a family. Capacity to shift roles increases the number of nonpathological homeostatic mechanisms available to reduce anxiety and control conflict. A rebellious child can be dealt with in a number of ways—by stern discipline, by reasoning, by joking, by diversion, or by example. In those families in which there is only one system of discipline, resentment smolders underneath. Continued stress then evokes anxiety. In those families in which differences are settled only by using muscular strength, a climate of fear of attack pervades the family atmosphere.††

The following vignette illustrates the importance of the child's experimenting with many roles, both rational and emotional.

A young man was brought up in a home in which the father was a self-styled miser. He never purchased a new car, always wore the same old suit and, in short, took pride in making do with the tattered and

---

††One can speculate about the relationship of emotional role and psychosomatic medicine. In the emotional complementarity of mother and child, for instance, there must be a time when the child is allowed complete dependence on his mother. If the mother does not allow this dependence, can the asthmatic cry be a substitute for a genuine cry for help? It is a well-known fact that genuine tears in an asthmatic child will often abort an attack of asthma.

the worn, and in how much pleasure he could deny himself. This was the value system with which he indoctrinated his children. He never borrowed money and always paid cash. His world was limited to that which he could control with his two hands and his two eyes.

The son eventually set up a business. At one point, it was evident that he would be obliged to borrow money. The idea caused him severe anxiety and, in fact, he delayed so long that his business almost failed. His problems in operating the business led him into phychotherapy, where he realized that his anxiety about going to the bank to borrow money stemmed from his fear that such a move might make him a "spendthrift." He had no practical or "emotional" experience in the role of "borrower," since this role had been completely closed off to him by his father's teachings. To borrow money was tantamount to losing all control. One swallow would make a summer. The expression "like father, like son" may reflect the fact that the same experimentation with roles which the father denies himself is often denied the son.‡‡

EMOTIONAL ROLES AND GROUP THERAPY

In emotional communication, or in functioning at the emotional level of adaptive mechanisms (see Chap. II), the family and the therapy group have much in common. In the family, interactional patterns and complementarities have long been established and follow along more natural lines; family members know each other's needs, frustrations, tolerances, conflictual areas and to a great extent, phantasies; in the group therapy setting, these come about through testing over a short time span, perhaps more artificially, starting with the inception of the group. For example, one group member is disturbed about his sexual behavior. Because of his own conflict, he becomes the spokesman when the topic of sex comes up and blurts out an aggressive remark about sex. This outburst serves to provoke some other member to take up the opposite side of the conflict, perhaps due to his own con-

‡‡ In studies of immigrant families, it is common to hear the first generation describe how successfully they have shed the values, goals, and customs of the immigrant parents. Yet, study of these offspring shows that within their own social roles, they still adhere to many of the same ways of life as did their parents. A highly-respected physician raised as much fuss in a restaurant when the food was slightly delayed as did his immigrant father. The latter, however, had been through actual food deprivation during his early life (Messer, 1963).

flicts. This new response evokes a counter-response from a third individual, at which point the first member may respond with a more conservative view. In this interchange, an emotional complementarity is set up. These people are actors in a drama, playing out various sides of emotional reciprocity. As dialogue continues, each member of the group puts forth his views in harmony with his own personality needs. In time, there is freedom and flexibility in different roles, and the group becomes healthier in terms of emotional growth of its members. One virtue of group therapy is that it gives members a chance to try out various emotional roles in a structured setting. After leaving the session they are then able to judge which role, or roles, are appropriate for them in other life situations as well.§§

In psychotherapy, the wise therapist practices the art: "If you have an obsessional patient, be hysterical; if you have an hysterical patient, be obsessional." If a patient is always seductive, it is best to play "hard to get" and thus help the patient become aware of his (or her) need to seduce. If the patient is a cold and calculating person, a "little romance" is useful. All of these maneuvers give the patient a chance to expand his emotional role functioning and role testing under ideal conditions. One of the tenets of traditional psychoanalytic therapy that seems to be undergoing modification is that the analyst remain entirely neutral. It is very difficult for a patient to play out certain unresolved conflicts under these circumstances.

---

§§Although family group treatment and group therapy groups have much in common, in the area of leadership there is marked disparity. Leadership in the family can shift, depending on specific needs and competence of any member. In the therapy group, if leadership shifts continually, the effectiveness of the group is diminished.

Chapter VI

Family Therapy: An Adaptational Approach

Bert Roberts was a young rascal of nine who refused to attend school. When he did attend, he developed severe panic, nausea, vomiting, and tremulousness. The only relief came when he left school and returned home. Every device of urging, pressuring, rewarding, and forcing on the part of the parents had come to naught. School officials were likewise unable to do anything. Consequently, Bert and his family were referred to a mental health clinic.

Bert was the youngest in a family of three children. The family itself had been through a crisis of illness during the months previous to the referral. The mother, forty-four, had been stricken with a coronary thrombosis while visiting her married daughter, Sandra, in another city. Mrs. R. was hospitalized for four weeks and then stayed with her daughter. Her convalescence was complicated by intestinal attacks attributed to adhesions from earlier surgery. As a result she had to be rehospitalized. While Mrs. R. was away, Bert and his older brother, Hal, nineteen, stayed with relatives. Bert was a very obstreperous visitor.

After returning to her own home, Mrs. R. had further episodes of abdominal pain and was twice again hospitalized. At that point, Sandra, her husband, and their two children arranged to move back home to be near her mother. They lived in the parents' home until they were able to get settled in their own home. The mother's illnesses had occurred during the spring of one year. That summer, Bert was sent to day camp but was not able to finish the session because of occasional severe attacks of stomach cramps and hyperventilation. He was taken out of camp and remained at home during August. Just prior to school starting, the mother was again taken to the hospital. Bert went to school for two weeks, but after the mother returned home from the hospital, he again refused to attend because of recurrence of the anxiety attacks. On his way to school, he would suffer from cramps, panic, and a fear that some unidentifiable catastrophe would overtake him at school.

Bert was of superior intelligence and had always been a good scholar. He was ashamed and afraid that outsiders would learn of his problem. The family was completely bewildered. The parents had always "sacrificed" for the children's education, and academic achievement was continually stressed at home. One other concurrent event that September was that Hal, the older brother, went off to college for his junior year. Previously, he had attended a local college. This was the first time he had lived away from home. (The treatment of this family will be detailed throughout the chapter.)

IN the previous chapter, some elements in the maintenance of family homeostasis were described. Th family is able to function during times of stress and conflict by utilizing certain homeostatic mechanisms. For example, one member of the family may be designated the scapegoat (black sheep); there may be a defensive alliance between several members of the family; the family members may be cold and withdrawn toward each other, and be a family in name only; the family may be a cat-and-dog type, discharging tensions by continual fighting. The family therapist concerns himself with the flexibility of these homeostatic mechanisms. In the healthy family, there is fluidity and flexibility of the mechanisms. If the homeostatic mechanisms become rigid and inflexible, they are akin to psychic defenses: irreversibility of pathology and loss of function result.

The hypothesis in the case presented here is that the child's phobia is a symbolic public expression of breakdown in the equilibrium of the family. Prior to the onset of the phobia, the family had been able to use various homeostatic mechanisms to neutralize pathologic interaction of its members. Even though these mechanisms interfered directly with the healthy growth of the individual family members, they did serve the defensive purpose of keeping anxiety within tolerable limits and allowing the family to keep functioning as a unit. Two concurrent events—the mother's illness and the older son's going off to college—necessitated sharp role changes in the family and rendered the previous functioning mechanisms inadequate. The school phobia then burst out as an open symptom of thc disequilibrium in the family (Messer, 1964).

As will be seen later, the phobic symptom disappeared once the family's equilibrium was restored. In this sense, the initial results are similar to those obtained using crisis intervention: relief of acute symptoms is achieved by a return to precrisis equilibrium. Here, however, the goal of family treatment was more ambitious:

to uncover the basic family conflicts which necessitated the use of pathologic mechanisms of control.

TREATMENT OF PHOBIAS

It has been traditional in psychiatric training to teach that phobias are "transmitted." Standard psychiatric texts state, in effect, that a phobic child is often the product of a phobic mother (Noyes and Kolb, 1968). Despite these statements, psychiatrists have paid more attention to the dynamics of the phobic individual. The attempt here is to take a look at the other half of the phobic equation—the mother and the family of the patient. Further, with regard to school phobia, a great deal has been written about the child's anxiety at being separated from the mother. Now we are also looking at the mother's personality organization and her response toward separation *from the child* (Johnson *et al.,* 1941; Sperling, 1961; Waldfogel *et al.,* 1957).

Freud's seminal paper on phobias, "Analysis of a Phobia in a Five-Year-Old Boy," was written in 1909. In this paper, he describes the outbreak of street phobia in four-year-old Hans and the successful treatment of the phobia via letters between Freud and the boy's father. In the theoretical discussion of the case, Freud suggested that the boy's street phobia represented a fear of castration by his father.

One is struck, however, by a statement in the epilogue that not only had little Hans responded well to "analysis," but he had been able to weather the severe storm of his parents' separation, divorce, and remarriages. Can a family perspective be applied to Hans' home life? The school phobia occurred in a setting of two parents heading for divorce. In the father's letters, there are repeated statements—apparently sarcastic—about the mother taking Hans into bed to "coax" with her. In several letters, the father blames the boy's problems on the mother's "overstimulation" of Hans, e.g. "No doubt the ground was prepared by sexual overexcitation due to his mother's tenderness." In the epilogue, Freud notes that with the separation of the parents, Hans was also separated from his sister, with whom he had a very close relationship. Certainly this must have contributed to the boy's anxiety.

Also, in Freud's case material, it is recounted that Hans started to show continual improvement after the single visit to Freud by the boy and his father. During this family session, Hans openly confessed his anger toward the father and the latter became aware of the boy's hostile feelings toward him. *Freud told Hans directly that his father was not angry with him and consequently would not abandon him.* Freud also noted Hans' ambivalent feelings toward the father; at first the boy hit his father's hand, then affectionately kissed it. The father's next letter indicates that, to the child, Freud was a new super-father and omnipotent person (*op. cit.*, p. 185).

EMERGENCE OF FAMILY THERAPY

Ackerman (1961) has pointed out the shift in emphasis at child guidance clinics over the past two decades. Influenced by traditional psychoanalysis, early practice in child guidance clinics generally consisted of play therapy: the child was seen individually, and his play behavior and play phantasies were explored in order to learn about conflicts, both conscious and unconscious. However, it became apparent that much of the therapeutic progress was being undone at home where the environment remained unchanged. Because of this fact, the mother gradually was involved in therapy: the child was seen by a psychiatrist and the mother by a social worker. (This is the period of the child guidance movement in which the staff were known as "mother killers": they "teamed up" on the side of the child against the mother.) In time, mothers and children were treated together, first by two different therapists and then by a single therapist. When the parental relationships of a child—particularly a boy child—were being explored, it was impossible to work out oedipal conflicts without involving the father. Gradually, then, the father was brought into the treatment situation. The whole family was now involved.

The history of treatment approaches in childhood schizophrenia is similar. In the past, when a diagnosis of childhood schizophrenia was made, one "sympathized" with the parents about this unfortunate turn of events, and usually provisions were made for hospitalization of the child. When child therapy was attempted, the pathologic interaction of mother and child began to arouse the therapist's curiosity, and mothers were brought into the treatment setting. Often enough, as the child improved, the mother decompensated. This clinical observation, plus genetic hypotheses about schizophrenia, led to the concept of the *schizophrenogenic mother*.

In keeping with the psychoanalytic approach, the first psychodynamic interpretation of the schizophrenogenic mother was in terms of instinctual gratification: she had deprived her child of the oral gratification necessary for his proper growth and development. But of what clinical use was this postulate? The focus of treatment had to be on the current interaction of the schizophrenic child and his mother. In time, the father's role in the family also came to be considered. Thus, the clinical entity of childhood schizophrenia* became the catalyst for studying the patient's environment, rather than investigating mainly the subjective phantasy life of the patient (Friedman *et al.*, 1965; Boszormenyi-Nagy and Framo, 1965).

No attempt is made here to review in any detail the gradual evolution of family treatment. The reader is referred to Spiegel and Bell (1959) and Parloff (1961) for an extensive review of this subject.

The debt that family theory and family therapy owe to psychoanalysis is well known. But this heritage is not without mixed blessing. Because most therapists are trained in individual psychotherapy and individual psychodynamics, the shift to an orientation involving family treatment is usually a mammoth undertaking. Since this shift involves new learning, the "disorganization" of the therapist is predictable (cf. Piaget, Chap. II). In clinical practice, the change in orientation from a primarily individual

---

*Schizophrenia played a somewhat similar role in the development of psychoanalysis. After his paper "On Narcissism" in 1914, Freud began to struggle with the treatment of the schizophrenic, in which therapeutic failures were the order of the day. Freud decided that schizophrenia fell into the category of "narcissistic neurosis": no transference relationship could be effected with the therapist. This speculation generated great interest in ego psychology, with its emphasis on the executive functioning of the patient, rather than on his instinctual organization.

approach to a family approach is made easier when there are
other family therapists around. With their support and encouragement, the journey is a bit less rocky. The interdependence
of the individual and family approach is clear, however. The most
gifted psychoanalyst is usually the most gifted family therapist,
and vice-versa. As a matter of fact, it is doubtful that a person not
thoroughly grounded in individual therapy can practice adequate
family therapy.

The question arises periodically as to why family therapy has
not been given its due until recent times. The past lack of interest
in family study is all the more curious since in 1936, the Ninth
International Congress of Psychoanalysis had as its topic, "The
Family Neurosis and the Neurotic Family." There are many
reasons for this state of affairs. Overshadowing all was Freud's
influence. He warned repeatedly against involving relatives in
treatment. Those trained in psychoanalysis had invested much
time and money in the field, and certainly they would be inclined
to continue practicing what they had been taught. Social workers
have always been involved in family investigation, but when the
marriage between psychoanalytic theory and social work took
place during the 1920's, there was influence mainly in one direction only: from psychoanalysis toward social work, not vice-versa.
(It is interesting that a beginning social worker trained in classical psychoanalytic theory is often more "analytically orthodox" in
her approach than is the graduate psychoanalyst.) Another factor
is that involvement with families brings one face-to-face with
many of the newer sociological and communications-theory concepts—areas with which many older psychoanalysts had no famil-
iarity. When faced with new and different concepts, many still
insisted on seeing all psychopathology as stemming from the vicissitudes of the sexual instinct. In this way, they did not have to
concern themselves with environmental and sociological factors.

The practice of treating the entire family together runs counter
to the American "tradition" of leaving one's family and striking
out on one's own. This tradition stems from two sources: (a) the
necessity for leaving the family in order to conquer the frontier,

and (b) the need to divorce oneself from tradition and culture related to the "old world" in order to become Americanized. Many patients entering analysis foresee a successful outcome of therapy as including "liberation" from the family of origin. As has been indicated in Chapter IV, this splitting of the family molecule may have been akin to throwing out the baby with the bath water. The sense of family identity and family history that members of the extended family provide gives an individual a location in the whole range of time and space (Messer, 1963).

The Patient's Social Environment

The contemporary psychiatrist is more directly in touch with the environment of his patients. He knows more about the patient's social, cultural, and economic life than did the therapist of a few decades ago. During an analytic hour, the vast majority of a patient's free associations are related to the social environment and are only indirectly related to early unconscious conflict. The psychiatrist who is unaware of the social demands on his patient may focus primarily on that part of the patient's free associations related to unconscious conflict.

The early analysts in Vienna were able to analyze their patients without great concern for social mobility, since the class structure was rigid and constant. A middle-class woman's tasks, for example, were to run the house, supervise maids in care of children, and attend church. Not so any longer. The contemporary woman has many functions. In addition to the foregoing, she is expected to be her husband's confidante. Businesses take this new role into full account. A large corporation will often interview the wife as well as the husband before deciding to hire him. Will she be able to fit into the "social structure" of the new company?

Today, people frequently move up in social class overnight. For example, in Washington, D.C., newly-arrived diplomats and congressmen and their families can attend a "school" where they are taught social graces, including how to curtsy, how to wear flowers, and how to eat oysters. The learning situation is such that these people can practice a social role without worrying about muffing it. Unfortunately, in most of life this is not always the way things work out; many an individual must take on a new role without preparation. There is no opportunity to practice in a learning situation.

Observing Family Interaction

Experience has shown that once a therapist practices family treatment, his approach to individual treatment is no longer the same. It is difficult for him to divorce what he hears from his analytic patient from what he envisions going on in the patient's family life. Instead of shunning relatives, he may invite them to participate. He is aware of the fact that improvement in his patient may cause breakdown somewhere else in the family.

By observing the family and its interaction, the therapist sees first-hand how the family handles the behavior of its members, particularly the children. A two-and-a-half-year-old child, for example, begins to desire a great deal of autonomy. His drive to possess all, or to do all, is taken by some parents as an indication that he is "spoiled." In point of fact, however, the child simply wants to try out new tools of control that are part of increasing maturation of the neuromuscular apparatus. The parent who feels that he must be master of the situation at all times will greet these expressions of independence or autonomy on the part of the child with outrage. The child must then seek other alternatives to express this need.

In the introductory chapter on adaptation, it was pointed out that assessment of behavior must take into account not only what is absent but also what is present. The same is true in considering family behavior. Health in the family cannot be viewed simply as the absence of pathology but must also be viewed from the standpoint of the family's fostering growth and sharing among members. Take the matter of symbiosis. No longer can the symbiotic tie be studied by considering the mother-child dyad only. What is the relationship between father and child, father and mother, and with relatives? Are the mother and child "forced" onto one another because of absence or disinterest of others in the family?

Also, it is necessary to distinguish between valid action and "acting-out" in a family. Too often, a patient's behavior has been labeled "acting-out." Perhaps the reason for this is that the psychiatrist had little idea of what was truly responsible behavior on the patient's part. He did not know what was going on in his patient's life.

A prime attribute of family study is the focus on empiricism. What is said, how is it said, and to whom? Are there clear nonverbal messages as well? These questions can be answered by observing the family directly. Who speaks, as well as who does not speak, is equally important. One of the criticisms of psychoanalytic theories is that they begin with the analyst and are then extended to the patient. Repeated clinical observations of psychoanalytic treatment show that patients dream in symbols and language that are in harmony with the theoretical frame of reference used by the analyst. After all, the patient seeks acceptance from the analyst and to adopt his frame of reference may simply be an unconscious expression of his desire for acceptance.

Just as group therapy enhances the reality testing of the individual members, so family investigation reduces the amount of speculation necessary for theory building. If a person says that he has a hostile, domineering mother, or a "rejecting" parent, what better way to determine the truth of his statement than to observe the family interaction?

> A daughter, seventeen, told of asking her father to meet her for lunch downtown. The father had refused, pleading business matters. However, the mother brought out the fact that the father had always refused to take his daughter anywhere unless there was someone else along. The mother went on to say that her husband was the height of integrity and discretion, "the most moral man I know." The family joked about the father's "shyness" and was willing to let it go at that. The therapist, however, persisted in investigating this behavior, and subsequently it was disclosed that the father would never allow himself to be seen in public with his daughter lest someone think she was his concubine.

During the course of treatment, if came out that the mother had tried to keep her husband and daughter apart, and the man was responding to her messages. Father and daughter needed to discover that it was perfectly permissible for the two of them to have a relationship which did not necessarily "go through" the mother. (A careful psychodynamic investigation of this man's behavior also revealed an unconscious longing on his part to establish some kind of relationship with a young woman. He constantly inhibited and controlled this wish, however, and, in doing so, overshot the mark.)

The Roberts Family: First Interview

Bert Roberts' parents were European born. Mr. R., fifty-four, worked as a tailor. He was the third boy in a family of eight children. His own father was a lumberman—a giant of a man, hard-working, harsh, and punitive. His mother was busy having children and looking after them. Mr. R. confessed a long-standing feeling of inadequacy because of his height (rickets had shortened his trunk); all the other men in his family were tall.

Mrs. R. described her early life very simply: "I never was a child." Her father was alcoholic and irresponsible, her mother chronically ill. Mrs. R. worked around the house and cared for a brother, six years her junior. Her mother died when Mrs. R. was twelve and she was then in complete charge of the house.

Mr. and Mrs. R. had met on a blind date and each liked the other's "sincerity." There was a short courtship before marriage. Mrs. R. helped her husband in his tailoring business, and both worked long hours. After the children were born, they were brought to the store and kept in a back room. The two older children were taught to look after themselves. When Bert came upon the scene and was brought to the store, the older children assumed responsibility for him. Bert was "unexpected," as Mrs. R. considered herself sterile. He was born almost eleven years after Hal.

In the six years prior to the present illness, Mrs. R. had had four major operations: a cholecystectomy, an appendectomy, uterine fibroid removal, and ovarian cyst excision. Thus, Mrs. R. was in and out of hospitals a great deal and was away from work. This put a far greater burden on her husband, as the two of them worked hand-in-hand, often as much as sixteen hours a day.

The family was seen together beginning with the first interview. The first four interviews were filmed with sound and thus could be studied over and over again. A fifth filmed interview was done approximately eighteen months after therapy began.

At the *first* interview Bert took over at the outset in an omnipotent way. He pranced around the room, making derisive and humiliating remarks about everyone, including the interviewer. He called his older brother, "garbage can." He talked about another baby coming into the family, either fathered by his father or himself.† Only the mother could silence him; this she accomplished by a look or a gesture. The brother and father sat silently by, helpless. The family began describing their bewilderment and frustration about the boy's not attending school. Most of the interaction during this session was on the part of Bert and his mother. The father sat hunched over—meek, passive, and sorrowfully depressed. Hal sat with his arms folded. Most of the time, it seemed as though he were in another room. His teeth were clenched, and when he spoke, it was in a low, controlled voice.

When the therapist shifted to a discussion of how the family felt about the mother's illness, he was met with denial. Only after repeated questioning were they able to acknowledge their actual feelings. Bert told of his fears that his mother would die, relating this to her many illnesses, the most recent being the coronary. He told of his profound loneliness going "way back" and his resentment at his parents' never being at home. In this expression, Hal joined him. But such statements were covered over with "There was always enough love for all!" With the therapist's assistance, Mr. R. finally confessed his anxiety about his wife's health. He stated that he and his wife were a team; they worked together and devotedly took care of each other through sickness and health. He confessed he did not know how he had been able to survive with her being so sick and added, "I'll die first." His voice and facial expression confirmed the depth of his feelings.

Later in the interview, Mrs. R. stated she felt that Bert's troubles began when Hal moved out, since the latter had been a "second father" to the boy. Bert agreed that he was lonely, but it was brought out that the mother and Hal had had a "romance" for years and had always kidded each other about being sweethearts. As a sequel to this conversation, Bert again brought up the fact that he would like to have a baby in the house.

Toward the end of the session the physician dealt directly with the school phobia, telling Bert that he probably wanted to stay home to watch over his mother so that nothing would happen to her. He then told the boy that the law was the law, that he had to go to school, and that someone in the family could take him if necessary.‡ The therapist

---

†There are many similarities between the phobic child in this family and Freud's Hans, particularly in regard to phantasy. Some of these will be evident in the case material. The rebirth phantasies were striking in both children.

‡There is general agreement that a school phobia is an emergency situation

told the boy that there was a family problem here, and that the family
would be helped in solving it.

As the therapist was telling the boy he must attend school, Mr. R.
looked vastly relieved while Mrs. R. looked down with a cloudy face.
She then countered effusively that *she* would take him.

The analysis of the first session was that this family orbited
around a dominant mother. She had been able to keep all of them
in line by verbal command, by gestures, or by direct threat. However, with the mother's coronary attack, the homeostasis was
upset. Roles had to change. A death anxiety hung over all. The
father became depressed, Hal withdrew by isolation, and Bert
refused to attend school. In his omnipotent phantasy, he would remain at home to protect his mother from death. His preoccupation with rebirth phantasies neutralized the threatened loss. But
the anxiety over his exposure to his mother's direct attack (as she
attacked all men) was handled by displacement onto the school.
Hal was no longer at home to protect him.§

The mother handled her own death anxiety by denial and by
clinging to her family. Her hesitation about the boy's returning to
school can be understood in this context. She needed him at home
to watch over her, particularly since Hal had left home.

AN ADAPTATIONAL APPROACH TO FAMILY THERAPY

Generally, the initial interview should be scheduled for an
hour and a half. Less time is usually inadequate for understanding the various levels of interaction among the members. Ninety
minutes also allows sufficient time to hear the personal life history
of each member. A longer session is fatiguing, both for the family
and the therapist. Ideally, it is best to see the family twice for
evaluation. Since this is not always possible, however, it is feasible
during the initial interview to take a short recess after a half hour
or forty-five minutes have elapsed. During this brief recess, the
family is escorted to the waiting room or perhaps to the lounge

---

which must be dealt with by sending the child back to school immediately. Medical
excuses are definitely contraindicated (Sperling, 1961).

§Freud differentiated between early infantile phobias in which there was a loss of
the protecting and gratifying object, and later phobias in which the origin of anxiety is fear of castration.

for water or refreshments. The therapist does not see the family during this break.

The purpose of this short intermission is to give the family and the therapist a chance to "recalibrate." Studies show that the first moments of any interview are used by the family members and the therapist to appraise one another on the basis of dress, speech, body signals, and other nonverbal communications (Birdwhistell, 1963). Some judgement about social class is also made. This calibration holds true in everyday situations: whether it is two people meeting for a business engagement, two politicians confronting each other on the stump, a patient meeting a therapist, or a couple on a blind date. The recess provides an opportunity for a second and fresh appraisal. (The same holds true in individual therapy evaluations as well. When a patient can only be seen once, a break of five minutes during the interview gives both patient and examiner a chance to recalibrate.)

In an authoritarian family, all the members may be cowed by the presence of the commanding authority and go along with his (or her) opinions and edicts, particularly with regard to scapegoating of one member. The manner in which the family enters the room, how they arrange themselves in chairs, and the gestures and body language used by each member must be noted by the therapist. These nonverbal messages frequently reveal more about family conflicts than do verbal communications (Scheflen, 1964).

The therapist first attempts to discuss, *What is wrong?* In this quest, he tries to involve all of the members. At the first interview, the family may be bewildered and able to focus only on the symptoms of one member. In the Roberts' family, for example, there was at first denial of conflicts or problems other than the matter of Bert's refusing to attend school. In other families, all individual assertivity may be compromised to maintain peace and harmony in the group. In still others, the quality of the interaction and involvement of the family members elsewhere may raise a question as to whether or not this is a functioning family unit. Have they reached the point where the forces for breakup of the family are greater than the forces for joining and learning?

In exploring the various homeostatic and defensive patterns

that exist, the therapist can next ask, *What could be better?* Here, the focus is on the family's ideals. The indirect approach is best. An adolescent may be reluctant to confess his frustrations but may willingly describe his wishes. The latter can be as revealing of family conflicts as the former.

By observing family interactions, the therapist can gauge the extent to which a child has been taught to be open and the extent to which he must restrain himself. Is the child allowed to "make a mess," or are the parents obsessed with cleanliness? In any adult, there may be islands of immaturity related to the fact that his own parents were overbearing in some particular area. A child whose parents react vehemently to his "making a mess" may, as an adult, "experiment" by disclosing some shocking behavior or phantasy to his spouse, just to see the reaction. He is testing to see if the earlier reaction of the parents will be repeated by the spouse.

Very often, families burdened by conflict and pathology have lost their sense of humor. One of the best approaches in family therapy is to reawaken the latent humor that exists in every family. Humor seems to be a natural part of the child's development as he tests the world and is probably the anlage for the capacity to laugh at one's self or one's foibles later on in life. Generally, this sense of humor can be awakened by asking a couple how they first met or how they felt on their honeymoon.

Another technique to help the family burdened by conflict is to have the members recognize and reward desirable performance of family roles. Husbands need to tell wives they are good mothers or good spouses; men need to be recognized as being good fathers or husbands. It is often therapeutically useful to have family members mentally exchange roles. The man who complains of coming home and finding his wife cranky might "exchange roles" with her during a therapy session. In this way, he can perceive some of the feelings engendered by a day of being badgered by children or a day of housecleaning. A woman can imagine the pressures of the business world or the pressures a child feels in school.||

||Having the family play charades together is another useful diagnostic tool. Each member can be told to select and impersonate another member of the group. Usu-

As will be stressed later, family treatment must sometimes be interrupted in order to deal with one member's deep-seated personal conflict. This type of interruption is different from seeing one member of the family while gathering information. For example, one member asks to be seen alone because of the nature of his information, such as the recounting of an extramarital situation, or a long-standing complaint dating back to childhood. It is frequently unnecessary for the other partner to know these details and, further, the hearer may not have the ego strength to handle the disclosure of these very intimate facts. One of the legends that abounds in our society is that husband and wife tell each other everything—literally everything. While secrets between married partners are not to be encouraged, this does not mean that every piece of behavior or personal phantasy should be discussed. (This notion is sometimes carried over in relationships between parents and children as well; a mother may want her child to confide "everything.")

It is useful in family or marriage therapy to indicate that the therapist does not automatically refuse to see members individually. This takes care of the need for privacy, should this need arise. This is particularly important with adolescents, for they go through periods in which they doubt themselves, their parents, and their parents' judgment. They are more comfortable talking with the therapist alone. As a rule, the therapist does not *encourage* individual sessions during the course of family treatment. The disadvantage is that members tend to "save up" ideas and complaints for these individual meetings rather than bring out provocative feelings during the family session. Feelings of rivalry are a case in point.

It is generally not recommended that younger children be seen separately from their parents, at least in the early stages of treatment. Separation of parents from children may stir feelings that the youngsters are "tattling" or are in alliance with the therapist

---

ally, a child will portray some aspect of one parent's behavior that is particularly gratifying or particularly frustrating. A five-year-old boy climbed on a chair and gestured wildly with his right hand. He was imitating the father always "lecturing the family."

against the parents. However, it may be necessary to see children apart from their parents if it is evident that the parents will not allow free and open discussion. After a small crack in the dike, the parents may forcibly signal that no further breaks are allowed, and quite suddenly and remarkably, everyone is on his best behavior. However, the therapist can head off splits between parents and children by reviewing with the parents at a later time the gist of the discussion between the therapist and children.

The homeostatic pattern of discharging tension by continual fighting has been described in Chapter IV. If this is a prominent mechanism used by a family (or couple) to handle conflict, the therapist might ask them to demonstrate such a "fight." This demonstration may have the effect of shifting the conflict "higher up in the cerebrum." The origins of the conflict can then be investigated, and the knowledge may lessen the need to fight. In treating a married couple or a family in which the therapist knows that a fight will occur during the unfolding of some conflict, he can take a short cut by saying, "Have your fight and get it over with."

When a family has been seen over a period of time, the therapist and the family sometimes begin to recognize repetitive cycles of interaction or redundancies of themes—for example, conflict over involvement with extended family. Once such a conflict has been discussed and understood, but yet keeps recurring at the end of the session, a useful technique is to adjourn at that point and allow the family to pursue the matter on their own. Hopefully, it will be settled. This technique gives the family a feeling that they are mobilizing themselves toward health, and the self-reward is important for growth in the family.¶

¶Hemingway's observation on work is in harmony with the above. During the years when he was writing very actively, Hemingway set himself a tight schedule during which he knew he must work. After he finished his stint of writing for the day, he went on to something else. In his writing, when he came to a scene where he was working on characters or action which he knew he could quickly and easily develop, he would stop at that point. The next day, he would sit down and complete the previous day's work readily. This gave him a "reward" and served as an impetus for his writing during that day (Hemingway, 1964).

The Roberts Family: Second and Third Interviews

A *second* filmed interview with the Roberts family took place two weeks after the first. Bert was back in school, and the parents expressed relief over this fact. The father had driven the boy to school, had taken him to his classroom, and that was that. Sandra, who was twenty-five and the oldest child, was present at this second interview. She confirmed the impression gained during the initial interview about the role relationships in this family. The mother was kingpin and would tolerate no assault from any quarter on her dominance and position. Bert was seductive with his mother, constantly fingering his genitals and his nose; at other times he was assaultive and destructive toward her.

There was a great deal of teasing that went on between the two, but when it seemed to get out of hand, Mrs. R. would pull rank on him, quieting him by a simple look or gesture. Sandra confirmed the fact that the family had been out of control since the mother's illness. She stated that all during her early life, the mother had managed to be in complete control of the family. She dictated their comings and goings and always wanted to know who they were with. She controlled the children either by direct intervention or by an enema hose. The same had been true with feeding in the family. Mrs. R. would tolerate no intervention in her forced feeding of all the children.

During the *third* filmed session, there was discussion of sexual matters. The children had never received adequate sexual education from the parents, although they were bright children and picked this up from their peers. It was clear that the mother rationed sex to her husband. She would ignore overtures unless she was in the mood.

Several other themes covered during the third session were the parents' description of Bert's messiness and their having to clean up after him; details of Bert's fondling himself; and the father's vile temper, long since buried.

It was also noted that Bert was born some years after elective surgery; Mrs. R. had been told that she could not conceive. Mrs. R. then quickly went on to say that they wanted the boy, and if anything, "We babied him too much." During the first part of her coronary illness and recuperation, Mrs. R. was left alone with Bert much of the time, but she insisted that the boy did not know how frightened she was of death. However, the family admitted the relatives constantly cautioned him to behave, lest his mother die.

During the third session, death anxiety still hung heavily over the family, but the therapist again assured them that there would be some help forthcoming. Bert had continued in school without further incident.

RESISTANCE TO CHANGE DURING THERAPY

A human trait seen repeatedly in individual treatment and which is perhaps more graphically seen in family treatment, is echoed in the phrase, "We are what we are, and we expect what we know."

> A woman of thirty was the oldest daughter in a middle-class family. Her father worked long hours in his own small business. He came home late, so that generally the children had little contact with him except on weekends. However, he felt that he had to participate in the children's activities and therefore tried to attend PTA meetings and social activities at schools or clubs. He generally had a few drinks before these events and frequently appeared in public somewhat inebriated. Because of the repetition of this scene, the daughter was left with the image that a man embarrasses and humiliates a woman.
>
> She was seen with her husband in therapy because of marital difficulties. The husband plaintively stated it was impossible to please his wife because she was always obsessed by what was wrong and undesirable, not what was right: "I can do one hundred things, and if ninety-nine are correct and one is wrong, my wife will always harp on the one." The therapist suggested individual treatment for the wife. She agreed but was markedly resistant to change. She had always defended herself from being humiliated and rejected by men by attacking them first. The resistance in treatment was thus closely related to her psychic defense.

Nowhere is the family therapist's need for understanding individual psychodynamic patterns greater than when he begins to meet resistance to change in the family members. For, as noted above, resistance in an individual is intimately related to a psychic defense. A defensive pattern, established to counter anxiety, is not easily altered. Many family therapies have gone on the rocks because an individual or the family itself could not tolerate the change. In a family in which the father is passive and compliant, treatment may be broken off by the family when he begins to shift to assertiveness and independence.

In most areas of life—political, social, and economic—change brings about polarization into two groups. One group fights to maintain the *status quo*; they want to rely on past and predictable behavior. The other group sees change as exciting, something to be given a chance. These attitudes can often be traced to the family life of individuals. What is the family's response to a new challenge? Does it fall back into a pattern of rigidity, or is there flexibility, with necessary role shifts, and a desire to meet the new challenge with zest and a sense of discovery? When a family is in therapy, the therapist tries to help the members relinquish old and burdensome patterns of response and substitute new ones. This increases the family's chances of handling subsequent stresses successfully. To any given stress, there can be a number (or *range*) of responses, not just one fixed or rigid response in every situation. Any of a number of homeostatic mechanisms can be used.

Some individuals are prone to crisis. Often, this individual brings on the crisis either directly or covertly.

> A couple was seen because of marital difficulties. The husband began a recitation of their problems which went back to the day they were married. He stated that they were "forced into marriage" because the girl's parents suspected them of sexual intimacy. The man was hesitant about marriage at the time but felt there was enough feeling between the two of them, so he went ahead. After marriage, there followed a series of crises: a sexual crisis on their honeymoon, a crisis about where they were going to live, a crisis with the birth of their first child. The present crisis was related to a suspicion that his wife was having an extramarital liaison. He often shadowed her, bursting in on her, expecting to find that she was involved with some other man. During this recounting, the wife sat by with an oddly bored expression which clearly indicated that she had heard all this many times over. When the therapist pointed out to the man that his life seemed to revolve around crises, he replied that this was the way it had always been. He was an unplanned child. His father and mother had always battled furiously with one another; as he grew up, he was cast in the role of mediator (he was an only child). This man was repeating in his current life what he had been taught in early life—if there is no crisis, provoke one.

The ability of the family therapist to help patients and families alter their responses, i.e. overcome resistances, is tempered by the fact that human beings do not easily change the rules of the

game.** In the play, *Toys in the Attic* (Hellman, 1960), two spin-
sters who are sisters, live on an old Southern plantation and have
dreams of recapturing their lost family wealth and traveling in
style to Europe. One sister is a clerk in a hardware store and the
other is a charwoman, but in their phantasies they are great ladies. They have a nephew who lives with them, and after several
real estate manipulations, he suddenly comes home one day with
new dresses, fur coats, and travel tickets to the continent—the fulfillment of all the sisters' phantasies. He has already called their
employers to tell them that the women will no longer be working.
There is disbelief and consternation on the part of the sisters at
first, followed by the realization that their phantasies have now
come true. Then resistance to change sets in. In the end, the
nephew is brutally beaten by one of the men with whom he con-
summated the real estate deal. He loses all of his newly-acquired
money and property, and the two women must beg their respec-
tive employers for their old jobs. There is a touching scene at the
end of the play in which the bruised and battered young man tells
the women that for some reason they seem more pleased at his
failure than they ever seemed at his success.

The Roberts Family: Fourth Interview

At the *fourth* interview, two weeks later, the Roberts family seemed
more hopeful. Bert was excelling in school once again. At the beginning of the session, he described some playthings he wanted, and as he
did so, he looked at his mother. When the therapist noted that the
power in the family seemed to reside with Mrs. R., the boy tried to
defend her but made a slip of the tongue, calling her "father." He
told about fights in the family, particularly between him and his
brother. When the therapist asked Bert if he ever fought with his
mother, the boy replied, "You're supposed to have respect for Mom
and Pop. You must."

Mrs. R. brought up the fact that things seemed to be better with
Bert and then asked the therapist if he could explain the improve-

---

**There is an amusing anecdote about Professor Albert Einstein being given a
container of shaving soap. He had always shaved with a straight razor and plain
water, but when he tried the shaving soap, he confessed to his friends that this was
a marvelous invention. However, when he had used all the shaving soap, he went
right back to using his straight razor and water.

ment. The therapist replied that perhaps Bert was responding to *her* improvement. He pointed out that she was less afraid, less controlling, and less invasive and that Bert was responding accordingly.

From repeated study of the filmed sessions, the dynamic equilibrium that existed prior to the mother's illness was reconstructed. Mrs. R. was the nucleus about whom the other members of the family orbited. Mr. R., longing to fulfill his dependency needs, competed with the children for the mother's attention. He tied her to him by means of overly long work hours. During these times, the children were left mainly to their own devices. No grumbling about this arrangement was allowed, since, as the parents constantly reminded the children, it was for their education that these sacrifices were being made. With this as a goal, the family was able to convince themselves that all was well, and this is how they appeared to the outside world. The homeostatic mechanism of "reaction formation" has been described in Chapter IV; there is an outward overharmony and overtogetherness in the unit, which serves to cover over internal conflict and stress.

With the advent of Mrs. R.'s illness, there was immediate decompensation in the family. At the first family interview, an air of depression and death hung heavily over the room. There was shame, panic, and bewilderment over Bert's refusal to attend school. Mr. R. remarked that he felt he was "drowning."

At the time of Bert's refusal to attend school, Mrs. R. was actively preoccupied with an outbreak of death anxiety. This had been precipitated both by her own illness and by Hal's going off to college. The latter event had awakened memories of early death and abandonment by her own parents.

As family treatment proceeded, the older children disclosed that they were desirous of a change in the family milieu but felt helpless to do anything. They were guilt-ridden over their mother's illness. Bert was the most active member of the group— giggling, teasing, displaying manic behavior and childish omnipotency. Since Mrs. R.'s illness, no one seemed capable of controlling him. A power vacuum had been created and he moved in.

The school phobia was a multidetermined symptom. Bert was a child with crippled executive capacities. The fear of losing his mother was therefore overwhelming. In his omnipotent phantasy, he would remain at home to make certain that his mother stayed alive and he would reunite the family in the equilibrium that existed before the illness. Then he would again be on familiar ground. Also, by being with his mother, she would mediate any of his conflicts with his father, brother, or anyone else that he perceived as a rival. (Schoolmates might similarly be perceived as rivals or enemies in this circumstance and hence engender anxiety at school.)

The other part of the equation was seen in the mother's response to Bert's being at home. Despite her repeated concern about the boy returning to school, her facial expressions and gestures indicated that, unconsciously, she needed Bert at home to neutralize the anxiety she felt over the "abandonment" by Hal. Bert would be her "omnipotent guardian."

The task posed in therapy was, of course, complicated by Mrs. R.'s illness. Her work tolerance was limited, and after overwork —which she repeatedly forced herself into—two or three days of complete bedrest would be necessary for her cardiac reserve to build up again. It was agreed that a return to the previous equilibrium was not feasible. Therefore the following tack was used.

A skilled homemaker was brought in to do the housework and take up part of the mothering role vacated by Mrs. R. There were further family therapy sessions aimed at achieving a new balance and honesty in the relationships in this family. The idea that complete harmony existed in the family was quickly dispelled. True, they had attained equilibrium before, but at a high price. Mrs. R. had assumed the pivotal position in the family and all had vied to be the favorite. Further, the mother had constantly reminded the children about all that the parents were sacrificing for them. It is interesting that, as a child, Sandra had had a severe bowel problem with frequent constipation. Her mother dealt with this by resorting, at times, to daily enemas. Sandra laughingly disclosed that on the day she married and moved out, her intestines stopped "growling" and there was an end to the bowel problems. Hal had no marked somatic complaints but had responded with isolation, withdrawal, and subsequent guilt. In the family sessions, when

Sandra and Bert objected to the parents' preachings, Hal joined in readily.

Most of the treatment involved family sessions. Individual hours with a single member were made available when requested or, occasionally, when the therapist felt that one individual's particular response or psychic defense impeded understanding in the group. Bert, however, was *never* seen alone at any time.

In individual sessions with Mr. R., his background in Europe was explored. Mr. R.'s statements that he had a "wonderful childhood" and that he was "probably the favorite" were quickly punctured. The very presence of rickets belied the former. He subsequently confided feelings of inadequacy because of his height. At the same time, he told of his prowess as a horseman, a biblical scholar, and his present capacity for work, which far surpassed that of most younger men. Thus, it was clear that the feelings of inadequacy and exaggerated need for someone to look after him were mainly illusory. The psychotherapeutic insights were aided by the fact that he was able to take over and run the house during his wife's illness, while still working long hours to achieve some financial balance. For the first time, he began counseling Hal about problems in college. Obviously, he had shifted into the role of family leader.

Mrs. R. had been acutely depressed after her first coronary attack, and the depression deepened after two further episodes of cardiac decompensation. In individual sessions, the depression was dealt with in terms of self-rage because of feelings of helplessness. From her tower of strength, she had fallen into a position of a bedridden, complaining grouch. The guilt, following the rage at her feeling of inadequacy, was everywhere in evidence. After exploring this guilt, Mrs. R. was asked if she thought she had "done enough" for others and could others now do for her? It was not easy for her to accept a homemaker. Her own early background of never having been a child, but rather having been thrust into caring for the family after her own mother's death, was explored. (It was of interest that while sick, she avidly began collecting money for heart foundations. Each time she saw the therapist, she would recount who among her hospital acquaintances with coronary disease had died. These concerns, as well as the depression, abated as therapy proceeded.)

Because of his schedule as a college student earning his own way, Hal found it difficult to attend family sessions. However, he asked to be seen individually by the therapist on several evenings. During the first session, Hal again maintained that everything had always been fine in the family, even though he stated that he had frequently felt depressed and socially inept. His characterization of himself was sprinkled with words such as "sterile" and "impotent." In succeeding sessions, he began to describe some of his early dissatisfactions, his anger at the impositions his family made upon him, and the guilt he felt about leaving home. Eventually Hal achieved some independence on his own and went overseas with several of his peers for a summer. He continued on to professional school and supported himself by scholarships and working.

A new equilibrium was gradually achieved in the family. Having gained an understanding of his passivity in terms of his early life's experience, Mr. R. now began to assume more authority in the family. Mrs. R. began to accept some of her physical limitations and, grudgingly, a more passive role. According to Hal, he had never seen his parents so happy with each other. Bert began to assume more the role of a nine-year-old boy .His fear of abandonment by his mother and brother and his constant need for reassurance abated.

The Roberts Family: Summary

During the summer when there was interruption of treatment the family suffered a relapse. Although Mrs. R. managed to stay out of the hospital—this was the first summer she had been able to do so—there were many episodes of congestive heart failure, and her depression returned. At the first visit, after six weeks absence, Mrs. R. was dyspneic. Mr. R. complained of headaches, chest pains, and gastrointestinal upset. He felt weak and fatigued. (They were seen only briefly before being sent to their local physician.) Mr. R. was not aware of his wife's discomfort until it was pointed out directly to him. Mrs. R. then related that during the summer, the two older children had bought her an air-conditioner, but her husband would insist that it be turned off at night, as he was afraid of "catching cold." She suffered much discomfort because of this but had to give in. Bert was in a day camp, but when at home was "impossible"—disobedient and demanding. He insisted on new clothes and new playthings. Both parents felt he was unmanageable.

The first interviews after the relapse were similar in many ways to the first filmed sessions. Mr. R. sat hunched over, was depressed, and stated, "If only she were herself, all would be well." Bert vacillated between childish omnipotence and pseudomaturity. His major complaints were that his parents did not "give him enough" and that there was "never enough time."

In subsequent sessions, Mrs. R. poured out her bitterness over the fact that her family now refused to recognize that she was ill. Mr. R. never referred to her heart disease by name, only as "her trouble." The only time he mentioned the words, "heart attack," was in referring to people he knew who had had attacks and were now fully recovered. This denial was called directly to his attention.

Bert referred to his mother's illness as "arthritis." When heart disease was mentioned, he burst out crying and wanted to leave, as he felt the therapist was saying his mother would die. The therapist pointed out that she was "alive and kicking." Bert's many demands and his obsession with time were related to his concern that his mother had only a little time left to live. There was discussion about the family's feelings toward the therapist's having been away for the summer and also about Hal's leaving again for college after being home during much of the summer.

Mrs. R. requested an individual session the following week. Her concern was that Hal was going out with a girl of a different religion. She felt this to be a "death blow." This was really the first girl that he had ever dated with any seriousness. Mrs. R. described the girl as a "simple soul" of the neighborhood who worshipped Hal. Mrs. R.'s only reaction was to ask continually what she had done wrong, and how could Hal think of doing this to her. The therapist countered by stating that although she must truly feel abandoned by Hal, it was only natural that he try to prove his manhood. She then confided somewhat ruefully that she felt Hal had always been a "mamma's boy," and perhaps he needed to "grow." It was left on the note that if Hal could prove himself a man with this girl, perhaps other girls, more appropriate from her standpoint, would follow.

Following this sequence of visits there was a *fifth* filmed interview at which only Mr. and Mrs. R. and Bert could be present. During this interview Bert was obstreperous and complained loudly about the fact that his mother was holding him down. His father joined in by saying that perhaps his wife had always been too strict. Mrs. R. countered with the fact that Bert, in his precocity, had attended some teen-age parties and had described the goings-on there to his mother. Frequently she forbade him from going to these parties, when she felt the age group was inappropriate, and this caused outright rebellion in the boy. When she did allow him to go, she worried constantly about his getting home safely. There was again some allusion to sexual matters, and Bert told about his parents having sex on Sunday morning and his trying to peep in the keyhole. Mrs. R. was shocked at these remarks, but Mr. R. seemed bemused. The father then went on to recount how his wife had always rationed him sexually; she always had to be "in the mood." When the therapist asked Mrs. R. whether the men in her family were too "frisky," she responded with a stormy look.

For several weeks thereafter, Mrs. R. was seen alone. She went back to the time before and after her mother's death. Mrs. R. was twelve years old when her mother died. She awoke one night after her mother's death to find her father molesting her. She was terrified and went to the house of an aunt where she slept for several nights. The incident was never discussed with her father, but for years she recalled being frightened and angry at him. During the next few weeks of therapy, Mrs. R. had many nightmares about her mother. In these dreams, she was uncertain whether her mother was dead or alive. The therapist suggested to her that the painful memories had been reawakened by Bert's sexual precocity: she was frightened by this just as she was frightened by her father's molestation. She had responded by trying to restrict the boy altogether.

Her dreams were interpreted as a longing for the return of her lost mother and the unconscious feeling that her father had killed her mother. As a result of this phantasy and the molestation by her alcoholic father, she reacted defensively toward men and thus became an "attacker" of men. They could not attack her if she attacked them first. Following this interpretation, the nightmares ceased. In subsequent family sessions, there was less concern on her part about Bert's going out to preadolescent parties and coming home by himself.

When last seen, the family was doing well. Bert had had no further trouble about attending school and, in fact, had been placed in advanced classes. Mrs. R.'s cardiac status was such that there were occasional episodes of decompensation necessitating medical care and home oxygen, but the family seemed to be weathering the storm satisfactorily.

THE FAMILY AND FAMILY TREATMENT

It goes without saying that all family members must recognize the intent of therapy—to work for understanding or change in family patterns that will make for improved relationships and functioning. During a session, when one family member tells another that he is disgusted with a certain piece of behavior, the therapist must stand ready to help this member accept the criticism as part of a learning or growth experience.

His job is to "protect" the members from assaults which might result from the freedom allowed in the therapeutic setting: an adolescent child may lambast his parents, knowing that he is under the wing of the therapist and will therefore not be chastised; a husband may tell his wife things that he might not be able to tell her in the one-to-one situation at home. The therapist represents an umbrella of safety, and he must use his position to make certain that these remarks are not taken simply as attacks but as tools for learning.

People can best take criticism when there is some previous milieu of support and protection. This fact is crucial in the practice of family therapy, with its maximum confrontation and evocation of emotion. Rado always insisted that his students learn the "sandwich" method of making interpretations to therapy patients: the therapist must soften interpretations or observations which would prove painfully humiliating to the patient's self-esteem. Then the interpretation to lay bare the defensive maneuver can be made. Following this, the therapist should again make a remark to enhance the patient's feeling of self-worth. The "painful" interpretation would thus be sandwiched between supportive statements.††

A useful technique to guard against humiliating family members is the use of the indirect question or the indirect observation. An only child complains that no one ever plays with him; rather than asking the parents directly whether or not they play with him, the therapist can simply ask, "Is there anyone around who

---

††Nothing is quite so disheartening to a clinician as seeing a psychiatric patient completely depressed as a result of history-taking. After reciting all of his current problems in detail, the patient may then start in on all of the early traumatic experiences of his childhood. At the end of such a session, an hour has transpired which has been completely humiliating to the patient, and he is keenly aware of his deficiencies, both in the here-and-now and in the past. The following is a rule which should be followed, then: if a patient comes in to talk about his sexual impotence, first talk about the patient's periods of sexual potency.

can play with him?" No finger is pointed and thus no direct guilt engendered. Similarly, if an adolescent boy shows need of male companionship and peer relationships, the therapist might ask him whether or not he has ever thought of going to camp. This does not put the parents on the spot to explain why they have not thought of it. It simply introduces into the lexicon of family thinking the notion that children often profit from going off to camp.

The therapist must also make it clear that information (or thoughts) disclosed during family sessions cannot be used for purposes of attack outside of treatment. The whole goal of treatment is defeated if a member feels that by being open in therapy, he becomes vunerable to later harassment.

Very often, the family therapist becomes a model for future behavior within the family. For example, by showing sympathy for a beleaguered father, the therapist demonstrates to the family that this man needs sympathy even though supposedly he is the "strong one," the head of the household. In the case of a rebellious and hostile child, the therapist's show of understanding, rather than punitiveness, towards the child can serve as a useful example for all those present. The ability of the therapist to "take" hostile outbursts is reassuring to all concerned, particularly the family member who had the outburst. All present can see that a hostile outburst does not "kill" or "maim" or "destroy."

The therapist may remain in a position of neutrality, or he may support a member of the family.

> A Southern family of old parentage was referred for evaluation. The family had lost most of its fortune and was left with a "name" as its most precious possession. Living with the family was a widowed aunt, the wife's mother's sister. The aunt accompanied the family to the interview. She had lived with them for twenty years, ever since her husband had died. He left her a substantial income so that she was able to travel abroad every summer and take winter vacations. Except for these trips, she stayed with the niece's family, where her main preoccupation in life was to complain.
>
> During the interview, it became apparent that the man of the house felt a great deal of resentment toward this aunt. To a casual question about financial arrangements, the man and wife stated that they would

never think of taking any money from the aunt. She, in turn, responded that she had often tried to help them financially—had even offered to hire a maid for them—but that they would not even consider it. The aunt said she had been made to feel so guilty about offering help that she had given up the idea. Her niece immediately countered that this offer had never been made graciously. The husband then stated categorically that he wanted to hear no more of this, that things would remain as they were, and that was that. He refused to discuss the issue further.

It was apparent to the therapist that if this man were put into a situation where he had to take money from his wife's aunt, it would be the final blow to this man's image. Thus the therapist deemed it necessary to support this man in this particular instance. To remain entirely neutral might have undermined the entire course of treatment.

Fostering a Sense of Historical Continuity in Families

Perhaps one of the most valid reasons for seeing parents and children together is that it provides children an opportunity to become aware of their parents as part of a historical continuity and not simply as isolated units. When three generations are present, the continuity is even more graphic.

A family was referred because of problems with an adolescent son. The couple had married at age seventeen. The father stated that he married early primarily to get away from home. His wife was a passive person who generally followed his commands, although she would occasionally throw up a minor roadblock as a means of indicating her resentment toward his authoritarian behavior. Of note in the man's background was the fact that his mother was a semi-invalid. From early childhood, he had had to pitch in and do much of the housework and chores that ordinarily would have been done by his mother. His father was a tyrannical person who would brook no rebellion on the part of his son. This man consequently grew up with the feeling that he had been "enslaved" during much of his life.

The adolescent boy whose behavior had occasioned the referral was in trouble with the law. He had taken a rifle and climbed to the top of a schoolhouse, threatening to shoot various members of the teaching staff. He was subsequently referred to a mental health center. The boy was the oldest of three children and had a long history of what the parents described as "nervousness." He could not tolerate loud noises or any ruckus in the family. During the interview, he told of feeling that his father was inordinately restrictive and controlling, but he (the son) refused to be passive or "give in" as the mother and other children had. The resentment this boy felt toward his father was enormous. During the course of several sessions, the father's background was reviewed in the presence of the entire family. His resentment at being made a "slave" during his own childhood was discussed. The father began to understand that a great deal of his need to "control" stemmed from the fact that he himself had always been "controlled." The family was able to understand this man's behavior in the light of his past, a past in which his father was a tyrant (and perhaps his grandfather and great-grandfather before him). The boy who was the identified patient could see that he, too, might incorporate much of this same behavior. Tyranny was what he knew.

A practical way of altering behavior in an individual such as this man is to make the behavior "ego-alien." This task is much easier when there is the sympathetic support of family members who understand the background of the character structure. It then becomes unnecessary for the individual to "fight" to maintain the defensive posture; the climate in which the defense had its origin is now extinct.

For example, what happens when someone tells a mate or friend that he or she "talks too much"? There is usually immediate anger and denial on the part of the accused individual. However, if the criticism is coupled with the observation that there is really no need to talk so much *now,* a defense emanating from a past family constellation in which the individual was seldom listened to is neutralized. The criticism is much more readily accepted by the individual, and alteration of behavior follows more easily.

Therapy With Several Generations

The older generation's behavior patterns are often repeated blatantly in the younger generation.

Mr. and Mrs. L. came for consultation because of bickering and sullen periods in their marriage. Mr. L. worked late at his office to avoid these quarrels, only to be scolded later by his wife for staying away from home. Mr. L. stated that his wife tended to demand inordinate reassurance of his concern for her at all times, and that he simply could not tolerate her "clinging." The couple had married after a brief college courtship, the marriage being hastened by the fact that the husband, a soldier, was to be sent overseas.

Mr. and Mrs. L. were invited to bring their parents and their children to the interviews. Only Mrs. L.'s parents were able to come. Her mother disclosed that Mrs. L., an only child, had been in psychotherapy intermittently since the age of 15 (she was now 27). When asked why, her mother stated that they had always been concerned about their daughter's shyness and inability to make friends. They had tried alternately to coax and to coerce her into being more outgoing and friendly, all to no avail. It was apparent that all during her early life, Mrs. L. was constantly invaded by the parents. The mother was dominant in the family, the father passive and quiet. Mrs. L.'s mother also disclosed the fact that, as a child, she too had been considered "nervous" by her parents and that they sent her away to a boarding school known for its close supervision of students. "I was glad to get away from home," she stated.

Mr. and Mrs. L. were concerned about their older girl, Beth, aged seven, because she said little to anyone and frequently sat in school stimulating herself sexually.

Since the children's births, Mrs. L. had always looked for shyness in the older child: "She reminds me of myself as a child. I was afraid that the shyness was going to be in Beth. I always felt guilty about not giving her as much mothering as I should have. She is seven and still sucks her fingers. She has a doll to which she is deeply attached. Sometimes I find her lying on top of the doll as if she had been masturbating. My own guilt about it is such that even though you tell me that it is not unusual and even though I can understand it, I can't stop worrying. I'm always looking for this. Here she is, seven. When will she stop this behavior? Will she keep it up until she's sixteen? I wonder." She went on to state that she kept looking for rebelliousness in the younger child: "She'll do something that I never could." There was a hopeful note in her voice.

It has been said that a child's behavior represents the unconscious imagery of the parent; the child is the tablet upon which the mother's (or father's) unconscious is written. In the case noted above, the mother was looking for confirmation of her neurotic projections in the child. Beth's behavior in school reflected problems in the home, especially in the mother-child relationship. In this home, the father was away too much and, when home, was too tired to bother with the children. Thus he did nothing to neutralize the mother's pathogenic effect. Unless there is some resolution of conflicts, the same type of behavior exhibited by the mother and grandmother will probably be found in the third generation also.

The goal of family therapy in such instances is not necessarily a harsh modification of parent-child relationships. (There are many jokes about a patient being finished with his analysis once he is able to curse his mother outright.) One cannot bring the "Bible-belt," teetotaling parents into the offspring's new home and serve them alcohol with the notion that "this is the way it's going to be!" It is well-nigh impossible to cut off the relationship between a child and parent, no matter what the personality factors are. What one hopes for is a *change in attitude*. Not only should children not serve whiskey to such parents when they come to visit but, indeed, they might even put away the whiskey bottles. On their own, though, they may imbibe liberally. Too often a mistaken belief of therapy is that an individual must express his independence or defiance of his family, no matter what. Rather, it is useful to demonstrate to the younger generation exactly how the parental generation acquired its attitudes.

Individual Therapy Within a Family Setting

The value of having all the members of a family understand conflictual behavior in one individual has been described above in the instance of the man whose parents were tyrants. It is sometimes necessary to go beyond this understanding and to do extensive individual psychotherapy in the presence of the entire family. By so doing, the relationship of this individual's own conflicts to pathology in the family is demonstrated. An adolescent involved in the struggle to achieve an identity as an adult is a case in point. Where parents have interfered with his maturation and separation, therapy in the family setting can recreate for the youngster the conditions under which pathological reactions had their origin. Learning is thus markedly enhanced. The difference between this approach and the standard family therapy approach is that, here, the focus of treatment is on one individual and his conflicts.

Only secondarily is there an attempt made to treat other members of the family. The following vignette will illustrate.

Larry was a seventeen-year-old boy referred for treatment because of abusive behavior toward his mother. He had threatened her repeatedly with physical harm, and a week before referral had thrown a flowerpot at her. The entire family was seen. During the first session, it was disclosed that Larry had sporadically refused to attend school over the past two years. The mother constantly goaded him about his nonattendance. His father dealt with the problem by attempting to humiliate the boy; he was not as "good" as other boys and was a "coward" because he refused to go to school. However, since the father left home at the crack of dawn each morning, there was less friction generated between the two males than between the boy and his mother.

Larry's parents had married overseas while his father was in military service. The father was a career Army officer and attempted to run the home in military fashion. The mother was of Mediterranean origin and a "softer," more emotional person. She frequently talked of going back to her native home for a visit, or even to stay. Whenever she brought this subject up, her husband became enraged and cursed her.

Larry was a "cryer" until he was four, and both parents became exasperated with him. Because of this fact, they decided to have no more children.‡‡ The son described innumerable arguments between his parents, dating as far back as he could remember. He did his best to mediate these squabbles but usually gave up and left the house until the storm blew over. Later, he would return and attempt to comfort his mother. The boy became her confidant, and she told him in great detail how unhappy she was. She could not think of leaving the marriage, however, as this was contrary to her religious beliefs.

From early childhood on, Larry was quite independent—tying his own shoes, staying out late in the evening playing, and putting himself to bed. He was not a particularly happy child. As an adolescent, he began to develop anxiety about school. His fears seemed to center around one class in particular—math—where he had difficulty doing the work. No matter how hard he tried, he could not master the subject, and this caused him to panic. Eventually he found excuses to stay home. As the panic increased, he avoided school entirely.

---

‡‡The more demands a child places on the parents that they are unable to fulfill, the greater the feelings of inadequacy in the parents. This produces guilt and hostility toward the child. These parents could not cope with Larry as a "cryer." In another instance, a child comes home and tells his mother that he wants her to make coconut custard "like I had at school." If she is unable to do so she may become extremely angry with the child because he has made her feel inadequate.

During the interviews, it became clear that the parents' marriage
had never been a good one. Prior to the son's birth, while the parents
were still overseas, things were fine. After the son's birth, however,
both parents felt tied down. The father was an obsessive and power-ori-
ented man, with little flexibility in his personality. The mother was a
hysteric—alternately seductive and hostile. She usually tried to placate
her husband, but during arguments between father and son, she sided
with the boy. It was felt by the therapist that the parents were "fixed
quantities," and that there was little hope of altering their behavior in
treatment.

The therapeutic goal thus became that of helping the boy become
aware of his great anger and his inner struggle to maintain control of
his rage. He was in constant fear that his feelings of anger and frustration would spill out. Larry had another problem at school which also
necessitated rigid control of his emotions. He was a dark and hand-
some lad, and girls usually approached him in a teasing, flirtatious
manner. This evoked memories of the seductive teasing by his mother,
who alternately teased and fought with him. In a sense, Larry manifested a "male hysteric reaction": the early sexual stimulation by his
mother now necessitated repression of all sexual feelings.

In the family therapy setting, Larry could readily understand the
basis of his hysteric reaction. When the mother sided with the boy
against the father, the therapist could point out the rivalry and the
father's subsequent anger. Similarly, Larry's resentment at his father's
domineering manner was quickly apparent. By being directly exposed
to the nuances and permutations of both parents' reactions, therapy
was made easier. Larry did not have to conjure up in phantasy the
parental responses, since they were there for him to see firsthand.

Family therapy often functions best by helping an individual
member of a family achieve a more secure individual identity. In
one family, the mother considered herself a drudge. The therapist
and family members challenged her to do something about her
feelings of low self-esteem by investigating a long-standing interest
in decorating. She enrolled in an interior decorating course, and
later became a buyer for a small antique shop. The marriage improved greatly. Of note in this woman's background was the fact
that she was the only girl in a family with several boys. She had
always been showered with attention and affection. She was an
"other-oriented" person who depended on cues from the environment to make her feel worthwhile. As she established a functioning
identity of her own, cues from the outside became less important.

Discouragement During Family Therapy

After treatment has proceeded for several months and there has been open communication among the members but little change in family patterns, despair and discouragement often set in. What should the therapist do in such a case? One possibility is to give up the notion of change. A common belief of therapy is that there has to be change. Perhaps this does not have to be the case at all, and both the therapist and the family should be able to give up change as the major objective of treatment. For example, in the family in which the wife "wears the pants," there may be good reason not to change this arrangement; her husband may be unable to function in any role other than the passive one.

Another technique to counteract feelings of despair is to discuss resistance with the family in terms of "learning theory." When an individual has been brought up on old math and then is taught new math, he goes through a period of disorganization: one technique is being "unlearned" while a new technique has not yet been completely mastered. The same may be true for family patterns. Operative patterns, while tinged with compromise or other homeostatic mechanisms, have worked in the past; it is hard to learn new patterns without some disorganization and resistance.§§

In the field of family therapy, there is repeated emphasis on the need of a family to "communicate." This has almost become a magical term and may reflect the biological fact that mankind cannot survive without sending and receiving messages. "Just get them to communicate, and things will be all right," goes the adage. We know, however, that this is not necessarily the case: one can alter the communication patterns between people with-

---

§§Some therapists deal with resistance by bringing in a co-therapist. The presence of this new person may stimulate further associations and reactions. However, it is my feeling that therapy with one therapist is more efficacious. When two therapists are present, there tends to be an automatic regression in the family: the members place one of the therapists into the maternal role and the other into the paternal role. Learning and growth may suffer because of the regression. There is no doubt that exposure to "parental images" can be of great benefit in some families, particularly if members have come from backgrounds with inadequate parenting. However, it is my belief that this replacement is best sought in areas other than the family treatment setting.

out affecting any personality changes whatsoever. Therefore, the responses to and the content and emotional correlates of the messages become all-important. (One is reminded of a past chapter in psychotherapy when patients were encouraged to come into the office and discharge their aggression, willynilly. There might be no integration with stimulus or source of frustration, but the aggression "had to be discharged.") It is said that much of the communication between the family members has been lost because of modern technology. In days gone by, the kitchen was the center for homey conversations and exchange. Not so any longer. Kitchens are efficient and shiny and electrified. Similarly, the open fireplace has been replaced by an open television screen, and the latter blots out conversation. Not only is there a loss of interaction but also a loss in terms of identity. The woman spends less time teaching her daughter how to be a woman and the man spends less time teaching his son how to become a man.

THERAPY AND THE THERAPIST

One of the major differences between psychiatric family therapy and counseling which is done by clergymen, is that the physician does not emphasize guilt in the "moral" sense. The psychiatrist emphasizes responsibility for behavior. A well-known minister wrote an article on how to save marriages. He suggested that the couple contemplating divorce sit down together in a room and quietly talk over the consequences of divorce—how this will affect the children, the financial problems, and so forth (Peale, 1964). While on the surface this may seem to be a valid approach since it appeals to the reason and innate decency in most individuals, clinically, it doesn't often work. It is like asking a drug addict to recognize the harm his habit does him, or challenging an alcoholic in his sober days to stop drinking because of all the problems his drinking creates. Most people capable of such lucid reasoning seldom come to see psychiatrists or counselors. They are able to work out their problems on their own. When emotions hold sway, reason has little opportunity to prevail.

One must be honest about the exacting nature of family therapy insofar as the therapist is concerned. Most people are brought up in families and therein lies the efficacy of family therapy. A person who has never been part of a family is a poor candidate for practicing this type of treatment. On the other hand, the therapist is exposed on a multitude of levels to interactions which may have been troubling him or which stir memories of his own life. What is the answer?

Ideally, the family therapist should have enough personal therapy or analysis to discover sources of unconscious conflict within himself. In particular, the family therapist must have had a chance to investigate thoroughly the personalities, the behavior, the characteristics, and the emotional messages that he himself received from his family of origin—from parents, siblings, and others in his background. He will then be able to move more freely within the emotional complexes of a family without being encumbered by unresolved conflicts from his own past. The drama of family therapy, as in stage drama, is so moving and so intense that the most "perfectly analyzed" individual cannot help but become directly involved. Thus, he may find himself lecturing the family, scolding the family, urging the parents to be firm with a child, urging children to be more aware of their parents' needs, condemning the family for abandoning an aged parent, or challenging them to allow the members to grow. Experience has shown that this tendency to become directly involved is not altogether unwise; it demonstrates to the family that the therapist is emotionally attuned to their problems. Fortunately, what he says is usually taken in the context of the circumstance. (The same holds true in individual psychoanalysis. When patients who have been analyzed are asked to describe the high spots of their analysis, they frequently relate some instance involving an emotional response on the part of the analyst. The patient then knows that the analyst is "involved." It may have been an angry outburst on the telephone; it may have been a genuine scolding given them by the analyst; or it may have been the patient's surreptitiously avoiding an emotional response, but then one day confessing this to the analyst and evoking an even deeper emotional response in return.)

After a highly moving play or drama, the viewer wants a chance to discuss the impact and the emotional message of the play with someone. This is true of family therapy as well. After a highly emotional experience with a family, the therapist needs an opportunity to discuss some of his reactions and findings with someone with whom he feels free from criticism. It should also be remembered that it is sheer hard work to do family therapy, and the therapist must take care not to overburden himself.

THE THERAPIST AND SOCIAL CLASS

Sociologic study of mental illness has been extended to include study of the effect of class differences between therapist and patient. Most psychiatrists tend to be of middle-class social background. How might this affect therapy with families of other social classes, particularly the lower socioeconomic groups?

Studies suggest that the psychiatrist must take both psychological and social factors into account in order to understand the meaning of symptoms in poverty families. In an Appalachian poverty-stricken family, an individual may have florid somatic symptoms and yet have no inkling that these are related to tensions brought on by his environment. Therapy may thus involve "treating the environment," i.e. helping the patient to modify the environment in accordance with his needs. Similarly, the so-called blue-collar family of the urban slum areas may not realize that some of their symptoms or complaints are related to frustrations in their lives.

> A forty-five-year-old woman was admitted to a hospital for severe excoriations of her forehead and face. These were beet red, and the physician first thought that the woman had erysipelas. However, this initial diagnosis proved incorrect and led the physician to investigate the patient's environment. Her life was full of frustration. She lived in a mountain area in East Tennessee and was the mother of four children. Her husband worked long hours and when not at work, was off hunting with the boys or carousing at the service station. The woman's role in life was fixed: she prepared the meals, cleaned the house, and took care of the children. When asked whether or not she was satisfied with her life, she could only shrug her shoulders and say, "That's the way it is." When asked if her husband satisfied her in any way—sexual or otherwise—she stated that he had his own life to live, and that was that. Her whole demeanor was that of a defeated, frustrated woman who felt

nothing could be done to improve her lot in life. She could only scratch herself out of sheer frustration.

Of importance in treating poverty families is this group's perception of the therapist's attitudes. Does the therapist make them feel that his investment of time and energy in this family is worthwhile? Most therapists seem to agree that this is a crucial factor in treatment of lower-class families; the middle-class psychiatrist tends to anticipate defeat because of his own social conditioning that these families are "hopeless." He approaches them with middle-class values, and the family soon detects the difference. In point of fact, the family itself must decide what it wants. The goals of treatment cannot be set by the therapist, since his goals of treatment may be completely out of line with what the family is capable of achieving or what the family actually wants. In *Social Class, Schizophrenia and the Psychiatrist*, there is the following statement:

> The psychiatrist places great emphasis on the patient's willingness to see her illness as the psychiatrist sees it. The patient from the same social class as the psychiatrist sees her illness as he does and thus is more effectively treated by him. This demonstrates how necessary it is for the psychiatrist to be more familiar with the attitudes of lower class patients toward mental illness and psychiatric treatment, if more effective treatment is to be made available (Moore *et al.*, 1963, p. 154).

In a study of socioeconomic variables and psychiatric treatment in a children's clinic, Wagner and Baker (1966) noted that there was no bias in accepting children for treatment. There was bias, however, in assigning therapists; those from higher social status were assigned more frequently to psychiatrists; those from lower socioeconomic status were assigned to social workers, medical students, and social work students.

Chapter VII

Psychoanalysis and Family Therapy

F amily therapy is approximately at the same stage today (early 1970's) that psychoanalysis was at the end of the last century. Freud and others demonstrated that, clinically, they had a tool—psychoanalysis—which would work; there was no question about that. But how were they to evolve a theory to explain these clinical observations? Beginning in 1905, Freud wrote a series of papers on metapsychology, and these were later elaborated on by many of his students. The conclusions Freud reached after 1905 have stirred endless debate among psychoanalytic theoreticians. There is, however, almost universal recognition of the validity of Freud's early clinical descriptions: his ideas about the psychopathology of everyday life, the importance of studying dreams, the theory of the unconscious, the principles of free association, and the fact that in psychotherapy the patient is entitled to a voice of his own and is not simply a pawn of the therapist.

Family treatment is also a method that works clinically. That long-standing symptoms in a family or one of its members can be resolved is demonstrable beyond question. The problem once again is to explain the clinical facts: how does a family operate, and what are the forces that tend to mold or skew a family? Family study may serve as a bridge to incorporate many of the newer insights of sociology, psychology, social work, and anthropology into the here-and-now understanding of the individual and his surroundings. The family is the principal environment of the developing child for almost a fourth of his life, and society entrusts the family with the task of providing nurturance for the child, fostering his creative growth, and teaching him social values.

Until recently, the tradition in psychotherapy has been to isolate the patient from his environment, whether it be a mental hospital or in the psychiatrist's office. However, as detailed in

176

Chapter I, studies now indicate that this practice may be questionable. Frequently, the individual who originally comes for treatment has been "designated" the carrier of the emotional disturbance for the family and may be the scapegoat for a more disturbed member of the family group. Further, many reports are now found in the psychiatric literature describing one individual's improvement in psychotherapy, only to have another member of the family break down. Certainly it is a common occurrence in the treatment of childhood schizophrenia that as the child improves, the mother may develop disabling symptoms.

How are psychoanalysis and family therapy different in conceptual approach? Psychoanalysis is the method, par excellence, for gathering data about an individual's subjective thoughts and feelings. One uses the patient's thoughts, dreams, phantasies, and motivations. Unconscious distortions come out mainly in the transference. The assumption is made that during analysis one modifies these distortions, and the person moves spontaneously toward health. In family therapy, a symptom in one member of a family may be viewed as a symbolic reflection of emotional difficulties in the entire family. The unit of health or pathology becomes the entire family, and this group is treated simultaneously. In psychoanalysis, transference becomes the main vehicle whereby patient and analyst see the effects of early traumatic relationships and by which the patient's distortions are modified. In family therapy, modifications result from direct reexperiencing of trauma with parents and siblings, or by observing the interaction of one family member with another member or the therapist. Obviously, there is a "transference" aspect here as well, i.e. irrational expectations and feelings from past relationships are transferred into the present.

Individual therapy and family therapy are two modes of treatment which can be used independently, simultaneously, or consecutively. Different goals are involved in each. In family therapy the focus is on the family interaction; in psychoanalysis the focus is on one individual's introspections. It is often apparent that family therapy should precede psychoanalysis; sometimes it is necessary to interrupt family treatment to deal in individual therapy with one person's deep-seated conflicts. Such an instance is described in the preceding chapter: the mother of the school-phobic boy had to be seen alone in order to deal with the conflict related to molestation by her father.

How can these observations be incorporated into everyday clinical practice? By seeing the identified patient together with his spouse or family at the initial interview, where practicable. In this way, the therapist can gauge whether the pathology is primarily a reflection of the present complementary relationship or whether it is a long-standing conflict in one individual. For the former, family therapy is indicated; for the latter, individual treatment.

A common example from everyday clinical practice is a woman referred for psychotherapy because of depression. She is in her thirties, is married, and has several children. She complains that her husband is always "too busy" to show her any affection, and the life she knows is drudgery. The therapist learns that she is the youngest child in a family that always showered her with adoration. By seeing both the woman and her husband together and observing the interaction, the therapist is better able to decide at which level treatment should begin. It may be that the husband finds his home life too demanding and tends to withdraw emotionally from his wife and family. On the other hand, the need for approval and attention on the wife's part may be "insatiable" and may reflect her feeling of inadequacy as a person.

On the basis of the initial evaluation, the therapist can appraise the total situation. It may be that family treatment is in order (in this hypothetical instance, the children would probably have been seen also), or individual therapy of either spouse might be recommended. In this way, treatment of the "wrong patient" is avoided. By stating directly what he feels the problem is, the therapist can unfreeze many other areas of interaction in the family. Another benefit of seeing the family: when individual therapy is suggested, the mate usually cooperates with the therapy rather than resisting or sabotaging it. The therapist becomes an ally and not a rival.

Both psychoanalysis and family therapy operate primarily on the level of the emotional mechanisms described in Chapter II, i.e. messages are sent between individuals either directly or symbolically and a response is sought. The fact that psychoanalysis is practiced in an intimate social setting (patient and analyst) facilitates working directly with the emotional mechanisms and their deviations. Psychoanalytic therapy is more analytic; family therapy is more synthetic. Family therapy is more evocative, more confrontational; psychoanalysis is more exploratory. In a sense, the two modes of entry—exploration and evocation—are two ends of a continuum. In psychoanalysis, one relies primarily on exploration but assumes that there will be enough evocation of reaction between patient and analyst, or the patient and his environment, to elicit understanding of the patient's emotional reactions. In family therapy, the primary tool is evocation of response, and the individual family member is led to explore his own responses. The self-exploration may require individual therapy or even reconstructive psychoanalysis, and the therapist should not hesitate to recommend analysis where it is indicated. The individual who has difficulty in the two-person, analytic setting might respond very well in the family or group setting where a whole range of responses are evoked. The opposite is also true. Thus, the therapist who wants to practice family therapy must have a thorough grounding in individual dynamics. No one understands family dynamics better than the psychoanalyst. After all, interactional data are always processed by one's own psyche and, in the end, behavior is determined by this processing.

Because the analyst works with only one individual in psychoanalytic therapy, there is little possibility of predicting or controlling the behavior of those with whom the patient is intimately involved. Modification of one individual's personality does not guarantee any change in reaction of those around him. Freud referred to this fact in his paper entitled, "Analysis Terminable and Interminable" (1937). He stated that an important factor in successful analysis is that the patient remain in a hospitable environment. Freud wrote, "If the patient who has made such a good recovery never produces any more symptoms calling for analysis, it still, of course, remains an open question how much of this immunity *is due to a benevolent fate which spares him too searching a test*" (p. 321). [*Italics mine.*]

Freud also noted in this essay that the ultimate desire of some men is to be in a passive role, and he emphasized the masculine protest in the female as well. In years gone by, the passive male position was unacceptable in most societies. However, today we know that some men can achieve satisfaction in a passive role. The passive man can work in a large corporation that offers "protection," he can work in a secluded office, he need not marry, he need not bother having children, and so on. The same holds true for "masculine protest": the woman can now fulfill herself in almost any field or fulfill any ambition important to her. Thus it is doubtful that masculine protest can be analyzed today as it was in Freud's time. The same holds true for sexual activity. The adolescent boy (or girl) is not so much troubled about inhibitions regarding sex, as he is by the constant challenge to participate aggressively in sexual activity.

It is hoped that this chapter will contribute to a refinement of criteria for involving patients in the various types of therapy. Not every patient is a candidate for psychoanalysis, but certainly during the 1940's and early 1950's, it was widely recommended for persons presenting themselves in psychiatrists' offices. An analogy might be drawn from medicine. Radiation therapy is not used for every swelling in the body. For some swellings (cancers) it is beneficial; for others it is completely toxic. Those familiar with the history of pseudoneurotic schizophrenia know that this diagnostic category came about primarily because of the large number of patients who were "analyzed" into state hospitals.

Family Treatment of a Man Who Failed In Psychoanalysis

An unmarried thirty-year-old man was referred one summer for psychoanalytic treatment of chronic depression, inability to adjust vocationally, and periods of sexual impotence. The patient had had two previous experiences in psychoanalytic therapy, the first for three years and the second for a year and a half. He stated that both experiences had helped him reach an intellectual awareness of his difficulties but had been of little help insofar as his actual symptoms and functioning on a day-to-day level were concerned.

The patient was the oldest in a family in which there were two younger sisters. He had been born two months prematurely and was asthmatic and sickly as a child. He needed special nurses and attended special schools. He had little self-confidence during childhood, and it was not until he went away to prep school for a year that he developed any degree of self-assurance. It was here, also, that he first formed lasting friendships. He finished college and then spent two successful years in the Army. He had always been shy and inhibited with girls, but while in service he attempted sexual activity for the first time. He recalled several traumatic episodes in which he was unable to function but eventually managed, while still in service, to overcome his sexual fears and to function adequately. After discharge he returned home to work at various jobs. Several times he worked for his father, but each time, due to quarrels, he would leave and find a job elsewhere. His inability to adjust vocationally led him to seek analysis.

The patient's mother was an only child from a small rural town. Before marriage, she had worked as a secretary. Her own father was a philanderer, and she recalled her mother's frequent lectures about the importance of finding a man who would be a faithful and steady husband. This she accomplished when she married the patient's father, who at the time of their marriage was thirty-four years old and was working endless hours each day to build up his own business. Because of the mother's experience with her own father, she brought up her children in a puritan-like fashion—hard work and little pleasure.

The patient's father was a man of imposing presence and restless nature. His own father had deserted when the boy was five. His mother then began working long hours, leaving him in the care of relatives. He started working at odd jobs when he was eleven and from then on cared for his mother and two younger brothers. At eighteen he started his own small business. It grew phenomenally, owing mainly to his hard work. In between all the work activities, the father managed to obtain some schooling in business procedure. What he lacked in terms of formal education was more than made up for by on-the-job training and experience. The father steadfastly denied that he needed anyone for comfort or support; he relied only on himself. Further, he denied that his own father's desertion in any way affected him. He stated he was able to shrug this off without any problem and that, indeed, he recalled the time after his father's desertion as being quite happy. He held firmly to this view despite many questions raised about it. The father recalled a significant relationship with his grandmother, a crusty old woman of pioneer stock. He saw her frequently as a youngster and remembered her stories, which stressed the importance of hard work and honesty.

The two daughters in the present family were born a decade after the son. The mother assumed she could have no more children when she failed to conceive for several years, and the daughters were "unexpected." At the time the family was seen, the girls were both in college and might best be characterized as "sweet young things" who spent most of their leisure time horseback riding.

Therapy Sessions

The son was seen alone for the first visit during which a history was taken. He was invited to bring his entire family thereafter. During the first family interview, the father participated only briefly and then in a manner that denigrated his son. He talked about how sickly the boy had always been, both physically and emotionally. He told of the huge sums of money he had spent on the boy's previous analyses, but coupled this statement with the fact that he was willing to do so again. He could not understand how his son had been accepted for military service. The therapist pointed out to the father that he seemed to respond only in a negative way to his son. The therapist also remarked that although the father said little, all the family members looked at him before speaking. Further, it was noted that no one seemed to support the boy when the father castigated him.

Although the father was willing to talk about his own personal history in this first session, at the end of the hour he stated that he would not return because he felt the entire procedure "wasn't worth a damn." The therapist turned to the other members of the family and asked how they felt. They all agreed that it was important that they try to work together because of the family's problems. The therapist explained to the father that the son's problems might be a reflection of a family problem and that the father would have to take part. Again the father demurred, and the therapist then told him that although his parents had abandoned him, this did not give him license to abandon his own family. He grudgingly agreed that he would come and never missed a session. For several weeks the entire family was seen together. Then, for several weeks, only the boy and his father came. Final sessions involved all the family members. The entire course of therapy was fourteen months.

During the course of treatment, the son complained bitterly that his father constantly humiliated him, refused to back him up, and had no faith in him whatsoever. At that time, the boy was back working for his father. If the son returned from the bank on company business during the middle of the day and the father happened to be in the office, he might accuse his son of having just come to work, without bothering to question his whereabouts. The father vehemently denied that he had ever treated his son badly, despite all of the boy's protestations. As evidence, he cited the fact that he always backed up those around him, even his employees.

One family session was crucial and needs to be recited in detail. The father told of a time when one of his employees had gotten into some trouble with the police. This employee's own father, who was prominent in the city and might easily have straightened the matter out, refused to help his son. Having no one to turn to, the boy called his employer (our patient's father) in the middle of the night. The man described how he had immediately called the police and straightened the whole matter out, backing his employee to the hilt. Quite suddenly, as he was relating this story, his voice choked up and he began to cry uncontrollably. He was unable to continue. He became exceedingly angry and embarrassed. He accused the therapist of having made him lose control—something he had never done before. The son was aghast at this unexpected behavior in his father.

The therapist explained that this behavior was not unique, that the father was responding emotionally to his awareness of need in another person, and that it was important for the family members to be aware that people need one another. The whole episode brought out into the open the father's own feelings about having been abandoned as a child. In the experience with his employee, he was in effect saying that he would never abandon one of his employees as he had been abandoned by his own father. The therapist was then able to point out to the father that he had never gotten over the loss of his own parents— the father by desertion, the mother by working long hours—and, fearing that he might be hurt again, never allowed himself to become emotionally involved and vulnerable with anyone. This emotional catharsis led the father to an understanding of some of the difficulties that his son was having.

The son immediately sensed the emotional current. He turned to the older man and stated several times that he wanted to feel close to him, that he wanted to feel that he could depend on him. During the emotional outpouring, the mother tried three times to divert attention from the father by saying how much they had done for the boy. The therapist told her repeatedly not to try to protect her husband, since in this case it was not protection he needed, but emotional catharsis and understanding of the reaction.

During the course of treatment, it became apparent that the father was a gifted man who would have succeeded in any endeavor. He was brought up in poverty and, as a consequence, was generally uncomfortable in his role as a wealthy man. (He was a millionaire many times over.) He made his own way by driving himself mercilessly and was a self-made man in the truest sense of the word. It was clear that the man's main source of self-esteem in life was success in his day-to-day performance. He demolished any competition before it arose to challenge him. He had a ready reserve of capital and would jump into any lucrative venture at a moment's notice.

The son improved significantly during treatment. His appetite was better, he gained weight, his sense of being pressured lifted, and he was generally more comfortable. He had no further experiences of sexual impotence, he continued to work with his father in business and, with the latter's encouragement, eventually went into business for himself. He dated regularly, although he had little thought of marriage. There was also improvement in family relationships. The mother learned to accept her children more for what they were. Her attitude became more warm and solicitous, and she stopped some of her lecturing. Both daughters married before completing college, and the men they chose were of a different social and religious background than their own.

THE SELF-MADE MAN

As often happens in family therapy, the focus of treatment shifted from the boy's subjective conflicts to some of the problems in the family interaction, in particular those between father and son. The first step, then, was to come to some understanding of the father's own psychopathology. In a sense, the father became the "patient." The father could not tolerate competition from any quarter, not even from his son. Not only did the father have one of the largest businesses east of the Mississippi, but he also had the biggest car, the biggest lake with the biggest fish, and so on. There were episodes which suggested that the father had sabotaged some of the boy's past attempts to venture out on his own. The father's psychopathology was treated in the presence of the son and helped the boy to understand what had interfered with the ordinary father-son relationship.

The story of this father is that of the typical self-made man. Many of the most successful men in this country had somewhat similar careers. They started out with only a few pennies in their pockets and eventually became outstanding successes in business. These individuals had little in the way of family ties or support and were almost totally devoid of the emotional satisfactions which are part of ordinary childhood. The only thing they were sure of was their ability to work; this they did with fanatical vigor and dedication.

What are some of the personality characteristics of the self-made man? First and foremost, he lacks a feeling of identity, the sense of self-appreciation and self-worth. Individual identity comes about through the process of identifying with parents, peers, and social acquaintances. The developing child has his first identity as a physical self: he is nurtured and cared for by a maternal figure during the infantile period of complete dependence. From this state of helplessness he gradually develops an identity as an individual who can accomplish things for himself. The individual who has had inadequate mothering and fathering often has difficulty envisioning himself as a worthwhile individual. He may attempt to make up for this inner feeling of worthlessness by constantly "proving" his importance. Everything he does and everything he has must be the biggest and the best. He has created a world in which his own performance and accomplishments are the mainstays of his identity. It is not surprising that this individual has difficulty retiring from work, since he has very little to fall back upon.

Many a self-made man has the feeling, "If you are not for me, you are against me." The child brought up under ordinary family circumstances learns that parents can discipline him or criticize him out of love or out of concern. The self-made man has usually not had this experience because of inadequate parenting. Thus, in later life, he will need constant acceptance and approval. He always needs to be infallible and correct. He cannot "take" criticism because, for him, criticism has never been a positive experience.

The self-made man will seldom allow competition—not even from a son or relative—because he feels threatened by other's ideas and progress. He has trouble sharing his knowledge and information. Having always been on his own and fending for himself, he has never known the satisfaction of a sustained relationship in which there was mutual trust and sharing.*

This was part of the problem that unfolded in the case cited. When the son, in attempting to learn the family business, ap-

*For a discussion of "Marriage and the Self-Made Man," see Chapter IX, pp. 242, 243.

proached his father with a problem, the man usually responded by suggesting that he solve it on his own. Later, the father would complain about the son's incompetence and inability. At other times, the father would tackle and solve the whole problem himself, afterwards telling his son there was nothing to be gained by constantly "stewing over things." It was no wonder that the son felt inadequate, helpless, and hopeless as well. Erikson (1950) has written about "overidentifications" in children which result from early unresolved crises in their development. These crises hinder the evolution of a more flexible and integrated personality. Conflicts are managed by rigid imitation of the parents' ways of handling conflict.

PSYCHOANALYTIC THERAPY AND FAMILY THERAPY

Why were the patient's previous analyses not completely successful?

True, the patient gained what he described as an intellectual awareness of his problems, but this did little to improve his day-to-day performance in life. Could a better result have been achieved in a more directive individual analysis? Could he have done well in group therapy? Or was family therapy, in which there was a direct confrontation between the patient and his father, necessary? The hypothesis used here is that direct confrontation was necessary while the father was still alive. The son's experience with his father was so laden with apprehension, and the fact that he was never able to assert himself in any way or declare his independence from his father was such a vivid and humiliating defeat, that the situation would have to be reversed to some degree before the boy could make significant progress. Some direct assault on this image of defeat and humiliation was accomplished during the confrontation in therapy.

Theoretically, one should be able to accomplish the same effect in psychoanalysis by analyzing the transference or by analyzing relationships with superiors or peers. The efficacy of the procedure depends upon how much one can revivify the earlier experience with the father in the situation being analyzed. (Of course, one can speculate about the degree to which this patient's previous

analyses contributed to the successful end result.) In routine analysis, the therapist often sees a patient struggling over and over
again with a problem intellectually or in phantasy. The analyst
soon recognizes that unless some change in the life situation of the
patient takes place, there is little hope of progress. The necessity
for "action" during psychotherapy has been noted in Chapter III.†

A question arises as to whether the boy was able to establish
any kind of transference relationship with the first two analysts.
Transference is not a built-in phenomenon. Rather it is evoked
by a situation. The psychotherapeutic situation is tailor-made for
this evocation. The circumstances were first detailed by Freud: he
noted that as his patients talked, more and more their thoughts
drifted to childhood experiences, and Freud found himself cast
into a role reminiscent of some past figure of importance in the
patient's life. However, the clinical fact is that there are many instances where the transference does not "take," due perhaps to the
personalities and experiences of analyst and patient. In the case
described here, the son as well as the father had difficulty trusting
any man.

A word might be said here about analysis of transference. What
seems to work best in analysis of transference are two parallel
emotional experiences going on simultaneously; in this case, for
example, if a change in relationship between the father and the
son took place at the same time as a similar change in analysis,
and the latter was being analyzed, learning would be much more
effective. It is doubtful that analysis of transference works out very
well when it goes on solely within the therapeutic relationship.
Personal reports by Freud's analysands disclose that Freud was intensely interested in what was going on in his patient's outside life.
Freud often complained that his patients were not doing enough;
he did not rely solely on what was happening in the therapeutic
relationship.‡ Also, unless the therapist asks directly about the patient's present life, he may miss vital facts which the patient has

---

†There is also the question about whether insight is a precondition of behavioral
change, or whether insight is a result of the change. For a fuller discussion of this
question, see Alexander and French (1946).

‡Abram Kardiner, personal communication.

selectively omitted. A woman may focus only on her childhood experiences and neglect to tell the analyst that she is contemplating divorce.

To return again to our case, the presence of the therapist was mandatory during the face-to-face confrontation of father and son. The son was not able, on his own, to be assertive with so awesome a figure as his father. His two analyses gave him some insight into the fact that there was something wrong in his relationships with his family, particularly with his father. But in spite of this understanding of his father's reactions in everyday life, he could do little about the older man's personality. An individual cannot control the environment around him unless it is a nonhuman environment. Each man's responses are his own. (Freud partially took care of this fact by instructing his patients not to make major changes or decisions in their lives until the analysis was completed.)

The fact that the father tended to belittle his son resulted in a great impairment in the capacity of the son to see himself realistically as a functioning person. Self-esteem in an individual evolves from mastering many situations and successfully completing many tasks. The son constantly tried to win some kind of approval and acceptance in the eyes of his father, but because the older man was uncomfortable in his masculine role and could tolerate no competition from his son, there was continual thwarting of growth in self-confidence and self-esteem. The boy finally gave up all attempts at gaining acceptance, knowing he could never "measure up" or achieve status in the eyes of his father. By giving up, there would be less insult to his self-esteem—nothing ventured, nothing lost.

In the face-to-face confrontation between the patient and his father, for the first time many of the son's conflicts were brought out into the open for all the family to see. The son had incorporated an image of a father as being deserting and ungiving, this image originating with both his father and his mother because of their own past experiences of being deserted.

The pathology in this family was an incapacity to neutralize the father's overbearing nature and provide support for the son's attempts at self-assertion. Secondly, a warm feminine response was lacking. A sense of gloom hung over the family, related to the traumatic experiences that both parents themselves had had as children. Family therapy was directed first to problems in the interaction, and once there was some modification in these patterns, individual personality reactions were then explored.

It is important to remember that this patient did not get "sick" alone nor could he get "well" alone. Family treatment is a natural level of entry into human relations. An individual learns about the emotions of love and hate, anger and fear, in his nuclear family. Harry Stack Sullivan (1953) described this phenomenon in working with schizophrenic patients; patients made the hospital staff their nuclear family.

Strictly speaking, a symptom in one individual should be described from an individual standpoint and not from a family standpoint. A symptom is characterized by its irrelevancy, inappropriateness, or stereotypy in a given situation. The soldier on the battlefield becomes phobic and obsessional, but these are not symptoms; the reactions are in keeping with the stimulus. A family may have many reactions to a conflict, but a symptom reflecting the conflict may be expressed in only one family member. Sexual impotence may reflect inadequacy in child-parent relationships, but it remains a symptom in one individual.

One person's capacity for adapting to stress is naturally determined by his degree of health or pathology. The individual with street phobia is limited in his reactions by this symptom; he cannot venture into the street without certain "safety factors." In evaluating a family in which the children complain repeatedly that the mother is short with them when they come home from school, it becomes necessary to look for possible stereotypy in the mother's reactions: if she has a phobia about dirt, she might respond to the child's dirty overalls or dirty shoes, rather than responding to the youngster as a whole being. The phobic symptom has limited her capacity to be flexible in her responses.

The same is true of autocratic-type families. If a father's perception of his maleness is inadequate, chances are that when problems arise, he will resort to brute strength or brute power in order to have his way. The more flexible he is, the more likely he will be able to enter into compromises.

FATHER-SON RELATEDNESS

What about "normal" developmental trends in father-son relatedness? After all, this dyadic sequence is all-important in terms of a boy learning self-assertion, self-confidence, and an identity as a man. For convenience of discussion, several distinct phases in this progression are outlined.

In the very early years of life the child clings to the father for comfort, support, and encouragement, much as he does the mother. He begins to learn something about the distinction between male and female body movements and vocal expressions. A father bounces a boy much differently than does a mother and demands more masculine-oriented performance from him. Roughhousing, whether in puppies or in children, appears to be extremely important in the growth and development of young offspring. By rough play with his peers, the boy learns something of his physical strength. In roughhousing with the father, the boy learns the limits of his physical strength. The actual physical contact makes it unnecessary to relegate thoughts about power or weakness to phantasy. This "living in phantasy" is characteristic of the very fearful child.§

Sexual gender indentification occurs during the first few years of life (Stoller, 1968). A boy of six or eight needs an idealized image of his father as a powerful man of infinite capacity, and he derives strength in telling his friends about how wonderful and strong his father is. He brags that his father is stronger than all other fathers. (Naturally, where a father is absent, such as in cases or death or desertion, the child can be sustained by an "image" of a strong father.)

In early adolescence this need for the father as a powerful figure continues, and, if necessary, the boy will lie about his father in this regard. The boy is struggling to achieve a masculine identity and to leave childhood behind. Therefore, he seeks to in-

---

§How often are children apprehended for homicide described by neighbors as "quiet, obedient youngsters."

corporate as much strength as possible from the paternal figure. It is not at all unusual to see a boy begin searching for "important" ancestors during this period—anyone who seems to have strength which he can incorporate.

As later adolescence comes along, a boy enters the phase of "separating" from his father; he begins to find fault with him and to disparage him. He is attempting to establish his own identity and, as part of this, there is need to compete with the older man. In time, there is resolution of the competitiveness and the boy begins to view his father in a realistic fashion. This attitude was aptly described by Mark Twain, who stated that at fourteen he assumed his father was quite stupid, but when he (Mark Twain) reached the age of twenty-one, he realized that his father had learned a great deal in that time.

When the father is an outstandingly successful man, it presents a double-barreled problem to a child; every son feels he must compete with or "surpass" the father in some way, whether in football, dress, or the ability to judge how much ground distance is in a mile. If the father cannot tolerate competition, it follows that he will not be able to support his son in this "rebellion." This, then, compounds the issue. Very often the son of an outstanding businessman will train for a professional career, the reason being, "There is no use competing with father, I can't win." Bronson (1959) has shown that significant stresses in the early relationship between boys and their fathers can result in "defensive overidentifications" in the sons or in complete rejection of "masculine" attitudes.

The self-made man described previously in this chapter is, in reality, a tyrant but pictures himself as a benevolent tyrant. He is in a constant state of so-called homosexual panic, i.e. he fears attack and humiliation from other men. This humiliation is visualized in sexual terms: he is being anally mounted ("shafted") or forced to submit to oral rape by another man. Accordingly, he is always on the defensive. He must immediately depreciate and humiliate those he meets, since, in his phantasy, they are out to depreciate and humiliate him. A son can only be tolerated if he is in the position of an inferior male, and many of these boys grow up with a tendency toward passivity and effeminacy. This theme was well-captured in the short play by Arthur Miller, *A View From the Bridge*. A girl's uncle set out to prove that the boy who was courting his niece was a weakling by treating this boy as if he were homosexual. At one point in the drama, the uncle adopts a completely homosexual pose himself in order to humiliate the boy (Miller, 1957). This type of man often suffers from hypochondriasis, which serves as a defense against increasing panic.

The writer once supervised a resident in the therapy of a patient who was orphaned at an early age. The boy had been placed in a foster home for several years and then was sent to live with his aged grandparents. They provided all of the boy's material needs and made it possible for him to attend college. He had difficulty concentrating during the second year of college and was referred for psychotherapy. Shortly after treatment began, he admitted that he was very much concerned about homosexual thoughts and impulses. As a matter of fact, he had "almost" participated in a homosexual episode. The patient stated that he was always looking for "something" from men. His behavior was interpreted by the resident as not being primarily homosexual but rather as a seeking of some other satisfaction or fathering from men. In his own mind, the patient felt his craving to be a sexual desire, and his anxiety was greatly relieved to learn that this was not the case. (He was the typical "pseudohomosexual.") He was able to stay in college while continuing therapy. In time, he began to have phantasies of the therapist in the role of father. In a very blunt way the resident informed him that he could not be his father, that he did not need a father, and that was that. The patient responded to this remark with depression and by participating in several overt homosexual episodes.

The family therapist meeting this problem, either in a family context or in individual therapy, is sensitive to the need for parenting on the part of all persons, particularly boys who have been brought up with little or no fathering. The therapist can help the patient become aware that his need and seeking for fathering has some legitimacy. He is hungry for the nurturance he never had.

A girl brought up in an orphanage, or by a mother who gave

her little nurturance, will have difficulty in mothering her own children. This difficulty will increase as the number of children increases. If such a mother has daughters, they may recognize that their own mother needs "mothering" herself. Occasionally, then, the daughters need to supply this mothering. If there are no girls around, then the husband must "mother" his wife. The same is true for a man who had little fathering during his life. It may be necessary for his sons to be paternalistic with him occasionally. The image of the rock-ribbed, energetic, stern father is not necessarily a sound one. It is better that a man have some emotional needs that the family can supply. They need to feel that he needs them.

In treating a family in which the father has a defective image of himself as a man, the man and his family must learn that simple family disagreements do not represent an attack on the father's position or masculine integrity. Such learning allows more flexible response in the family, i.e. the use of more homeostatic mechanisms. The family members need not always be on guard that what they say may be interpreted by the father as an attack or humiliation. The greater the flexibility, the more readily the family will be able to meet challenge and stress without decompensation.

Where members of the extended family are present, a corrective is usually built in; grandfathers, uncles, etc., of differing personalities can serve as models of identification for children and can also lend support to a father with a defective image as a man.

In a similar vein, more schools are experimenting with team-teaching, i.e. two or three teachers per class. Students then have a wider exposure to teachers of differing personalities, which enhances emotional role experimentation with adults (p. 128). This kind of exposure becomes more significant with speedup of maturation, e.g. puberty is a year earlier in 1970 as compared with 1870. The faster one travels, the more reference points he needs.

Chapter VIII

Social Homeostasis
Individual—Family—Social Interaction

The Ping-Pong Couple

Mr. and Mrs. Jeff Brown were referred for marriage therapy by their family physician because of continual quarreling. Originally, Mr. Brown had gone to his physician with abdominal pains. These pains often woke him up at night, and a presumptive diagnosis of peptic ulcer was made. X-ray studies were negative, however, as were other tests, and when the family physician pressed Mr. Brown, he finally admitted that he and his wife had lengthy quarrels on many evenings. No wonder the pains. This led the physician to ask to see the wife. When the two of them appeared jointly for interview, one of the major complaints of the husband was that his wife avoided sex and they often quarreled about this. But Mr. Brown also stated that on nights when there seemed to be marital harmony, his wife always had cleaning or ironing to do, or something to prepare for their children. These chores kept her busy until well past midnight, long after the husband had fallen asleep. Mrs. Brown conceded that she did "avoid" sex, primarily because she did not like to bother with female contraceptive devices: they were "too messy." She had some fear of pregnancy as well. Her husband countered by saying that often he was perfectly willing to use a contraceptive, but that even so, she still refused. The wife then remarked, with an air of self-sacrifice, that she felt sex would be more enjoyable to him if she were the one to take precautions.

Since they were desirous of limiting the size of their family and were using contraceptive devices already, the matter of the "pill" was brought up. The husband was most eager to discuss this, but the wife stated that she had heard about bad side effects and was uncertain. She admitted that using pills would probably make both of them more spontaneous about sex, but the stories of the side effects had caused her to reject the idea. The family physician did a physical examination and evaluation, and when he saw no contraindications, he put her on the standard regimen of medication for control of conception. The physiological side effects were minimal.

However, there was an intensification of the marital squabbles and a worsening of the husband's gastric distress. Consequently, they were referred to a psychiatrist for consultation. In all, about eight months had elapsed since Mr. Brown originally saw his own physician.

At the first psychiatric interview, they were indeed in misery. They hardly looked at or listened to each other. Both used the phrase, "If it weren't for the chidren. . . ." The sequence of events recounted above was reviewed. The husband felt that his sexual demands were "reasonble" and not excessive, and Mrs. Brown reluctantly agreed.

The couple had been wed for six years. Marriage took place after a courtship of eighteen months. Both felt they had been "very much in love." They liked travel and dancing, and the early years of marriage were harmonious. There had been petting and fondling of the sexual parts prior to marriage, but no actual intercourse. Both felt the sexual adjustment after marriage had been "Okay, but we didn't think too much about it." Mr. Brown worked in the sales department of a large company and felt satisfied with the work and opportunities for advancement. His wife had been an office manager but stopped working two years after marriage. They had two children in rapid succession, a girl and a boy, and decided to limit their family to this size.

Individual histories of both partners were then taken. On the basis of this information, the therapist concluded that individual therapy with the wife offered the best chance for amelioration of the couple's problems. (The husband's biography will be detailed later.)

Mrs. Brown was a middle child. There was an older and a younger brother. She recalled many fights with both. Mrs. Brown was the apple of her father's eye, and the "two of us were like peas in a pod." She recalled some resentment on the part of her mother over the fact that her father took her with him each Sunday morning to get the newspaper and left the other children at home. The description of the father's behavior was that of a very seductive parent. During adolescence, the girl remembered that she rather suddenly began to avoid him whenever possible. Further inquiry established a typical story: a young girl is overstimulated by her father and in time senses her mother's resentment over the close alliance between father and daughter. She becomes fearful and guilty over this. During adolescence, when she begins to experience sexual drives, any stimulation of these drives by physical contact with the father must be repressed. Further, she begins to avoid any physical contact with her father as much as possible.

How were these experiences reflected in this patient's marriage? She always did her best to avoid sex, often using the "socially legitimate" excuses of fear of pregnancy and messiness of contraceptive devices. When her husband pressed her about sex, the guilt related to it often provoked a hostile outburst toward him:

he was the one who was forcing her into guilt-laden activity.* The therapeutic challenge, then, was to have the wife come to grips with a problem related to her own background, a problem she had dealt with prior to marriage by avoidance and repression.

As noted, after marriage Mrs. Brown had used culturally-acceptable conventions (or rationalizations) —fear of pregnancy and dislike of contraceptive devices—to aid in "solving" her problem. After being placed on pills, these culturally-acceptable excuses were no longer available to her, and thus the marital difficulties intensified. The husband no longer had as much patience with her, since he felt there was no legitimate excuse for her to avoid sex. The pills thus forced the couple to a new level of integration: the wife must now find some other means of express-ing her conflict about sex or, hopefully, she must learn about the origins of her conflicts and understand the effects of her upbring-ing on her present adaptation in the sexual role.

This case is recounted to emphasize the necessity of gathering data in at least three areas of investigation when there are physical and psychiatric complaints in an individual.

These areas are (a) the individual's subjective feelings and phantasies about the problem, (b) observation of interpersonal reactions, and (c) the culturally-linked modes of behavior by which conflicts are expressed. (Who knows how many other vari-ables will have to be considered in the future. Certainly, genetic data is one.) In the present case, the family physician also gathered data from clinical inspection, i.e. physical examinations, labora-tory and x-ray findings, and so on, in addition to the data obtained by talking (introspection) .

Mrs. Brown was seen in individual psychotherapy for a year. She was able to understand the effects of her early environment on her present-day sexual adjustment. Marital embrace with her husband revitalized the earlier conflict of having a seductive father and the wrath of a vengeful mother. The guilt engendered in the father-daughter dyad was also explored. As a result of treat-

---

*How similar to the situation which occurs in everyday psychiatric practice: en-couraging an individual to deal with guilt-laden ("forbidden") areas of his life evokes a hostile response toward the psychiatrist.

ment, Mrs. Brown moved to a new level of integration—one in which she could respond more freely and spontaneously in sexual activity. What happened in the marriage now that the woman had dealt with her own major "psychodynamic" conflicts? She was more spontaneous in approaching sex and pressured her husband in this matter. (Perhaps there was even an element of "revenge" in her demands.) Trouble once more developed. The husband began staying late at work and had mounting physical complaints: headaches, insomnia, and excessive fatigue. There were no notable gastrointestinal symptoms. In time, he called the psychiatrist again, and the couple were seen together. The situation was reviewed, and a brief period of individual psychotherapy was recommended for the husband.

> Mr. Brown was the younger brother in a family of two boys. Both his parents worked, and after school he was cared for by an aunt. His father was a successful merchant who had built up his own business. When the sons reached adolescence, they began helping out in the store. The father constantly goaded them to "do more." His mother also worked in the business and tried as best she could to make the home a pleasant one, "at least on weekends." The patient was successful at school, college, and in the Army.
>
> In psychotherapy, Mr. Brown reviewed the stresses placed on a child by a working mother and a goading father. Although he could have entered the family business, he chose not to. This early experience in which his adequacy as a male was challenged was now being reflected in his doubts about his manliness when his wife pressured him regarding sex. Also, in his present business, which was a competitive one, he felt he had to produce more than his associates. As he came to understand these factors, both past and present, he too reached a new level of integration. At the end of Mr. Brown's individual therapy, both husband and wife were again seen briefly. At last report, their personal and marital adjustments were satisfactory. Affect and trust between the two was "healthy."

In summary, this case demonstrates the necessity for studying an individual's complaints in more than one dimension. The sequence began when the husband went to his physician because of gastric distress. The physician knew enough about the man's psychosocial background to recognize that this symptom could be an expression of emotional conflict. This led him to an investigation of the marital stresses and the wife's individual psychotherapy. Once she understood the origin of her sexual fears, she responded to sex with freedom and anticipation of pleasure. The couple had then achieved a new equilibrium, or as it turned out, disequilibrium: the socially accepted devices of avoiding sex had been removed; the psychological blocks to the woman's full participation in sex had also been removed, and the husband's own latent sexual problems and doubts about his masculinity were exposed.† (Of course, a man without significant conflicts relating to his own sexuality or masculinity would experience enormous relief once the quarrels were over.)

The existence of sexual conflicts in a man can be the basis for widespread symptomatology if his wife has a hysterectomy, her fallopian tubes tied, or is placed on contraceptive pills: he is expected to respond to this change in circumstance with gargantuan sexual appetite. Before medical or surgical intervention, the husband's own sexual conflicts were covered over in the culturally acceptable concern about the wife's becoming pregnant.

A woman of middle-class background who has a sexual conflict might tell her friends that she dislikes the "messiness" of sex. If she were of lower-class background, her friends would better understand if she characterized her husband as being a "brute," always demanding sex. It is important, therefore, that the psychiatrist know the relevant facts about a patient's socioeconomic background and how this background influences the choice of symptoms.

SOCIOLOGIC STUDIES AND MENTAL ILLNESS

This past decade has been characterized by an upsurge in studies of the individual's mental health in relation to his environment. It is not surprising that this should happen. As a matter of fact, it is a greater surprise that it did not happen sooner. Thirty years ago, in the orthopedic surgery department of a medical school, a fracture was defined as "dissolution of tissue in an indi-

---

†Kohl (1962) stresses the need for studying both marital partners, even when one is in individual therapy. One mate often sabotages the spouse's psychotherapy. He (or she) cannot tolerate the change in equilibrium.

vidual with loss of function." Note the phrase, "in an individual." What the orthopedist recognized at the time, and which psychiatrists are now emphasizing, is that the same type of fracture in two people—a charwoman who needs to work for a living and a socialite who can lie in bed and be cared for by private nurses—might be two entirely different kettles of fish.

Let us say there is a fracture of the surgical neck of the humerus. The day after the charwoman's surgery, she is out exercising the shoulder by swinging weights. The socialite, however, lies in bed and answers telephone calls about her injury. She leaves the hospital under the care of private nurses and perhaps retains some residual loss of function.

Similarly, at Cornell, Harold Wolff (1953) preached the ecological approach to medicine and stressed the fact that even pneumonia occurs in an individual *at a given time and place*. Wolff focused on the fact that the environmental surroundings of the individual were important elements in understanding the pathogenesis of illness, even with so discrete an entity as pnemonia.

The same ecological approach exists with regard to passing laws or promoting values in a given society. Those in leadership draw primarily from their own experience at home or among their peers. Formerly, contact of the rich with the lower class was mainly in terms of giving alms. In this country in the latter part of the nineteenth century—the great progressive era of growth—the whole concept of social Darwinism, and the carry-over of the individualistic tradition from Europe became important parts of political and economic life. This concept was reflected in a number of ways, including psychiatric understanding. Many of the psychiatric diagnostic categories were established primarily through study of upward-striving individuals, usually of the middle or upper class.

The importance of the environment as support for effective psychiatric treatment of an individual is aptly demonstrated by the lessons of battle-front psychiatry during the latter part of World War II and the Korean conflict. Soldiers suffering from "battle fatigue" were quickly and effectively treated using three basic therapeutic principles: (1) *The principle of immediacy*: the patient must be treated as soon as possible after his breakdown. (2) *The principle of proximity:* the patient must be treated as near as possible to the place where he had his emotional breakdown. He thus remains a part of his unit. (3) *The principle of expectancy*: the patient must expect, and be expected, to return to his former duty after a short period of self-organization (Artiss, 1963).‡

The importance of studying social class structure and its relationship to psychiatric diagnosis has already been mentioned. The studies of Hollingshead and Redlich (1958) show that the diagnosis of mental illness and the prescribed treatment often depend on the social class of the patient, as well as the social class of the psychiatrist. In the blue-collar group, the diagnosis of schizophrenia was more frequent and electric shock and drugs more often the prescribed treatment. In the white-collar groups, the tendency was to define illness more in terms of a neurotic problem, with psychotherapy the recommended treatment.

The matter of silence in psychotherapy must also be viewed in this light. In the traditional psychoanalytic model, a patient's silence meant resistance and repression. However, in lower-class patients, silence may be the suppression of speech stemming from past negative experiences. Or, such patients may be frightened in the therapeutic situation, particularly if it is a first interview. In their work, Hollingshead and Redlich found that, in general, patients in the two classes representing the lowest socioeconomic groups gained little understanding from their psychotherapy. Most approaches in psychotherapy are geared to the middle-class patient and physician; it is easy to see how a lower-class patient might be viewed as hostile, resistive, or even retarded in this setting. One relatively simple modification of therapy is that the therapist become more active, rather than sit passively and wait for the patient to "produce."

SOCIAL HOMEOSTASIS

In previous chapters, the maintenance of homeostasis in the in-

---

‡Veterans of Vietnam often develop "battle fatigue" *after* returning home; they have fought in an unpopular war, and have great difficulty justifying the death of their buddies

dividual and in the family unit by the use of various mechanisms has been described. Are there comparable mechanisms or equili-bratory devices that apply to society as a whole? Laws are passed to maintain order. Leaders are chosen to govern. Customs and tra-ditions give people a ready means of integrating past history with present-day life. There are endless examples of such regulatory de-vices. For purposes here, focus will be on one dynamic mechanism by which society regulates itself: the concept of deviance. The rel-evance of studying deviance as it relates to mental illness, and as it parallels the homeostatic mechanisms of individual and family, will be apparent.

How has the social scientist influenced the psychiatrist? One of the pioneers in this field was Emile Durkheim (1960), who stud-ied suicide and crime extensively. He noted that while crime pro-voked social outrage among people, it also served to bring them together in a common cause: concern with crime. Therefore, from the standpoint of society, a crime must be viewed not only with respect to transgression and appropriate punishment but also as part of the social order—social disorder also being a part of social order. This awareness led to the study of deviant behavior and so-ciety's relation to this behavior. As noted in Chapter I, deviance is a significant determinant in deciding who is mentally ill. It is hard to quantify behavior as deviant; perhaps it is best to use an operational definition: any behavior which deviates can be la-beled deviant. Disheveled dress is a good example; not shaving is another. Very often a person who goes through an entirely rou-tine day except for one piece of behavior can be adjudged deviant on the basis of this single departure from the norm (Kai Erikson, 1966).

A question can be raised as to how society picks out a certain piece of behavior and labels it deviant. It is easy to judge in the case of murder, but what about alcoholism? Social acceptance of alcoholism invalidates the idea that society outlaws only behavior which is harmful to the group. How, then, are the boundaries which distinguish acceptable behavior from unacceptable behav-ior (deviance) established? Is a particular kind of speech libel-ous? What behavior is legally indecent? In court questions, the so-called Brandeis Manifesto is part of the hearing: the data of so-cial (and behavioral) science are important elements in making an adjudication. Separate but equal school facilities were declared unconstitutional largely on the grounds that children so treated suffered great psychological harm.

Society puts great stress on motivation; there is a sharp line drawn between premeditated murder and unpremeditated murder. The sociologist looks at the behavior, e.g. the number of crimes committed and the circumstances; the psychiatrist looks at the motivation for the behavior.

Whenever there is an outcry in society against certain behavior, it usually is an indication that the boundaries are shifting. An example is homosexuality. Periodically, there are outcries about the number of homosexuals, and this usually correlates with a shift in society's greater tolerance of homosexual behavior. Durkheim emphasized that there is persistent deviance in a society, just as there are always some tensions within an individual and in a family. This rate of deviance can be calculated by adding up all the crimes, mental illnesses, drunken episodes, and so forth, in a particular society.

While deviant behavior is seen as a threat to society, it also performs a necessary function. It defines the boundaries of acceptable behavior and thus helps to maintain society's equilibrium. Murder alerts society to the fact that murder should not be committed. The sociologist looks for the boundaries within each group. In families, certain behavior is acceptable and other behavior is not acceptable. Boundaries constantly fluctuate and are in a dynamic equilibrium with the needs of the group. Those needs which are considered most central to the group have very sharp boundaries. In the United States, private property is all-important. Thus, thefts of any kind are regarded as sharply deviant behavior. In mainland China today, there is more concern with political ideology; accordingly, more arrests are made for sedition. In political trials, offenders are often called "deviationists."

Deviant behavior is publicized in order to show society its boundaries. Now that there are newspapers, public confinement of the deviant in stocks and bonds in the town square is no longer necessary. Many forms of behavior become polarized around those values which are important in a particular society. The criminal and the policeman have much in common: the former with breaking the law, the latter with upholding it. The psychiatrist and his patient have much in common in that both are concerned with the boundaries of mental illness. Thus, in any given culture those pieces of behavior which constitute the "highest morality" and those which constitute the "highest immorality" are closely related, and someone from a different culture may not see much difference between the two.

This view of deviance as an equilibratory device is a more dynamic one than simply considering deviant behavior the result of breakdown or disintegration in a society. Again, there are parallels found in the family group, as is noted in Chapter IV. In a family, conflict is often resolved when someone is designated as the scapegoat or black sheep, for example. Once a family member is labeled a scapegoat, he can then be "blamed" for all of the family conflicts and may therefore be kept in this role. The same follows in society. The group tends to induce and sustain deviant behavior. It is useless to study dropouts in a particular school without studying the attitudes of the school system, the attitudes of students toward education and toward dropping out, and the familys' attitudes. In any Army platoon, there are always a number of "oddballs" or "clowns." Once the deviant members of the group are removed, "the group . . . would realign its members so that these roles would become occupied by other members" (Dentler and Erikson, 1959, p. 107). Because deviance subserves a necessary function, the deviant may even be "rewarded" for his behavior, e.g. a rebel is often glamorized.

As noted in Chapter I, there is a filtering system by which any behavior can be labeled deviant. For example, in describing mental illness as deviant behavior, two elements are at work: (1) a "social diagnosis" is made by an individual's family or neighbors (or by himself) when the individual's behavior is considered aberrant; he is said to be in need of psychiatric care; (2) a "medical diagnosis" is made by a psychiatrist.

Labeling the patient by social observation alone is not enough, because society responds more to *disturbing* behavior than to *disturbed* behavior. If two persons are being evaluated for possible admittance to a mental hospital—one of whom is loud and boisterous, and the other silent and introspective—a jury of ten citizens will probably say that the individual who is boisterous and raucous is the one more in need of hospitalization. They may not recognize that the silent, noncommunicative person can be the more severely disturbed.

Some writers have suggested that mental illness is a myth since this type of "deviant behavior" is so widespread (Szasz, 1961). Diagnosis of mental illness is often made on the basis of someone's outward behavior being widely deviant from that which is acceptable to his social group or family. The child who is obstreperous in school, for whatever reason, may be referred by the teacher for psychiatric counseling simply to "get him out of her hair." The adolescent who does not follow the family's dictates insofar as education or profession is concerned may be referred to a psychiatrist in the hope that a "mental problem" might be found; with treatment, he would then supposedly steer himself in a manner compatible with the family's wishes.

What is missing in these instances are the individual's subjective perceptions. The fact that a seventeen-year-old girl does not date often may be upsetting to her parents if they want and expect their daughter to be popular. They may suggest that she seek psychiatric counseling because of her "isolation or shyness." Her "deviant behavior" may be simply a matter of not fitting the family mold. She may not date simply because she would rather stay at home and read. A psychiatrist may find the girl to be a wholesome and self-assured person with no significant problems. But the implications of her behavior would be entirely different if she does not go out on dates for fear she will get "too flustered" and lose control when a boy becomes amorous with her.

An example of "social evaluation" of behavior miscarrying is the following. There is a summer cocktail party at a very fashionable estate given by a prominent citizen in the community. In order to make sure that there are no gate-crashers, the host hires several local policemen to stand guard at the gate. They also help park cars and direct guests. At the end of the cocktail party, some of the guests come wobbling back to their cars. What happens? The police officers who had parked their cars now help them into the driver's seat, help them start the car, and point them in the right direction. The drivers weave off, with the effects of the party showing noticeably. If such a driver should be stopped by a policeman on his way home, he would probably be arrested for drunk driving. However, a member of this same police force has sanctioned this behavior by closing his eyes to the facts.

PSYCHOPATHOLOGY AND CULTURAL FACTORS

Weinstein (1962) makes a good case for studying cultural factors along with psychopathology. Reporting on two years' experience as a psychiatrist in the Virgin Islands, he suggests that delusions are an adaptational (homeostatic) mechanism to cope with social and cultural stress; they stem from difficulty in interpersonal relationships. The delusion is not primarily a symbolic manifestation of instinctual drive: rather, it is a complex representation of many of the cultural values in a given society.

Weinstein describes four distinct ethnic groups with whom he worked. These were (1) the native Virgin Islanders who are descendants of plantation slaves and who make up about half the population; (2) immigrants from the British West Indies, who constitute about 25 percent of the population; (3) immigrants from Puerto Rico who represent another 25 percent; and (4) a handful of French descendants of escapees from the penal colony at Cayenne. In the latter two groups, the Puerto Ricans and French descendants, the families are tight, paternalistic units. In the native group and the British West Indian immigrants, the families are much looser and are mother-centered. The native Virgin Islanders place a high premium on having many children. There is about 50 percent illegitimacy, and children are welcomed into the home, out-of-wedlock or not. As a matter of fact, women are reluctant to marry because they fear marriage will subordinate them to men, and thus common-law marriages are frequent. Most mothers are employed, and the children are left in the care of older people or British West Indian maids. The men are more proud of parenthood than of marriage, acknowledge paternity readily, and support their children willingly. Thus, there are homes in which the man in the household is father to none of the children there but may have fathered many other children in other households. Marital infidelity is tolerated, although serial monogamy is preferred.

Natives who become psychotic frequently have delusions about mistreatment or death of a child. Auditory hallucinations involving young children are commonly reported. The native groups seldom resort to physical violence and even evidence a fear of violence. They are gossipers and liars and will indulge in any kind of sexual activity to get a job. However, there is no sexual assault or sexual jealousy because of the freedom in sexual activities.

In the other two groups, the French descendants and the Puerto Ricans, the father is clearly the head of the household. There are strong concepts of masculinity and femininity, which is not the case among the native Virgin Islanders or the British West Indian immigrants. The Puerto Rican and French men react vigorously to any suggestion that they are not manly and may become suddenly violent at such an intimation. Weinstein found homosexuality and pathological jealously in these two groups, but almost none among the natives. Thus, the environment must be studied in order to understand properly even so structured a psychiatric symptom as a delusion.

At Manhattan State Hospital on Wards Island, New York City, records are available dating from the first patient treated in 1859 to the present. It is interesting to read of patients admitted in the period 1860 to 1880 with the delusion that they were suffering in the same manner as the American Indians: they were being attacked by white men and their land taken away. Also admitted were many patients suffering from the delusion that they were responsible for the death of Lincoln.

Nowhere is the awareness of sociocultural factors greater in clinical medicine than in the study and treatment of obesity. The psychiatrist who treated obese patients in the past usually operated on psychodynamic principles: the weight represented power or grandiosity; excess eating was an attempt to "cannibalize" adversaries; or, obesity in a young girl was an effective way of warding off sexual temptation. There is no doubt that these elements are significant in many instances, but we are learning that an examination of family or societal factors may be more pertinent than study of the subjective perceptions of a patient. Is food "pushed" on the family as a symbol of plenty? Is heftiness accorded more importance than the "lean, healthy look"? Are three square meals a day considered mandatory, or is it permissable to eat lightly and even skip a meal?

Moore *et al.* (1962) discovered that obesity was seven times greater in the lower socioeconomic class than in the higher classes. In the latter group, people congratulate each other on a lean appearance. Not so in the former group. (One element might be that in the lower socioeconomic group there is more concern with having plenty of food, since deprivation is felt in so many areas of life.)

In the middle and upper socioeconomic groups, obese persons who stay obese are probably more influenced by emotional factors. It is true that in all classes overweightness tends to be a family trait; thus, as with any character trait, one must study family attitudes toward food and eating insofar as the rearing of children is concerned.§

For the person who can afford it, there are now available exclusive salons for both men and women who want to reduce. This is accomplished by a combination of caloric reduction, exercise, and attitude. A humorous anecdote is the man whose girlfriend weighed over two hundred pounds. He sent her to a salon, insisting that she shed thirty pounds. However, when he took her out in the evening, he always insisted she have champagne and caviar. At the end of four weeks she left the salon, minus $2500, plus 15 percent gratuities, but not minus any pounds (Lear, 1966). The threat of his girlfriend's becoming slim and attractive to other men proved too much for this man.

---

§Bruch and Touraine (1940) have reported on a number of obese adults who were brought up in homes where, as children, a cookie was stuffed into their mouths indiscriminately at the slightest indication of any frustration. In later life, when under any kind of stress, they were prone to resort to eating for relief. This suggests a severe disturbance of the hedonic mechanisms of adaptation.

This same situation can sometimes be seen in a family with a very obese parent. Although the children constantly protest about the parent's overweight, the spouse is more silent. As a matter of fact, analysis of family patterns may reveal that the spouse does a great deal to foster the obesity. The presence of a lean and attractive mate might engender feelings of competition or rivalry, something the spouse does not feel able to tolerate.||

THE "WRONG" PATIENT REFERRED
FOR PSYCHOTHERAPY

The intersection of three variables—individual, interpersonal, and cultural—are further illustrated in the following case history of a woman referred for psychiatric evaluation. In time, it became apparent that the husband's problems were more significant than the wife's. This situation often occurs in marital interaction: the "healthier" partner tries to adapt to the needs of the "sicker" one. In attempting to make this adaptation, great anxiety may be generated in the more flexible partner. The more rigid partner may not experience much anxiety in the relationship because his personality (psychic) defenses remain intact.

The identified patient was a white married woman admitted to a general hospital for study of anemia, obesity, menstrual irregularity and depression. She was married to a lawyer. When her personal physician suggested psychiatric consultation and possible therapy, she agreed willingly. She had never been able to do so previously because of her husband's opposition.

The couple had been married for almost twenty years, and there were four children in the family—two boys and two girls. At the initial interview, the woman described her feelings of depression and discouragement and stated that she had felt this way for many years, but she could not understand why. The woman gave a history of a happy childhood in a comfortable middle-class home. She had two older brothers, both successful businessmen. When she finished high school, she studied music and art in college, and after graduation took a job as a high school teacher. She met her husband, who had recently begun law practice, while she was teaching school. She stated that she

---

||The psychiatrist making a home visit should always look into the freezer. Gallons of ice cream may be stored there; yet the overweight person cannot "understand" his obesity.

felt the marriage was "very happy": her husband was a good provider, active in church work, and a pillar in the community.

During the course of several sessions, the woman unfolded the story of her life, describing one prohibition after another imposed on her by the husband. Whereas she had enjoyed singing before groups in the first few years of marriage, her husband insisted that she stop. As the children were born, he demanded that she stay home, look after them, and give up the volunteer work she was doing. When the therapist pointed out the repeated restrictions, the woman unleashed a torrent of tears, stating that she had been aware of this for many years, but had never come to grips with it so directly. When the therapist asked to see her husband also, the woman insisted he would never agree to come and, indeed, that there was no reason for him to come. As a matter of fact, the first time she invited him to accompany her, he refused. The therapist then asked him to come for "his wife's sake," and he did so. At the interview, both maintained that everything was very well indeed.

The husband had one younger sister. His parents and grandparents were missionaries, and there were a number of relatives who were missionaries both in the United States and overseas. He was a gifted student, did well in school, and had no problem obtaining his law degree. After finishing law school, he opened a practice in the county seat near where he was born and became an eminent attorney. His major activity outside of his law practice was church work. He gave more money to the church than any other member. He stated that some day he might give up his law practice and become a missionary "like everyone else in my family."

It was pointed out that perhaps he had some feelings of guilt about not being a missionary now, but he vehemently denied this was so. However, the wife questioned the denial. This topic was explored at subsequent sessions to which the wife came alone. She asked for these sessions because she was troubled by the increasing awareness of how her activities had been restricted by her husband. The woman was overburdened by the anger she felt toward her husband and the subsequent guilt that followed. Ventilation of her feelings helped considerably, and she slept better and was able to diet and lose some weight.

During the third month of therapy, she asked to bring the older son in to see the psychiatrist. She stated that there had always been a lot of trouble with this boy, who was now a sophomore in college. The boy was an extremely bright young man who stated that he did not know for sure what he wanted to do. However, he was toying with the idea of leaving college and becoming a "wanderer." (The father, mother, and son had been invited together, but the father was absent.) The son agreed with the notion that his father was troubled by the fact that he had left the fold of missionaries. He described a great deal of conflict with his father, particularly during adolescence. There were conflicts about going to church and about going out with friends. The boy occasionally liked to drink or smoke with his peers and this was against the father's wishes. Both mother and son related many of their own problems to the father's guilt about his lack of fulfilling the family ideal. The son stated that he had been aware of this fact for a long time, but in the family it was never discussed. He felt the psychiatrist should talk to the other children as well. Accordingly, the entire family—all six members—were seen together for interview.

During the course of treatment, which extended over a period of a year, it was found that many of the family's conflicts were related to the father's burdensome guilt over not having followed the tradition of missionary work.

Several areas of exploration were crucial in understanding the expression of psychopathology in this family. First, the main task was to make the family aware that the overt consensus that everything was fine simply was not true. This belief was not easily shaken, since in the mother's cultural background, serious marital or family disagreement was intolerable. She stated frequently that she would sacrifice anything to keep her family intact; to protest or rebel was contradictory to all she had been taught. The second factor dealt with was the social determinants that were responsible for inhibiting the expression of dissatisfaction in the family. Third, the father's unconscious guilt over his failure to follow in the family footsteps had to be discussed.

The final issue was the matter of scapegoating of the son. Any member's show of initiative in any area not sanctioned by the father was seen as rebellion and could not be tolerated, since this evoked feelings of guilt in the father over his own "rebellion" at not becoming a missionary. Because of the family's unconscious awareness of this fact, they joined in the condemnation of any member who strayed from the fold by showing individual initiative or enterprise. Treatment was terminated with the proviso that they return should other conflicts arise. They seemed much happier together, there was more freedom of communication, and, as one of the girls stated, they enjoyed their churchgoing and religion more because they no longer felt coerced into these activities.

Disaffected Youth

Nowhere are the problems of individual-family-social interaction more directly visible than in the "Now Generation" of the 1960's and 1970's. This under-30 generation, raised in a world of instant communications, three wars, and the spectre of nuclear annihilation, shows marked distance from, and disaffection with, the over-30 generation. There is widespread rejection of parental value systems: traditional schooling; the Protestant ethic of hard work and dedication to career with its future rewards; family and sexual fidelity. Many of these disaffected youth float worldwide from country to country and find kinship with their peers in a new subculture. (Television shows them "where the action is.") How many members make up this group is speculative, but they are a vocal and vitriolic minority who have had a significant impact on society's outlook regarding morality, dress, music, and the use of hallucinogenic drugs. On college campuses, adolescents experiment with different types of "family arrangements," e.g. communes and serial monogamy.

Aside from their disillusion with society for failing to solve pressing social problems instantly, their reacton is in part due to a more difficult transition from adolescence to adulthood: fewer "rites of passage" along religious and social lines exist today. Some youths who find the transition too rigorous flee from the fray entirely and become "hippies," never seeming to enter adult status. Some become militant activists who attempt to destroy society's institutions entirely in the hope that they can "restructure" society to their own liking.

If an adolescent drops out for a year or two to "find" himself, the family should try to maintain some contact with the offspring —through a third party, if necessary. Otherwise, the youngster may identify so intensely with the new subculture, that he never returns to the fold. Society can ill afford to lose the talents of this group of youngsters

Chapter IX

For Better, But Not For Worse
Marriage Dynamics and Therapy

A few years ago at a symposium in California entitled, "The Family's Search for Survival," a physician who had been in practice for forty years startled everyone by stating that he felt monogamy had outlived its usefulness.

"Men really suffer more in marriage than do women . . . His responsibilities are greater; he contributes more and gets less out of marriage than the female" (Lee, 1965, p. 132). Because of the countless number of patients he saw with marital difficulties, he felt that marriage should undergo a change so that human capabilities and weaknesses are better accommodated. A man needs more room to roam and should have it; this is the way of nature; the strongest buck or stallion collects as many females as he can cover and protect. In his view, the solution to give the male more freedom would not only stabilize marriage but, with a return to the state of primal horde, those men unsuited for marriage—the homosexual, the mentally ill, the impotent, and the economically helpless—would be eliminated by the process of natural selection or "survival of the fittest." Also, the strongest and most aggressive men would sire the succeeding generations.

The speech made headlines around the country and caused a great stir. It was another cry that something is wrong with modern marriage and family life. Statistics on divorce, adultery, desertion, alcoholism, and suicide are cited as proof. Many people insist that society needs to go back to the old-fashioned values of "integrity and stability."

In a curious way, the suggestion of the physician quoted above is a solution that goes *back* not just to the old-fashioned values but *way back* to the values governing the conduct of our mammalian ancestors. In the primal horde family, the strongest male

212

did collect as many females as he could manage, but he was ever vigilant to challenge by any other male who appeared on the scene. Most of his energy was devoted to anticipation of this challenge. In marriage today, there are many motivations for union between two people. First, there is the need for love and affection, including the security of companionship and a sense of belonging. This involves a complementary fulfillment of needs (see p. 218). Second, there is the satisfaction of sexual need. Third, marriage allows the creation of a home and family and, with the advent of children, an illusion of posterity for each of the mates. (The mode of marriage alluded to is that of most Western societies, in which free choice of the mate is customary.) The basic trust and love which exist in an emotionally-satisfying marriage hark back to the primary dyadic relationship of mother and infant. This trust allows each partner to go about his business each day without worrying about what is happening to the spouse. The man going off to work in the morning need not concern himself that his wife will be lured away by another male. Similarly, the woman at home can devote herself to endeavors other than worrying about her husband capturing another female. The vigilance and the readiness to fight a rival that characterized the primal horde is no longer necessary.

"GOING STEADY" AND COURTSHIP

It should be noted that the avoidance of competition is an element in the "going steady" craze among teen-agers. With modern travel, with increased population, and with unlimited exposure of boys to girls, there is a feeling of competitiveness on the part of a boy or girl: the one he or she likes will be lured away by someone else. The whole problem is solved by going steady, since it diminishes competition. (One of the drawbacks of this system is that it does not allow enough exposure of a teen-ager to other teen-agers; when there is pairing off into "steadies," these individuals are taken off the market.) It seems clear, also, that adolescents who are most secure go steady the least.

Frequently, the "love" that adolescents feel for one another is based not so much on deep emotional feeling as on the reassurance that they will not be left out. Often enough, when this kind of relationship culminates in early marriage, the feeling of "love" may not be there any longer, since the necessity for the reassurance of anxiety over abandonment is abated. This couple may then experience their marriage as meaning an end to "love" and romance. It is due to misinterpretation of the emotion. To teenagers, the phrase, "I love you," is usually tendered because it is expected.

> A couple in their early twenties were referred for "last chance" consultation by their attorney prior to filing for divorce. Each professed disinterest in the spouse. Yet they both stated they were "madly in love" when they married. Shortly after they began going steady, the girl's father had a bad stroke and lingered for a year before he died. During this time, the girl experienced much emotional turmoil, and the boy was her comforter. With so much "need" for each other, they married at eighteen. Five years later, with two children, a mortgage, a car note, and other responsibilities, they found they had little in common except concern for their children. The "mad love" had been based primarily on the girl's need for nurturance and reassurance and the boy's feeling of satisfaction and self-esteem at being able to fulfill these needs.

Early teen-age marriage often occurs because the needs of most teen-agers are universal. In adulthood, needs are more individual and specific. Hence, teen-agers who marry may find later on that their unconscious needs are not satisfied by the mate. The same holds true for many of the "accidental" marriages that take place as the result of a dare, or because the individual is fleeing an intolerable home situation.

A "proper" engagement period for a couple contemplating marriage was customary a few decades ago. Today, this engagement period is often bypassed. Being engaged is quite different from going steady; the former is serious business in that it announces to the world that two people are considering marriage. Going steady carries with it few obligations but, as noted, it has the advantage of doing away with "too much" competition and freedom of easy termination. It is apparent from study of teen-agers that when a couple become engaged, there is pressure from peers to stay engaged. It is as if they were saying, "Don't upset the system—going steady is one thing, engagement is another."

Can courtship be structured so that some of the "work" of joining is accomplished before marriage? In nature, there are elaborate rituals and practices followed by species prior to mating. Anyone who has seen male and female foxes do a "foxtrot" cannot help but be impressed by this courtship procedure.

If two youngsters are going steady and thinking about marriage, an engagement allows families and friends to entertain the couple and gives them maximum exposure to each other under many different circumstances. The "work" of marriage is partly accomplished during this period; both get an inkling as to whether they can form a joint identity as a couple and begin to evolve "traditions" of their own as a new family. Terminated engagements are most often looked upon by adult society as a show of strength rather than an expression of failure. When two adolescents have been going steady for a long time and the parents try to "bust it up," this attempt may precipitate a marriage, mainly out of rebellion.

A girl of eighteen was admitted to the emergency ward of a hospital because she had swallowed "pills"—twenty-six aspirin tablets. She told her story to the psychiatrist in a matter-of-fact fashion. For two years she had gone steady with a neighborhood boy. A month previous, the subject of marriage came up and the two discussed it casually. Then one evening the boy told her that he was not at all ready to think about marriage and suggested that they stop seeing each other for a while. That night the girl swallowed the pills. It was apparent during the psychiatric examination that this was not a highly lethal suicide attempt. The girl's motivation seemed to be, "I'll abandon you before you abandon me."

The next morning, she and her boyfriend, who had been pacing in the waiting room all night, had a long talk. Afterwards, the girl excitedly told the psychiatrist that they had "talked it all over" and had decided to get married immediately. The therapist called the boy in and raised the question as to whether or not this was a good time to decide on such a serious step as marriage. He suggested that they explore the subject further before making a final decision. The boy was delighted with the suggestion, and after a few joint sessions, both decided that they had best wait before marrying. Meanwhile they would date other people to "compare."

Exposure of one partner to another in varying circumstances can also open up differences in social class, religion, or ethnicity. This refers primarily to the different learning experiences that each person has had as a child. These include the area of education as well as personal tastes in speech, food, topics of conversation and, above all, life values. Is financial success treasured over artistic achievement? Are firm roots in one locale necessary, or can one pick up and move as new opportunities arise? Is adventure more valued than security?

> A couple and their two children were referred for evaluation by their clergyman. The woman was an only child of an old, socially-prominent New England family. The husband was born to immigrant parents. The couple met while she was in college and he in graduate school. When the man completed his graduate training, he was drafted so they decided to get married; after all, they had "gone steady" for two years and found they had much in common. There were the ordinary disagreements of marriage for several years, but not until the oldest child was ten was there real trouble. The woman insisted the boy go off to private school; the man was just as adamant that he go to public school. This circumstance opened up a whole chasm of disagreement between the two involving their values and ideals. They admitted that this had really never come up during courtship or early marriage. When asked about exposure to each other's home and family, they conceded that there had been practically none.

The difference in social class did not become crucial until decisions concerning the children's education had to be made. What was seemingly psychopathology in marriage was more properly an expression of differences in social class. The old-fashioned advice about "marrying your own kind" seems to have more and more efficacy. Once the aspect of romantic love (see below) is diminished, class differences between the partners come to the fore. The princess and the pauper marriage is often doomed to failure after the solely romantic aspect has passed with time; so too is the marriage that springs out of rebellion against parental edict.

ROMANTIC LOVE VERSUS MARRIED LOVE

George Bernard Shaw has written, "People in love are under the influence of the most violent, most insane, most illusive and most transient of passions, and they are required to swear that they will remain in that excited, abnormal, exhausting condition until death do them part."

How do we distinguish between romantic love and married love? In romantic love there is an illusory gratification of needs; in married love, there is a feeling of mutual responsibility and desire to protect one's mate. Married love is deeper, firmer, and more reciprocal; romantic love is more illusory and can end easily. Popular ballads tell us that the natural outcome of being in love is marriage. This is all right if romantic love merges into married love. But romantic love is reinforced by movies and stories about how lovers overcome mammoth obstacles that keep them apart; thus they titillate human phantasy. Marriage takes place for many reasons, including romance. A good description of romantic love evolving into married love is *Swann's Way*, by Proust. In this story, Swann fell in love with Odette, who was of different class and position. In the "falling in love" stage, Swann went through agonies of feeling for her. Once he decided to marry her, many of the extremes of feeling disappeared and were replaced by a steady partnership and mutual acceptance. Eventually Odette was accepted by the aristocratic society in which Swann found himself; even when he died she continued as a leading member of that society.

A humorous summation of the concept of romantic love is a play entitled *Cinderella Married*, written some forty years ago. In the original story, Prince Charming rescues Cinderella from a life of misery and drudgery and brings her into the highest social position. Fulfillment of phantasy is complete (and so is the reader's). What happened a few months after they married and the "romance" wore off? In *Cinderella Married*, Cinderella sits at home, neglected and brooding, while Prince Charming amuses himself with the ladies at court. A leopard does not change his spots overnight.

Still, romantic love has some basis in social custom and in human development. Mankind is unique among all living species in his need for comfort and fulfillment of desires and phantasies throughout life. In our society, marital partners are chosen presumably because each partner senses that the other can provide this "emotional fulfillment." Also, human beings have a desire for "exclusive possession" of a mate (probably a recapitulation of the infant's desire to possess the maternal figure). The happy marriage has within it a preponderance of "married love," but on occasion the couple try to recapture the spirit and phantasies that go along with "romantic love."

The need for stability in marriage was captured well by the Beatles in the following song:

> When I get older, losing my hair,
> Many years from now.
> Will you still be sending me a Valentine,
> Birthday greetings, bottle of wine?
> If I'd been out till quarter to three
> Would you lock the door?
> Will you still need me, will you still feed me,
> When I'm sixty-four?

MARITAL COMPLEMENTARITY

Here is how an anonymous seventeenth century writer characterized the roles of husband and wife:

> The dutie of the husband is to seeke living; and the wives dutie is to keepe the house. The dutie of the husband is to get money and provision; and of the wives, not vainly to spend it. The dutie of the huband is to deale with many men; and of the wives to talk with few. The dutie of the husband is to be entermedling; and of the wife to be solitarie and withdrawn. The dutie of the man is to be skillful in talke; and of the wife to boast in silence. The dutie of the husband is to be a givern: and of the wife, to be a saver. Now where the husband and wife performeth the duties in their house we may call it College of Qyietness: the house wherein they are neglected we may term it hell.

This charming verse does not hold true for our society today. Witness the change in the concepts of "femininity" and "masculinity." Rather, it is best to conceptualize the marital relationship in terms of a complementary union between two people, resulting in a whole that is far greater than the sum of the two parts. The necessary tasks or roles—performance roles and expressive roles—of life are apportioned between the two members (see Chap. V).

There can be a shift in roles when necessary. Through marriage, each partner attempts to add to his own personality those attributes of personality in which he or she feels deficient. Marital complementarity can be schematized by the following lock and key diagrams (Fig. III).

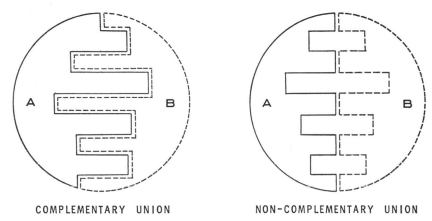

COMPLEMENTARY UNION   NON-COMPLEMENTARY UNION

FIGURE III

If A is nurturing and generous and B is receptive and dependent, each gratifies the other's needs, and the union is said to have a high degree of complementarity. Thus, in everyday life, the individual with a great need to be dependent and protected marries a Samson; the bookworm marries the partygoer; the person who spends lavishly marries the individual who saves prudently; and the obsessive physician frequently marries the hysteric nurse.

It is necessary to differentiate between complementary "needs" and what might be labeled "likes." A person going out on a date is delighted to have a companion who *likes* the same things: baseball, movies, horseback riding, or just talking. *Needs,* on the other hand, are largely unconscious. (The individual can, of course, react consciously to these needs by fervently denying their existence.) "Likes" are primarily conscious and rational choices.*

---

*The difference between "likes" and "needs" puts a sharp limitation on the chances of finding a suitable marriage partner by filling out computerized forms that are matched by electronic machines. The "match game" can be a lot of fun in finding a date or starting a conversation, but when it comes to finding a mate, the need is for someone with complementary (usually opposite) personality characteristics.

Ackerman has attempted to define complementarity—in psychodynamic terms—as being "specific patterns of family role relations that provide satisfactions, avenues of solution of conflict, support for a needed self-image, and buttressing of crucial forms of defenses against anxiety" (1958, p. 86). However, it is clear that as the individual undergoes changes in his biological and social life cycles, his need patterns will similarly change. A couple in which the wife has a high nurturant quality and the husband a strong need to be nurtured may initially have a satisfactory marriage. When this couple have a child, however, there may be a sharp change in the complementary relationship. The woman now has a child to nurture, and she may need a good deal of nurturing herself; the man may be called upon to supply this nurturance. On the other hand, if a woman has difficulty in mothering her children, the man must take up some of the slack. As pointed out previously, when two overly-dependent individuals marry, and the illusory gratifications of early marriage have receded, personality defects become more apparent. Sometimes the best therapy in such instances is to bring in a homemaker or in-law to "feed" both mates.

Occasionally, a couple will marry out of a mutual need to resolve early "separation anxiety." They cling to each other so intensely that, in time, they overwhelm each other. They are like two boxers in a perpetual clinch: they hold each other up, but nothing happens in the bout unless the referee separates them. In this type of marriage, each mate needs more reassurance than the other can supply.

In marital interaction, several needs (or motivations) may coexist side by side. A wife may push her husband to obtain more schooling because she lacks sufficient schooling and feels frustrated in this area. He is to make up for her "deficit." Or, at the same time, she may want him to be outstandingly successful in order that some of his success "rub off on her." Or, she may be aware that his success would give them financial security. Any one of these motivations may be in ascendance at a particular time.

During marriage treatment, the therapist listens to a recital of each partner's gross complaints about the other, but an investigation of complementary needs can best be accomplished by raising questions related to the subtle aspects of the mates' personalities. Is there a "giver" and is there a "taker"? Is there someone who needs reassurance and, if so, is there someone to do the reassuring? If one partner is in great need of being nurtured, does the other supply the nurturance? Further, in healthy marriages there is a shift back and forth in these roles, depending on the needs of each individual.

This is one of the key differentiating factors between a healthy marriage and a pathological marriage: in health there is flexibility and capacity for shift, whereas in pathology there is stereotypy and rigidity. If a husband has an innate desire to be passive and receptive but finds this aspect of his personality unacceptable because he thinks it is unmanly, he may by reaction formation become a stern, rigid, "hypermasculine" person. When a shift in roles or in complementary positions is necessary, the marriage may be in trouble.

Figure III, illustrating complementarity, can also be used to explain why love and hate are opposite sides of the same coin: the individual who supplies all of the needs (real or phantasied) of the mate is also capable of withdrawing these gratifications. Therefore, behind love lurks fear, and in turn fear leads to anxiety, resentment or hate.†

Sustained close relationships of any kind tend to become regressive with time. Childhood patterns may be repeated and momentary flare-ups of temper typical of adolescence may occur. Or, to put it simply, people who live intimately together grate on each other's nerves occasionally. This phenomenon was clearly recognized by Admiral Byrd on one of his South Pole expeditions. He needed some weather observations 125 miles away from the main camp. Two men volunteered to go, and all arrangements were made. At the last moment, Byrd decided to go by himself. He

---

†The anlage for the capacity to surrender oneself is probably the infant's feeling of being completely loved by the mother and feeling that he completely possesses her. The individual who has not had this loving (and trusting) experience in early life can seldom surrender himself to another person, nor does he feel he can completely possess another person.

knew that two people cooped up in an igloo for any extended period of time would soon be at each other's throats.

In Chapter IV, the reasons for loss of the extended family are described. Naturally, the absence of parents, grandparents, aunts, and uncles intensifies the pressures on each mate to fulfill most, or all, of the needs of the spouse. In other words, each mate must be a confidant, nurturer, parent-surrogate, healer, and so on as necessary. The marital unit, like the family unit, can be analogized to a repertory company of actors: all the roles have to be filled by whoever is available. When extended family members were present, they could fill some of these roles. (In our time, the couple's children may take the place of the extended family in this respect.) When a spouse seeks *all* of his or her fulfillment from the mate, e.g. parenting, grandparenting, counseling, check balancing, home decorating, or entertaining, the marriage is "overloaded."

> A couple whose marriage was foundering sought help. The husband complained that he could never fulfill his wife's demands—"emotional, sexual, or material." From the moment they entered therapy, the wife's behavior confirmed this. She called the therapist daily for advice, then would hang up with, "I don't give a damn what you think." She complained of the hours, charges, and distance to the office. She "hated" the waiting room. In background, the wife had been one of two children whose parents never "gave" to the children but "demanded" a great deal. It was impossible for the husband to make up in marriage for all the past deficits and frustrations. She wanted and expected too much from marriage.

COMMUNICATION OF NEEDS IN MARRIAGE

Since need patterns periodically shift and undergo change, a couple must be able to communicate their needs to one another if the marriage is to retain its complementary nature and viability. In practice, there are two periods, easily recognizable, when communication of needs between a couple is greatest: (1) during times of maximum closeness, such as in the "honeymoon" or early romantic phase of marriage, and (2) during times of maximum apartness, typified by arguments and marital fights (Fig. IV).

During the early period of marriage, there may be frequent swings between the two extremes. As years go by, with the arrival

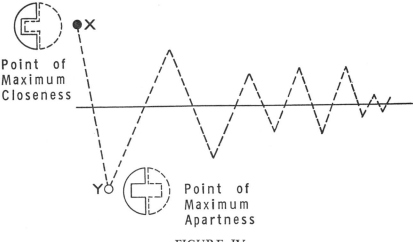

Point of
Maximum
Closeness

Point of
Maximum
Apartness

FIGURE IV

of children and involvement in business and social activities, the marriage tends to center around the midline. Those marriages which swing precipitously from one extreme to another have been given the euphemism, "gruesome twosomes." (In Chapter IV the need to discharge tension periodically by fighting is described as one of the family homeostatic mechanisms.)

At the two extreme points, the couple readily tell one another about their innermost desires and frustrations. At point X, which may or may not be coincident with the honeymoon phase of marriage, each individual experiences pleasure by providing satisfaction for the mate and by being aware of what it can bring in return. In other words, there is reciprocal enjoyment. The couple are intoxicated with happiness; there is fulfillment by illusory phantasy and by suspension of demands on the mate. In this state of blissful harmony, one partner is usually able to communicate needs, desires, or perceptions to the mate.

From this point of nirvana the two start downward on the curve as they become aware of deficiencies—which may be ordinary human deficiencies—in the mate or when there is the realization that the provider of complete happiness can also withdraw gratification and leave a feeling of abandonment. In any situation capable of arousing strong feeling and emotion, sensitivity is increased; thus a slight provocation that ordinarily would be passed over may be perceived as an insult or humiliation.

Marital Fights

At point Y in Figure IV, the point of maximum apartness, the couple may communicate by shouts and protests, all part of a marital fight. At this point, also, needs and frustrations are confessed, verbally and/or physically. Marital fights therefore serve a useful purpose if the couple stop protecting one another and communicate needs that might generally not be communicated. The "fight" then serves to actualize emotions and bring them into conscious awareness. Those marriages that exist without any type of fighting are generally frozen or inflexible marriages in which other aspects of the relationship are compromised in order to maintain a facade of peace and harmony. In studying marriage fights, it is found that usually there has been an addition of a number of frustrations, and when enough of these are totaled up, a point is reached at which further stress or frustration can no longer be tolerated, and there is an explosion. One partner will then drag out a catalog of these incidents in an attempt to "slay" the other partner.

In other words, marriage fights have the character of a pitched battle—not only does one want to defeat the opposition but defeat him so soundly that he will never rise again. There is the aspect of "overkill" in these situations.

What is said in the heat of battle cannot, of course, be taken as the whole truth. Unwarranted accusations and insults hurled at one another should be dismissed as being a natural part of any severe argument. The couple must learn that it is best to think about the *theme* of the fight and not about the *content*. During marriage treatment, one mate will often drag up an episode of many years past: "Do you know what he said to me ten years ago in Omaha?" By noting that this remark was hurled during a marital fight, the therapist can quickly decompress the whole matter.

When does a fight end? Usually when most of the frustrations have been talked out or discharged in some symbolic way—perhaps the woman cries, the man repents. At this point, one partner usually makes a gesture to let the spouse know he or she is willing to begin reversing the curve. The other member should recognize that failure to respond in an appropriate way to this gesture will probably mean that another cycle of fighting will begin. The one who has made the gesture and has failed to receive an appropriate response will feel humiliated. He (or she) will then withdraw or renew the battle, not because of the original source of trouble but because of the new humiliation. It is useful to counsel couples about this aspect of ending a fight. The peace gesture itself may be quite innocuous: a woman may decide to cook something her husband particularly likes, or mend his socks; a man may decide to buy a particular household item that the couple had talked about purchasing.

Figure IV delineates the boundaries which cannot be exceeded if the marriage is to endure. How are these boundaries established? The spouses, early in marriage, let each other know what kind of behavior will not be tolerated. For example, beyond point X, one mate may say that the other is becoming too "narcissistic," or needs "too much fulfillment"; beyond point Y, behavior might be described as "too cruel." Figure IV also illustrates the wisdom of having a legal as well as an emotional commitment in marriage; at point Y, many marriages would actually go asunder if there were no legal tie. The kind of behavior that will be tolerated during a fight may be limited to harsh words or going off to a neighborhood bar. Physical abuse is often intolerable in a marriage.

The purpose of studying communication patterns in marriage is to help couples become aware of the needs of each member so that frustration of these needs and the resulting conflicts can be minimized. Further, the more the couple are able to communicate needs in nonfluctuating, stable periods—that is, away from the areas of extremes—the better the marriage.

In marriage treatment, as one spouse becomes aware of the mate's innate needs, he or she must try to meet some of these needs, perhaps artifically at first, based on the new understanding. Later, needs are responded to more routinely or automatically. The couple should learn that the most surfeited individual has the most to give of himself. The man who has received a substantial promotion and salary increase at work may feel like stopping on the way home to buy a remembrance for his wife. On the other hand, if he has been working on a major deal which falls through, it is doubtful he will be in a generous or giving mood. The same holds true for a woman. She may take time to prepare an especially creative dinner when she is content in many areas of her life. At other times, when she feels unable to cope with excessive emotional demands of her children, or perhaps feels emotionally unfulfilled in some area, she may be prone to make liver and onions the main fare for dinner.

THE MARITAL LIFE CYCLE

Marriage manuals and women's magazines notwithstanding, we know little about the total life cycle of the marital relationship. In the trajectory, one would include courtship, engagement, and the various phases of marriage. The early "work" of marriage, whereby two people of different backgrounds and personalities form a joint identity as a marital pair, was described at the beginning of this chapter.

How early one marries depends on many factors—some cultural, some situational. Many college girls in their senior year experience a panic reaction ("senior girl's panic") if they are not engaged before graduation. They feel, "This is my last chance to meet so many acceptable boys."

At any clinical conference, one always hears the report, "He married her because of his neurotic need for. . . ." No doubt neurotic interaction forms the basis for many marriages, but—without being simplistic—one must not forget "love" or chemistry. This is particularly necessary when doing marriage treatment. After listening to a recital of woes by both spouses, harking back to the days of their early courtship may serve as an antidote for some of the immediate pain. (Freud threw up his hands in frustration when asked to detail how one should go about seeking a mate.)

If a couple do not form a joint identity, the children may sense this conflict and dedicate themselves to healing the breach. Readiness to satisfy the needs of the mate, or readiness for parenthood, depends on what is left over after each individual has satisfied his own needs of adaptation. It was once said that a couple with marital problems should have a child. Supposedly this would make them more "responsible."Nothing could be more absurd as a solution for marital problems. Having a child before a couple feel emotionally secure in marriage can only constitute a further strain. One such couple did have a child, as per instruction, and the overwhelming guilt felt by the mother—stemming from her resentment of the child—was expressed by her inability to respond to the child except when he was sick. Needless to say, the child was taken to the doctor frequently. However, as with so many martyr-type parents, the mother made the child feel guilty about all that was being done for him. Some of the mother's resentment was being expressed in this overconcern with his health. She was "killing her child with kindness." (Unfortunately, some children are taught to feel that such martyrdom is a form of love, which it is not, and often they tend to confuse the two. They grow up feeling guilty about their inability to respond to this "warmth," and this defect may warp their relationships in later life.)

No license is needed for parenthood. There are many studies of what happens when children arrive, but very little systematic research on the effect of children on the marriage. Not every couple should have children; as a matter of fact, some couples are rigidly "complete" without children, and when offspring do arrive there is "no room in the inn." It is not hard to spot such a couple when they are observed together with their youngsters. The marital pair often sit tightly clasped to one another, whether it be at home on the sofa, at a movie, or going for a drive. The children try unsuccessfully to get in between.

The roles of husband and wife change to include the parental roles—father and mother—when a child is born. The crisis that occurs whenever any member joins or leaves the family is distinct. One need only visit a family during the period before an adolescent leaves for college. There are repeated squabbles, remarks about his being "glad to get out of this house," parental sulks, and fighting between younger children. Some conflict is related to the college-bound youth's uncertainty of himself in an independent role; part relates to the family's realization that other members must shift and take up the roles filled by the departing member.

Most surveys show some decreasing satisfactions with marriage as time goes on. The basis for this finding is unclear. Few studies have been done on the so-called middle phase of marriage. One common observation, however, is the fact that one spouse has not "grown" in consonance with the mate, and disequilibrium results. The physician who has been supported all through training by a working wife is constantly challenged intellectually and culturally by his patients and associates. As a result, a gulf may develop between husband and wife insofar as interests and conversation are concerned. Unless the couple are aware of the disequilibrium and try to restore an equilibrium, the marriage may be in for trouble.

Other critical points and/or crises in family life occur when there are job changes, disabling illness, death of a family member, or when relatives come to live with the family. As has been discussed in Chapter IV, when a crisis supervenes, some change in role is usually necessary. If the role change is accomplished with ease, the crisis is met with minimal loss of family functioning, and equilibrium is restored.

Analogous to the shift that takes place when the first child is born is the one which takes place when the last child leaves home. The couple resume their primary roles of husband and wife. This latter role shift has been studied least. Parents who live too much of their lives "through" their children and derive most of their emotional gratification from them, rather than from the spouse, may feel a void in their marriage after the last child departs. These so-called "20-year fractures" are increasing at an alarming rate. Study of breakup of long-standing marriages suggests that one preventive measure is for the couple periodically to reinvigorate the husband-wife relationship. Also, social reinforcement of marriage, e.g. celebration of anniversaries, family reunions, and so forth, does much to solidify the marital and family relationship (Messer, 1969a).

One of the givens in any relationship, particularly marital, is that there are constant changes in the complementary needs of both partners. A couple must pay attention to this fact and either talk about it directly or sit down periodically to try to assess the change. If the assessment adds up to "no change," then this indicates that one or both spouses are not paying attention to the needs of the mate.

In studying long-standing marriages that break up, one sometimes finds that the wife has had much anxiety in her role as mother. The husband was put in the role of "reassurer" for his wife's anxieties about motherhood.

Or, a man struggling to get ahead in business may feel that it is his work above all that matters; the wife may have been his "reassurer" and confidante.

If either mate feels constantly coerced into the role of reassurer, resentment and humiliation mount. By the time the children are grown, or by the time the businessman is secure in his work, the situation can be irreversible. Needs are not met. The "hurt" partner may turn to other outlets for emotional gratification, whether it be sports, children, or even extramarital liaison.

Now, what about change? After the young wife feels secure in her role as mother and after the man's train seems to be heading into a successful career station, each spouse then has energies available to explore new vistas in life and in marriage. It is this change and growth that makes marriage exciting and invigorates the relationship. Nothing is more disheartening to a marriage therapist than to hear couples complain of the sheer boredom that exists in their relationship. (This boredom, of course, can represent a reaction to feeling stymied in a particular role, such as being the constant "reassurer" as described above.)

Rapid changes in physical surroundings and mores are the hallmark of contemporary life. The shift in definition of roles as it pertains to masculinity and femininity has already been alluded to. Take the situation with regard to college life. Prior to World War II, the custom was for a man to put off marriage until he had become independent financially. The longer he wanted to study, the more years he remained single. Not so any longer. At most universities, construction of quarters for married students has priority. While a generation ago a man took a wife only if he could provide for her, nowadays a man often marries with the idea that his wife can support him while he finishes school.

The couple are often separated by pressures of homework and school obligations. Material acquisitions as well as children need to be delayed. Then the roles have to be reversed when the man becomes the provider and the woman becomes a housewife and mother. Many women become depressed by feelings of "worthlessness" after this role reversal; where once she was the "giver," now she is the "receiver."

CHANGING SEXUAL MORES

The change in sexual mores from the 1950's to the 1970's is also pronounced. Miniskirts, see-through dresses, and the "peacock" look in men are obvious manifestations of the change. What was once private sexual behavior between two people is now portrayed publicly on the stage. In addition, satisfaction of every one of the "polymorphous perverse" phantasies is also provided on stage, e.g. exhibitionism, voyeurism, fondling, sucking, smelling. Pressure for sexual activity among teen-agers is a factor in the rise in homosexuality and "unisexuality"; both represent defense against anxiety provoked by the pressure for premature sexuality.

Surveys today indicate that many adolescents (and adults) feel that sex is an acceptable part of an exploratory relationship—a kind of trial marriage—so long as no children are produced. It is therefore not surprising that as many as one-third of the brides are pregnant as they march to the altar.

For generation after generation, sexual exploration and participation have been interdicted among young people who could not realistically care for offspring. This interdiction, whether on religious grounds or not, was reinforced by ideas that (a) mental illness can result from masturbation; (b) the girl who engages in premarital sex can become pregnant and a social outcast; (c) venereal disease can permanently maim the individual; and (d) "terrible" anatomic damage can result.

None of these fears can be justified in the present era of science and technology. Anatomy and physiology are understood, pregnancy can be prevented by "the pill," and venereal disease can be controlled by antibiotics. Thus the major thrust in interdicting premarital sex in contemporary times has to be in the area of the "desired image" of virginity—if that be the case—or the injunction that the individual must be responsible for his sexual activities. Scientific advances have allowed more freedom for sexual activity without fear of disease or pregnancy; with increased freedom goes increased responsibility.

A concrete example of the change in "morality": learning about contraceptives and purchasing them once meant "premeditated sex." One was supposed to feel guilty about this. If sexual activity was impulsive, then presumably it grew out of love and was not tinged with "immorality" in the minds of the participants. Not so any longer. As one teen-ager stated on a television panel, "Today everybody thinks about sex and knows how to prevent pregnancy."‡

In many surveys conducted to determine the type of marital problems for which physicians are consulted, sex ranks at the top of the list. However, according to divorce court statistics, lack of fulfillment in marriage and concern with money—not sexual disharmony—are first in rank. This fact is supported by the clinical experience of many psychiatrists. What generally happens is that sex becomes the barometer for the total relationship. Part of the overconcern with sex comes from overemphasis on the subject in marriage manuals. Look at the titles of some of these volumes. Also there is frenzied preoccupation with the mechanics of sex, e.g. anatomical positions, minutes elapsed. Yet the fact is that sexual activity can be looked upon as an experiment between two people, and the couple who share a deep and abiding love for each other will find mutually satisfying physical expressions of this love—the key being a voluntary desire to do for the mate.

---

‡The late 1960's have, in fact, given rise to a "New Victorianism." A century ago, love was not necessarily linked with sex—a man often sought a sexual partner who was a fallen woman; a woman had sex with her husband primarily to produce offspring. Now, the credo for many, at least on college campuses, is sex without love. A boy may expect to be "paid off" for a date with sex; a girl may begin to wonder if she has "bad breath" if a boy does not make a pass.

CHANGING ATTITUDE TOWARD DIVORCE

There are many reasons for the change in society's attitude toward divorce. Some individuals tend to blame psychiatry—and the application of psychiatric principles—for this state of affairs. While this may be true to some extent, it is more a product of the essential value which psychiatry preaches, i.e. self-realization. The great advances made by Freud and other giants of psychiatry were in emphasizing that we all have an inner life and that our behavior is governed to a large extent by these internal drives and only partly by our environment.

The increase in the divorce rate in present-day society does not necessarily mean that there are more unhappy marriages any more than does the fact that more people consult doctors today than in the past means that there is more sickness than there used to be. The increase in divorce may be due to the fact that there is acceptance of divorce today without scorn. It is also a reflection of affluence in our society. (More people can afford divorce financially.) Furthermore, it means that both partners expect more fulfillment in their marriage.

A question can be raised as to how a claim on happiness and fulfillment in marriage for both partners has come about. Not too many years ago, it is doubtful whether the words "happy" and "unhappy" would have been applied to marriage at all. This is still the case today in certain countries and in certain religious groups, but even here modifications are being made. The same holds true for sexual fulfillment. The female now has a claim on sexual satisfaction, a claim that had little weight a few decades ago. The pressures of law, religion, and society to keep marriages intact are much less stringent today. Many societies are moving toward granting divorce on "noncompatibility" grounds. If, after a period of several years, a couple mutually agree that they are incompatible and can show that responsibilities to any children have been fulfilled, a divorce will be granted. (Clinically, the vengeful hostility which accompanies divorce may be part of mourning—mourning for the dead marriage.)

In the United States, the change in attitude toward divorce

probably follows more from the shift in political and social factors. This country was settled by Pilgrims who wanted new homes, new opportunities, and new freedoms. As time evolved, it was found that the person who worked hard enough and long enough could achieve almost anything he truly desired. These themes were echoed in the Declaration of Independence, the Emancipation Proclamation, and the concept of universal suffrage. In recent years, with the advances in science and technology, with better medical care, and with more leisure time, it is possible to achieve an even better life.

The Pilgrims left much of their British "reserve" and reliance upon "character" behind them. Americans work more with concepts of pragmatism and change. Nowadays, if a woman has an excessively large nose and receding chin, she does not get much solace or sympathy. She can go to a plastic surgeon and have the nose shortened and the chin built up.

If everything else can be changed for the better, why not husbands and wives as well? The renowned British psychiatrist, Lord Taylor, has observed this phenomenon and termed it "American hypomania."

The "Phaedra Complex"

One result of an easier approach to divorce is the problem of stepparent-stepchild relationship in remarriage.

If Oedipus and Electra were the complexes of Freud's day, more and more the "Phaedra complex" becomes significant for our time. Phaedra was a young Cretan woman who married King Theseus, a much older man. She fell hopelessly in love with Hippolytus, Theseus' son from a former marriage. The drama ends in tragedy with the death of all three.

The Phaedra complex deals with stepparent-stepchild attraction and is to that relationship what the Oedipus complex is to the natural parent-child relationship. A major difference, however, is that in the Phaedra complex, the incest taboo between stepparent and stepchild is diluted because no blood tie exists between the two.

For example, what is the fate of the "normal" family romance—

the young child's sensual feelings toward the parent of the opposite sex—in a reconstituted family?

The degree of intimacy involved in the family romance varies from individual to individual and from family to family. In some families, there is cold formality and aloofness; in other families there is much warmth and physical affection between spouses and between parents and children. But in the natural family unit, the incest taboo is very strong indeed. In the reconstituted family involving stepparents and stepchildren, this incest taboo may not be as viable.

As an extension of the family romance, any parent can see a child in a potential sexual role. Thus, the more society can "institutionalize" the phenomenon of family romance, the less problem of actual incest. Reducing the secrecy and furtiveness and guilt in the natural or reconstituted family reduces the tendency for the family romance to swing to pathological proportions (incest); the same applies to stepparents and stepchildren. By institutionalizing the family romance, a girl can sing, "My Heart Belongs to Daddy"; a boy can sing, "I Want A Girl Just Like the Girl. . . ." Social functions involving fathers (or stepfathers) and daughters (or stepdaughters), and mothers (or stepmothers) and sons (or stepsons) will aid significantly in making the family romance a part of everyday life (Messer, 1969b).

MARRIAGE THERAPY

Why has marriage treatment fallen into disrepute among psychiatrists?

Generally, the field has been left to the so-called marriage counselors who may or may not have sufficient training for this task. Some people turn to their clergyman for advice, but mainly it is to friends, or newspaper or magazine advice columnists. The problem with this type of advice is that, frequently, it has a "cookbook" flavor: prescriptions and formulas for marital happiness are given much as one might provide a recipe. Also, it usually takes into account only one partner's views, without considering the other's point of view.

To the marriage therapist, some knowledge of psychodynamics

is mandatory in order that he make the couple aware of some of their needs which hark back to earlier conflicts. If, in the process, these needs can be modified, fine. But this is not always possible, and some couples are willing to settle for less. Thus, where changes in behavior are not possible, *changes in attitude toward behavior* can be the goal of therapy.

A factor involved in lack of esteem for marriage counseling among psychiatrists has been the influence of Freud. As noted in the chapter on family homeostasis, his writings are replete with warnings to psychiatrists not to involve themselves with a patient's relatives. However, Freud in part remedied this situation by making it a condition of treatment that his patients make no major decisions or major changes in their lives until treatment was finished. In this way, he did not have to face the problem of divorce or serious upsets in the lives of his patients. We know how graphically analysis of one married partner affects the mate. Marriage is an interactional system, and one cannot alter half the equation without affecting the other half.

During marriage treatment, the couple may vie for the therapist's attention, wanting him to take the side of one against the other. One way to handle this situation is to make it clear to the couple at the outset that it will be impossible for the therapist not to be influenced and react to things that are said or done and that when this is the case, it is because he is "only human." However, the therapist should assure them that he is on "both of their sides," and this then neutralizes some of the struggle of each one to "possess" the therapist.§

Although joint therapy reduces secretiveness, a couple should be aware that they do not have to tell each other "everything," i.e. private phantasies, thoughts, or episodes that might humiliate the spouse. Individual identity need not be completely inundated by the joint identity. When one mate has an inordinate need to "confess" everything to the spouse, it may cause serious problems.

---

§Just as the psychiatrist may tell an angry, obsessional patient, "Look, I'm on your side," so marital fights can often be nipped in the bud by one spouse saying to the other, "Don't forget, we're on the same team."

This need generally springs from a deep sense of guilt and may necessitate individual treatment for the confessor.

Efficacy of Marriage Therapy

What are some of the advantages of marriage therapy over individual therapy? They can be enumerated in several ways.

1. Marriage therapy can bring to light one partner's sabotage of attempted change in behavior (i.e. growth) in the mate.

> A wife complained that her husband never "stood up to his parents." What bothered her in particular was that his parents constantly told her how to raise her children. They also popped in at random, never waiting for an invitation. One day they called, wanting her to bring the children over to their home for the afternoon. She had other plans but said she would try. After she hung up, she called her husband and berated him about his parents' conduct. He thereupon called his parents, told them his wife and children would not be over and asked them please to wait for an invitation before visiting again. He then called his wife and informed her of what he had done.
>
> Not an hour went by before the wife called her in-laws, saying she hoped her husband had not been "too rough" on them. Only at their next joint session did she become aware that she had completely undermined the change in her husband's behavior. Despite her loud protestations to the contrary, she had trouble accepting her husband as an assertive person.

2. When a couple are treated together, the presence of a third party (the therapist) often makes the partners "open up." Each mate must be his or her own advocate. He may try to justify his behavior or "defeat" the partner. As stressed above, one of the givens in the marital relationship is the fact that there must be constant readjustment to changes in both partners. Most people use a lack of awareness of this change as a rationalization to maintain their own personality (neurotic) constellation.

> After several visits, a couple expressed pessimism and hopelessness about the outcome of treatment. Both had doubts about their marriage enduring. In one session, the woman stated that it was very hard work that they were undertaking. Her husband agreed and then made reference to one of his employees who had an organic illness. He commented that this man would have to adjust to an almost "impossible situation"; he was, of course, referring indirectly to his own marriage.

The therapist sensed some feeling of defensiveness on the wife's part and began to inquire about some of her habits. It turned out that she was an extremely compulsive person, a characteristic which she had never before recognized in herself. She could never leave the dishes in the sink, could never leave the beds unmade, and was constantly sweeping, dusting and straightening everything. She insisted that her children eat everything on their plates, was always hounding them about their manners, and so forth. The husband felt trapped in this system but was not consciously aware of his resentment. The therapist began talking about the compulsive aspects of her behavior. The wife's mother had been hypercompulsive, and had so indoctrinated her daughter, who was continuing the pattern. As this was elaborated, the patient remarked that she realized she was constantly angry at herself because of this behavior but that she simply "could not help it."

The marriage had to be recalibrated and new ways of interacting had to be opened up. As the woman became aware of how past experiences affected her behavior, she was able to choose alternate ways of responding. Her husband stopped giving in to all of her demands, since it did neither of them any good. This forced the wife to examine her reactions in the here-and-now and helped her overcome repetition of pathological responses related to her own childhood. (The husband had a vested interest in her compulsivity based on his own conflicts. This was also explored during therapy.)

There is one rule that the therapist should at some point make clear to the couple: if they want to preserve their marriage, and are willing to work at it, then each partner must help neutralize the other's anxieties as these are uncovered during the course of treatment.

3. When biographies are reviewed in the presence of both partners, past conflicts and problems become illuminated. Each partner is then more readily inclined to be willing to make up for deficits in the spouse's early life. It is astounding how frequently facts of prime significance about one mate are brought out during marriage therapy, only to discover that the other mate was totally unaware of these events.

A woman had been abandoned by her father during early childhood; as a result, she needed constant reassurance from her husband that he would never abandon her. Before therapy, he had felt that his wife's "clinging" was an attempt to smother or control him. When he became aware that his wife had a bona fide need for reassurance, it became a simple matter for him to provide it. For example, he learned that it was important to call home every evening when he was off on a business trip.||

When such learning takes place during treatment, the awareness is sometimes overwhelming. Often, this simple bit of insight prompts one partner to say, "Is that all you have been craving all these years?"

The same holds true in family therapy. Children often bring up problems about which the parents had no inkling whatsoever.

Each person brings into marriage those values with which he has been brought up. This includes a total range of behavior: how many times a day one eats, whether one sits erect or hunched over, whether one likes to read novels, go to the theatre, go hunting, or go to football games. It follows that we will want to continue this same behavior after marriage, since we are "comfortable" with it. A frequent complaint voiced during therapy is that one partner has tried constantly to change the other since the day they were married. Usually, this is simply a reflection of trying to adjust the environment so that one is as comfortable with the new surroundings as with the old.

A couple were seen because they were concerned about their children's pervasive anxieties. The father had never completely resolved certain traumata related to his early life. When he was a child, his own father had abandoned the family. This left the mother with three children, and they had to be placed in foster homes from time to time. As an adult, whenever pressures got too much for him, this man would threaten to desert his family. Frequently, he would put on his hat and coat and leave the house, saying to his family that he was not sure whether he would return. It was not difficult to see how such behavior was affecting the children. Brief therapy soon brought to light the reason for this behavior.

||A clinical note in this era of tranquilizers: I have seen several chronically-depressed individuals with a history of abandonment. There is always anxiety about further abandonment. When there is a change in the life situation, such as a woman's husband receiving a significant job promotion, the woman's anxiety over abandonment skyrockets, but the anxiety holds her together. If she is given large doses of tranquilizers which neutralize the anxiety, she may become a suicide statistic.

Mankind is notoriously a creature of habit. In other words, behavior tends to be repetitive. The trouble with repetitious behavior is that it makes no difference whether it is "good" or "bad"; we tend to stay with what we know.¶ The man who has always been dominated by his mother may seek to perpetuate the same relationship with his wife. The woman who is an only child and who has had her parents' adoration all her life may seek this same kind of adulation in marriage.

Another example:

> A man was brought up in a home where, as a child, strict attention was paid to his every movement. Even as an adolescent he was never allowed to go anywhere without giving his parents a detailed account of where he was going, who he would be with, and exactly what time he would be home. As a result, he grew up thirsting for "freedom" and a chance to roam about on his own. After marriage, he often went out alone in the evening, perhaps stopping at a neighborhood bar for a drink, visiting a pool hall, or seeing a movie.
>
> This led to conflict, since the wife was usually left sitting at home with the children. She resented his evenings out, never knowing where he was or what time he would be home. The more she hounded her husband about this behavior, the more he stayed away. In therapy, as the wife became aware of the background of his behavior, she began to change her attitude. When the wife ceased to make an issue of it and, in fact, began sanctioning this behavior, the husband went out less frequently.

In the above case, a primary law of human behavior was operative: the best way to get one partner to change his behavior is to give license for it to continue (Haley, 1963). It is similar to the tack used to quiet a screaming child. He will usually stop when told, "Scream louder," since continuing the temper tantrum would represent obedience rather than defiance.

4. The problem of one partner not being aware of growth in the other partner has already been alluded to. During marriage treatment, this fact can be recognized.

¶In South America, the United States Aid Mission transported a group of Indians from a rocky, desolate slope and resettled them in a fertile, green valley. The Aid Mission clapped their hands in glee over their "typically American" achievement. It took the Indians only 60 days to wander back to the desolation.

A couple came for treatment because of "trouble" in their marriage. The husband was a dentist. He had met his wife during hospital training, and at the time his intent was to go into academic medicine. However, after finishing training and completing his military service, he returned to civilian life and settled down to begin private practice. His wife had at first been satisfied with their life, but later, as difficulty began to develop in the marriage, she continually harped on the fact that he should have gone into academic research: he would have been "so much happier." Much of her trouble stemmed from the fact that she felt responsible for her husband's having abandoned his original goal. They already had a child before his discharge from military service, and because of financial pressure he decided against further study. Despite constant reassurance that he was happier in private practice than he would have been in academic work, she continually felt guilty about this.

During treatment the wife came to understand that her husband had gone through a change in life cycle. He was comfortable and happy in private practice, and was no longer interested in academic work. When the wife was able to see that she was unnecessarily burdening herself with guilt about this situation, many of the marital problems tended to dissolve.

5. **A primary task in marriage therapy is often a simple definition of the rules of conduct in marriage.**

Mr. C. goes off to work early each morning after having gotten his own breakfast as well as the children's. Mr. C. resents this bitterly, but his resentment is deeply buried most of the time. In the evening, Mrs. C. makes one telephone call after another to various girlfriends—"After all, we never go anywhere." Mr. C. complains that his wife is always "too busy" with other things to take an interest in him.

There were many other problems that brought this couple into therapy. The therapist took a marital and personal history from both of them. Afterwards, considerable time was devoted to formulating some rules of marriage which might allay the frustrations of both mates. It took a long time for Mr. C. to admit how angry he was that his wife never got up and made breakfast. She confessed that his never suggesting that they go out together embittered her. A new code was set up for their marriage: she would get up, make his breakfast and feed the children, and once a month they would go off together by themselves.

6. **In the complementary relationship, one mate can need reassurance in times of stress and the other mate be in the role of reassurer. It often happens that individuals must be taught how to**

"give" reassurance. Take the hard-pressed businessman who has trouble with his boss. When he tries to describe some of these woes to his wife, she explodes with, "When are you going to tell him off?" Far from helping neutralize his anxiety, she has only made him feel more inadequate and depressed. If, on the other hand, she tells him, "One of these days, I'm sure you'll be able to straighten out those matters in your office," her husband feels supported and understood. Someone close to him has caught the essence of his conflict and is lending reassurance.

Pathologic need for reassurance may sometimes be at the root of sexual incompatibility.

> A woman described her frustration that took place at the culmination of intercourse. There was always a great deal of tenderness and caressing during foreplay, but after completion of the act, her husband wanted to sleep. She, on the other hand, was completely wide awake at this point and desired more embrace. She needed, on an unconscious level, reassurance relating to her guilt about sex. Her husband turned away because he could not understand her demands, nor was there much desire to try to fulfill them. Some men learn to cope with this situation simply by mouthing words to satisfy this type of anxiety in their mates.**

One of the difficulties in our society is that we tend to feel that the partner should always be ready to receive and express feelings of tenderness and love. (Hollywood and television have helped to foster this belief.) In point of fact, there must be a readiness or motive state for this type of emotional expression; in therapy, couples frequently must be taught this fact of life. This knowledge can counteract the feeling of humiliation in a partner who feels the mate has spurned his (or her) love. It may simply be that it was not the time or place.

One of the most difficult tasks in marriage treatment is dealing with a couple in which one member has had an extramarital liaison. Despite the humiliation and hurt felt by the "wronged" partner, the experience can be used to foster learning and growth in the marriage. One mate may feel that his (or her) needs were not

---

**There is evidence from neurophysiological research that once orgasm is attained, neuronal discharge in the reticular activating substance is diminished, and this brings about the desire for sleep.

being fulfilled, and the frustrations and dissatisfaction led to the seeking of gratification elsewhere. The movie, *The Pumpkin Eater,* illustrates this point. In this story, both partners had traumatic pasts; during marriage, extramarital liaisons were entered into. However, because of the understanding that was achieved, each moved to a more stable level of adaptation (and interaction). The extramarital relationships were clearly therapeutic relationships.

Couples Group Therapy

Just as group therapy gives individuals an opportunity for reality testing, couples group therapy does the same for married partners. In this setting, a couple have a chance to discuss their problems with other couples in a sympathetic and therapeutic setting. There are no judges. The presence of the therapist lends neutrality to the situation. One couple can learn from another couple. It soon becomes apparent that many couples have similar problems. In the drama, *Who's Afraid of Virginia Woolf?* the conflicts of two couples were unfolded. The play provided an opportunity for any married couple to contrast their relationship with the ones portrayed. Some individuals have been brought up in homes where they knew only marital discord; in a couples group, they are exposed to periods of marital harmony as well.

MARRIAGE AND THE SELF-MADE MAN

A particular type of marriage (and marital problem) is that involving the "self-made man." A clinical example of such a man was recounted in Chapter VII. What type of woman does this man marry? Most frequently, it is the "doll type," the candy blonde whom the man parades around like a jewel. Usually this woman makes little demand on her husband. Her own narcissism is satisfied by receiving worldly goods, and she does not need her husband to reassure her that she is very important to him. He feels enhanced by her irridescent glow; the "outside" shines brightly and makes up for some of the inner feelings of low self-esteem or emptiness. Such a man wants the world to judge him by the prettiness of his jewel. It follows that when the jewel stops glowing, the man may look elsewhere for another shiny jewel. (The self-made man likewise wants to associate with "important" people—political figures, clergymen, bankers, and so on—thereby enchancing his own self-esteem by numbering these among his friends and basking in the aura of their importance.)

The other type of woman frequently married to this individual is the shy, retiring type, the woman who accommodates herself in every way to her husband, submerging most of her own needs for independence. She is able to give her husband the illusion that he is all-powerful and mighty.

Where the self-made man runs into trouble is when he finds himself married to a woman who makes demands on him for emotional fulfillment. She wants to explore many of the complementary roles in life, but her husband is ill-equipped for this exchange. The more pressure he feels for this fulfillment, i.e., the more demanding his wife becomes, the more anger will be generated in the husband. He may attempt to placate her by deferring to her in most situations. She chooses the place for dinner, the vacation spot, or the color of a new product in his business. However, if this proves insufficient, he may "escape" through any of several avenues open to him: desertion, divorce, extramarital relationships, alcoholism, or frequently enough, by throwing himself even more fervently into his business enterprises.

Chapter X

Regarding The Future

The definition of mental illness has gone through a great many cycles, from the ancient Greeks, to the Inquisitionists of the Middle Ages, to the organically-oriented psychiatrists, to emphasis on intrapsychic conflicts, to the present-day consideration of the "sociology of mental illness." Who knows what other dimensions will be added in the future? The aim of this book has been to view mental health and mental illness in a tripartite context: the individual's own perceptions, the interaction with his family, and the impact of social forces which, at a given time, can label particular behavior as deviant. Psychiatric diagnosis and therapy must take into account all three factors. There is no reason, for example, why a patient cannot simultaneously be treated in individual therapy and as part of a family group.

Future psychiatric research will be, in the main, team-oriented, and a prime member of the research group will be the *physiologist*. The necessity for coming to grips with a neurological and neurophysiological study of the brain has been stressed by the eminent physiologist, Dr. José Delgado, of Yale University. He states that attention should be redirected from the study and control of natural elements in scientific research to the study of analysis and patterning of human mental activity. "There is a sense of urgency in this redirection because the most important problem of our present age is the reorganization of man's social relations. . . . Investigators will not be able to prevent the clash of conflicting desires or ideologies, but they can discover the neuronal mechanisms of anger, hate, aggressiveness, or territoriality, providing clues for the direction of emotions and for the education of more sociable and less cruel human beings" (1965, p. 46). Delgado details the many experiments now being done which allow control of behavior by implantation of electrodes in various parts of the brain.

244

Further, he argues that once more effective means of locating these cortical centers for pleasure, anxiety, or aggression are established, it will aid both in understanding and in treating these conditions which lead to pathologic reaction.

At the next most basic level will be the individual whose expertise is knowledge of the patient's emotional responses: the *psychiatrist* (psychodynamicist; psychoanalyst).

"Psychoanalysis" is defined here as the learning of emotional reorientation in an individual. This definition is in harmony with the emotional mechanisms of adaptation listed in Chapter II. Great confusion can result from the use of intellectual mechanisms as a primary tool of analytic work. Thus, Szasz (1965) describes psychoanalysis as a model "for achieving a better understanding of ethics, politics, and social relations generally." Unfortunately, this deviates from the emotional core of psychoanalytic treatment and it is no wonder that Szasz finds psychoanalysis a very limited procedure. In his view, the therapist does very little but attempt to fulfill "the original moral mandate of psychoanalysis" which is "to aid in the struggle of the individual patient not only against his illness, but also against those who, by their conduct, cause him to be ill."

In a number of recent papers and books, there is the tendency to denigrate traditional psychoanalysis as an important tool in treatment and research. These criticisms range from considering Freud a charlatan and attacking the doctrinairism of "orthodox Freudian" analysts today, to suggesting that psychoanalysis has now offered all that it can to psychiatry and medicine. Unfortunately, if the title of a book indicates some criticism of psychoanalysis, it is destined to sell widely. (One wonders if this might not be the motivation behind some of these writings.) Criticism— healthy criticism— is certainly appropriate, but to consider Freud a charlatan is ridiculous. Further, throughout much of his writing, Freud is clearly a scientist intrigued by method; he makes many references to the fact that all the answers are not at hand and that future work in physiology and biochemistry may hold answers to many of the questions raised by his and other psychoanalytic investigations. That psychoanalytic treatment is not a cure-all is certainly true. Most psychoanalysts would agree, however, that psychoanalytic treatment was undoubtedly oversold in the 1940's and 1950's. Typically, the patient with the most severe psychopathology was considered the best candidate for analysis, because psychoanalysis had about it an aura of having "the real key." As in all of general medicine, the patient with the most severe disability receives primarily symptomatic treatment; the amount that can be done for the patient with chronic arthritis is limited. In a similar way, chronic or severe mental illness imposes a limitation on what can be accomplished therapeutically. This fact was somehow lost sight of and is one of the reasons why the "image" of psychoanalysis has suffered. Still the psychoanalytic method and principles of therapy will always remain at the core of psychiatric training.

The third member of the team is the *specialist in family diagnosis and family treatment.* Emotional communication is the hallmark of family living and, naturally, the family specialist needs training in psychodynamics as well.

The impact of human family emotionality is demonstrated in the book and movie, *Born Free.* A lion cub was found in the wilds and adopted by a human family. Reared in an atmosphere of warmth and love, the lioness became a social being in the human society and had to learn how to become a lioness in the jungle when she was returned to her natural habitat (Adamson, 1960).

Contrast this story with that of a human child brought up in a home with harsh discipline and lack of affective contact. He may become a cruel and heartless adult and be completely in his element when inflicting cruel and inhuman suffering on others.

As technology and mobility in our society increase, it is clear that more and more of the functions that traditionally were the domain of the family—education, health, housing, economic support, and vocational training—will be taken over by society-at-large. This means that the family will be left primarily with the crucial tasks of providing emotional nurturance to its members, particularly the children and the aged, and indoctrinating the family with ethic (value) systems.

Finally, it will be necessary to include the *sociologist* in this team. He is aware of community pressures and reactions and their influence on the individual's behavior.

If the symptoms in an individual are described under the rubric, "deviant behavior," what is the total context of this behavior? In a family, one member may be the scapegoat or "carrier" for the family's problems. His pathology, although "deviant," serves to maintain the family's equilibrium. On the individual (intrapsychic) level, this same behavior may be a defense against unacceptable impulses. The ever-pleasant, smiling individual may be defending himself against unconscious feelings of anger. Therefore, psychiatric or psychoanalytic practice which isolates the individual from his family and community deals mainly with the individual's subjective phantasies. Similarly, the sociologist who does questionnaire surveys, such as the Kinsey Report, is also dealing with only one-fourth of the pie.

With the advent of Community Mental Health Centers, it will be much more feasible to see the patient and his family together to determine the degree to which pathology is a reflection of individual conflict, and the degree to which it is a reflection of family or community problems. In the past, when adolescents were referred for psychotherapy, parents frequently asked if they might come in to talk to the psychiatrist about the problem as they saw it. What better way of dealing with such a situation than having the parents and child confront each other directly, rather than the parents making separate visits "in secret"?

The question must be raised as to why this team approach, with its obvious advantages, has not been used extensively heretofore. First, perhaps there have been communication difficulties. Even today, when a psychiatrist and a sociologist work together, they often have trouble talking to one another. Take the word "symptom," for example. In medical usage this connotes a subjective awareness of some difficulty in an individual. Can there be a family symptom? Can there be a community symptom? If there are symptoms in these two latter categories, who labels them as such? How are they measured and defined? An individual can say, "I have a pain in my stomach," but can one define economic depression in a community as a symptom?

Second, man tends to be parochial in nature. We do not bother with the things we do not really know; we do not deal with those areas in which we are not conversant. A good example of this tendency occurred at a medical meeting during which a surgeon described new approaches in the resection of diseased blood vessels, particularly aneurysms. Up to that time, the method used was to wrap the diseased areas with wire in order to form clots, which eventually would become scar tissue. With new blood pressure drugs and heart-lung machines, it has become possible to excise the diseased wall and replace the resected part with a synthetic material. These findings were presented at the meetings. The discussant of the paper, a distinguished surgeon of many years' renown, mounted the podium and stated that surgical excisions of aneurysms could not be done. He reviewed all the failures in surgical resection, but recounted some successes in wiring. Here he had just listened to a paper describing successful resection, and yet talked about the fact that they could not be done! What better proof of man's parochialism?*

Initially, what does one emphasize in psychiatric investigation? The answer depends upon the point of view of the investigator or therapist. In contemporary times, emphasis seems to be on community psychiatry. In former periods, focus was primarily on structural changes in the brain, and later, on psychoanalysis. A family therapist feels that one must begin by viewing the entire family. Similarly, the neurophysiologist feels that a deeper understanding of the physiological and reflex mechanisms of the organism will lead to a better understanding of the origins of mental health. In other words, each one rides his own hobby horse. The best answer, therefore, would be to strive for a multidimensional approach, certainly in diagnosis and evaluation.

It is heartening to see that work in family diagnosis, family treatment, and group treatment is now being incorporated into most psychiatric training. Similarly, the basic sciences of psychiatry—psychology, psychodynamics, anthropology, sociology, and communications—are being taught to medical students and psychiatric residents. (The parallel basic sciences of medicine are

*Dr. Charles Hatcher, F.A.C.S., personal communication, 1970.

physiology, anatomy, and biochemistry. The physician-in-training has always spent many hours in lectures and laboratory work mastering the basic sciences of medicine before assuming responsibility for the medical care of patients. In the area of teaching the basic sciences of its speciality, psychiatry is only now catching up.)

This multidisciplinary approach was the theme of Alexander's last essay concerning the future development of psychiatry. Alexander wrote:

> In addition to the prolonged psychoanalysis and psychotherapy, which attempt to bring about changes in the patient's internal emotional economy, the precise knowledge of the psychophysiologic interaction characteristic of different types of patients allows their purposeful total management. Many years of experience have taught me that there are different avenues toward bringing about a proper adaptive balance between the person and his environment. . . . Future advancements of psychotherapy will evolve from such an integrated comprehensive approach to man as a biologic organism, a personality, and a member of a social system. Neglecting any of these three major parameters results in a distorted and operationally unsatisfactory personality theory and therapy (1964, pp. 19, 23).

A conclusion that will disturb some people stems from the fact that a symptom in a child can be viewed primarily as a symbolic representation of disturbance in the family's equilibrium. This means that treatment of children will have to be modified to involve the family directly and that "classical" child analysis will die a slow but unlamented death. No longer can the family be relegated to the waiting room; no longer can the mother be seen by the social worker and the father excluded. No longer can a child use the "secrecy" of his psychotherapy as a club to batter the parents. The entire family group must be involved, at least for an initial evaluation and understanding of the symptoms.

In the scheme outlined for evaluating an individual and his interaction with society, the psychiatrist cannot shrink from assuming a pivotal role. Only he among mental health professionals is trained in biology and medicine, and his particular expertise is recognizing emotional patterns that are normal or that are aberrant. (Also, he must be able to recognize psychiatric symptoms that reflect underlying organic disease. As mental health becomes more and more "popular," patients are prone to walk into a psychiatrist's office "off the street," rather than being referred by another physician. Therefore, the psychiatrist must not forget to be a physician first, when necessary, and a psychiatrist second.)

Each member of the team will need to know something about proprioceptive (kinesic) and linguistic communication. The kicking of the foot, the blanching of the face, the hunching of the shoulders—all can be viewed as messages which provide valuable data for study.

For example, one of the burning issues in psychoanalytic treatment is the question of the analyst's neutrality. In general, the position has been that the analyst be a sort of blank screen. The patient could then easily project past relationships into the present therapeutic relationship. If the analyst is neutral and impartial, distortions in the therapeutic relationship could then be analyzed in terms of unresolved problems related to key figures in the patient's past. However, it is quite evident today from research in "proprioceptive language" that the individual communicates via many channels, not just verbally. Similarly, the analyst may breathe, snort, or doodle more vigorously at certain times during the patient's sessions. In other words, just as the patient with a severe illness can sometimes tell the prognosis simply by looking at his doctor's face, so the analytic patient may "read" the analyst's feelings by being attuned to extraneous, nonverbal communication.

Further, it is clear that the physician's own beliefs exert a bias, at least to some degree, and he may unknowingly visit these upon the patient. A study was made of a number of drugs used to combat depression. In those instances where the physician had some doubt about the efficacy of the medication, the results were less favorable than in instances where the physician was convinced of their value. Similarly, Rosenthal and Fode (1963) have shown that a group of experimenters given a number of identically-bred rats, and told that some were bred to be retarded and some to be bright, will validate this dissimilation in their findings. In other words, the experimenter's bias is reflected in his conclusions.† An analyst should therefore be flexible enough to indicate his emotional feelings to a patient when these become an issue in therapy. The patient then has a chance to react to these emotions on a conscious level, rather than responding unconsciously to covert messages. Learning to perceive emotional messages is enhanced.

This emphasis on the therapist as a person is well stated by Karush (1967). The patient's identification of certain real qualities in the analyst—integrity, tolerance, stick-to-itiveness, dedication to challenge—serve also as an ego ideal which enhances the therapeutic alliance between analyst and patient. "Working through," the process of altering defenses and feeling states, is also enhanced by this identification.

Similarly, as family diagnosis and family treatment become a part of every form of psychotherapy—individual, group, child, community psychiatry, and vocational counseling—it is doubtful that diverse professional societies which restrict themselves to study of only one area are in the best interest of the patient or of science in general. There is no need for a society for study of family pathology, as distinguished from a society for the study of sibling therapy.

---

†Another experiment found that when teachers were told that "test" results indicate that particular students have great academic potential, sure enough, these students showed a spurt in learning ability and IQ. However, no tests were given, and the students were randomly selected (Rosenthal and Jacobson, 1968).

References

ACKERMAN, N. W.: *The Psychodynamics of Family Life.* New York, Basic Books, 1958.

ACKERMAN, N. W.: Emergence of family psychotherapy on the present scene. In Stein, M. I. (Ed.): *Contemporary Psychotherapies.* New York, Free Press, 1961.

ADAMSON, J.: *Born Free.* New York, Pantheon Books, 1960.

ALEXANDER, F.: The dynamics of psychotherapy in the light of learning theory. *Amer J Psychiat, 120*:440-448, 1963.

ALEXANDER, F.: The development of psychosomatic medicine. In Wahl, C. W. (Ed.): *New Dimensions in Psychosomatic Medicine.* Boston, Little, 1964.

ALEXANDER, F., and FRENCH, T. M.: *Psychoanalytic Therapy.* New York, Ronald Press, 1946.

ALLEE, W. C., and SCHMIDT, C. P.: *Ecological Animal Geography,* 2nd ed. New York, Wiley & Sons, 1951.

ARDREY, R.: *The Territorial Imperative.* New York, Atheneum, 1966.

ARTISS, K. L.: Human behavior under stress—From combat to social psychiatry. *Military Medicine, 128*:1011-1015, 1963.

BANNISTER, R.: *The Four Minute Mile.* New York, Dodd, Mead & Co., 1955.

BERKSON, G.: Development of an infant in a captive Gibbon group. *J Genet Psychol, 108*:311-325, 1966.

BERNARD, C.: *Introduction to the Study of Experimental Medicine.* New York, MacMillan, 1927.

BIRDWHISTELL, R. L.: The kinesic level in the investigation of the emotions. In Knapp, P. H. (Ed.): *Expression of the Emotions of Man.* New York, International Universities Press, 1963.

BOSZORMENYI-NAGY, I., and FRAMO, J. L.: *Intensive Family Therapy.* New York, Harper & Row, 1965.

BOWEN, M., DYSINGER, R. H., and BASAMANIA, B.: The role of the father in families with a schizophrenic patient. *Amer J Psychiat, 115*:1017-1020, 1959.

BOWLBY, J.: Pathological mourning and childhood mourning. *J Amer Psychoanal Assn, 11*:500-541, 1963.

BRONSON, W. C.: Dimensions of ego and infantile identification. *J Personality, 27*:532-545, 1959.

BRUCH, H., and TOURAINE, G.: Obesity in childhood: V. The family frame of obese children. *Psychosom Med, 2*:141-206, 1940.

BRUNER, J. S.: *The Process of Education.* Cambridge, Harvard U. P., 1960.

BURGESS, E. W., and LOCKE, H. J.: *The Family*, 2nd ed. New York, American Book, 1960.

CANNON, W. B.: *Bodily Changes in Pain, Hunger, Fear and Rage*, 2nd ed. New York, Appleton, 1929.

CANNON, W. B.: *The Wisdom of the Body*. New York, Norton, 1932.

CANTRIL, H.: Perception and interpersonal relations. *Amer J Psychiat*, *114*:119-126, 1957.

DELGADO, J. M. R.: *Evolution of Physical Control of the Brain*. (James Arthur Lecture on the Evolution of the Human Brain.) New York, American Museum of Natural History, 1965.

DENTLER, R. A., and ERIKSON, K. T.: The functions of deviance in groups. *Social Problems*, 7:98-107, 1959.

DUBOS, R.: *Man Adapting*. New Haven, Yale University Press, 1965.

DURKHEIM, E.: *Suicide: A Study in Sociology*, translated by John A. Spaulding and George Simpson. Glencoe, Free Press, 1960.

EISSLER, R. S.: Scapegoats of society. In Eissler, Kurt R. (Ed.): *Searchlights on Delinquency*. New York, International Universities Press, 1949.

ERIKSON, E.: *Childhood and Society*. New York, Norton, 1950.

ERIKSON, K. T.: *Wayward Puritans*. New York, Wiley & Sons, 1966.

FERENCZI, S.: Stages in the development of the sense of reality. In Ferenczi, S. (Ed.): *Sex in Psychoanalysis*. New York, Robert Brunner, 1950.

FERREIRA, A. J.: Psychosis and family myth. *Amer J Psychother*, *21*:186-197, 1967.

FLAVELL, J. H.: *The Developmental Psychology of Jean Piaget*. Princeton, Van Nostrand, 1963.

FRAIBERG, S.: The science of thought control. *Commentary*, *33*:420-429, 1962.

FREUD, A.: *The Ego and Mechanisms of Defense*. New York, International Universities Press, 1946.

FREUD, S. (1909) : Analysis of a phobia in a five-year-old boy. In Jones, Ernest (Ed) .: *Collected Papers*. London, Hogarth Press, 1953, Vol. III, pp. 149-289.

FREUD, S. (1914) : On narcissism: An introduction. In Jones, Ernest (Ed.) : *Collected Papers*. London, Hogarth Press, 1953, Vol. IV, pp. 30-59.

FREUD, S. (1915) : Thoughts for the times on war and death. In Jones, Ernest (Ed): *Collected Papers*. London, Hogarth Press, 1953. Vol. IV, pp. 288-317.

FREUD, S. (1917): Mourning and melancholia. In Jones, Ernest (Ed.): *Collected Papers*. London, Hogarth Press, 1953, Vol. IV, pp. 152-170.

FREUD, S. (1937): Analysis terminable and interminable. In Jones, Ernest (Ed.) : *Collected Papers*. London, Hogarth Press, 1953, Vol. V, pp. 316-357.

FREUD, S.: *The Ego and the Id*. London, Hogarth Press, 1927.

FREUD, S.: *The Problem of Anxiety*. New York, Norton, 1936.

FREUD, S.: Totem and taboo. In Brill, A. A. (Ed.): *The Basic Writings.* New York Modern Library, 1938 pp. 807-883.

FREUD, S.: *A General Introduction to Psychoanalysis.* New York, Garden City, 1943.

FREUD, S.: *Civilization and Its Discontents.* London, Hogarth Press, 1953.

FRIEDMAN, A. S., et al.: *Psychotherapy for the Whole Family*, New York, Springer, 1965.

GALDSTON, I.: The family and the patient. In Masserman, J. H. (Ed.): *Individual and Familial Dynamics.* New York, Grune & Stratton, 1959, Vol. II.

GALDSTON, R.: Observations on children who have been physically abused and their parents. *Amer J Psychiat, 122*:440-443, 1965.

GAYLIN, W. (Ed.) : *The Meaning of Despair.* New York, Science House, 1968.

GEHRKE, S., and KIRSCHENBAUM, M.: Survival patterns in family conjoint therapy. *Family Process, 6*:67-80, 1967.

GELLHORN, E.: *Principles of Autonomic-somatic Integrations.* Minneapolis, Univ. of Minn. Press, 1967.

HAAN, N.: Proposed model of ego functioning: Coping and defense mechanisms in relationship to IQ change. *Psychol Monogr, 77*: Whole No. 571, 1963.

HALEY, J.: *Strategies of Psychotherapy.* New York, Grune & Stratton, 1963.

HARE, R.D.: Psychopathy autonomic functioning, and the orienting response. *J Abnormal Soc Psychol* (Suppl.), 73, (No. 3) : Part 2, June 1968.

HARLOW, H. F., and HARLOW, M. K.: The affectional systems. In Schrier, Allan M.; Harlow, Harry F., and Stollnitz, F. (Eds.) : *Behavior of Nonhuman Primates.* New York, Academic Press, 1965, Vol. II.

HARTMANN, H.: Ego psychology and the problem of adaptation. In Rapaport, D. (Ed.): *Organization and Pathology of Thought.* New York, Columbia University Press, 1951.

HARTMANN, H., KRIS, E., and LOEWENSTEIN, R.: Comments on the formation of psychic structure. In *The Psychoanalytic Study of the Child.* New York, International Universities Press, 1946, Vol. II.

HEATH, R. G. (Ed.): *Serological Fractions in Schizophrenia.* New York, Harper & Row, 1963.

HEBB, D. O.: *The Organization of Behavior.* New York, Wiley & Sons, 1959.

HELLMAN, L.: *Toys in the Attic.* New York, Random House, 1960.

HEMINGWAY, E.: *A Moveable Feast.* New York, Scribner, 1964.

HESTON, L. L.: The genetics of schizophrenic and schizoid disease. *Science, 167*:249-256, Jan. 16, 1970.

HOLLAND, B. C., and WARD, R. S.: Homeostasis and psychosomatic medicine. In Arieti, S. (Ed.): *American Handbook of Psychiatry.* New York, Basic Books, 1966, Vol. III.

HOLLINGSHEAD, A. B., and REDLICH, F. C.: *Social Class and Mental Illness.* New York, Wiley & Sons, 1958.

HORNEY, K.: *The Neurotic Personality of Our Time.* New York, Norton, 1937.

IBSEN, H.: A doll's house. In McFarlane, James W. (Ed.): *The Oxford Ibsen.* London, Oxford University Press, 1961, Vol. V.

JACKSON, D. D.: The question of family homeostasis. Part I. *Psychiat Quart (Suppl.), 31:*79-90, 1957.

JOHNSON, A. M.; FALSTEIN, E. I.; SZUREK, S. A., and SVENDSEN, M.: School phobia. *Amer J Orthopsychiat, 11:*702-711, 1941.

JOHNSON, A. M., and SZUREK, S. A.: The genesis of antisocial acting out in children and adults. *Psychoanal Quart, 21:*323-343, 1952.

KALLMANN, F. J.: The genetic theory of schizophrenia. *Amer J Psychiat, 103:*309-322, 1946.

KARDINER, A.: *The Individual and His Society.* New York, Columbia University Press, 1939.

KARDINER, A.: *The Psychological Frontiers of Society.* New York, Columbia, University Press, 1945.

KARDINER, A., KARUSH, A., and OVESEY, L.: A methodological study of Freudian theory: II. The libido theory. *J Nerv Ment Dis, 129:*133-143, 1959.

KARUSH, A.: Working through. *Psychoanal Quart, 36:*497-531, 1967.

KARUSH, A., and OVESEY, L.: Unconscious mechanisms of magical repair. *Arch Gen Psychiat, 5:*77-91, 1961.

KOHL, R. N.: Pathologic reactions of marital partners to improvement of patients. *Amer J Psychiat, 118:*1036-1041, 1962.

KOOS, E. L.: *Families in Trouble.* New York, King's Crown Press, 1950.

KROBER, T. C.: The coping functions of the ego mechanisms. In White, R. W. (Ed.): *The Study of Lives.* New York, Atherton, 1963.

LANGSLEY, D. G., PITTMAN, F. S., and KALMAN, F.: Family crisis therapy—Results and implications. *Family Process, 7:*145-158, 1968.

LEAR, M. W.: A greenhouse for wilted women. *New York Times Sunday Magazine,* June 19, 1966.

LEE, R. V.: The agony of conforming: The male parent. In Farber, S. M., Mustacchi, P., and Wilson, R. H. L. (Eds.): *Man and Civilization: The Family's Search for Survival.* New York, McGraw-Hill, 1965.

LIDZ, T., CORNELISON, A. R., FLECK, S., and TERRY, D.: The Intra-familial environment of schizophrenic patients. II. Marital schism and marital skew. *Amer J Psychiat, 114:*241-248, 1957.

LORENZ, K. Z.: *King Solomon's Ring.* New York, Crowell, 1952.

LORENZ, K. Z.: *On Aggression,* translated by Marjorie K. Wilson. New York, Harcourt, Brace & World, 1966.

MAHLER, M. S.: On child psychosis and schizophrenia: Autistic and symbiotic infantile psychoses. In *The Psychoanalytic Study of the Child.* New York, International Universities Press, 1952, Vol. VII.

MEAD, M.: *Culture and Commitment: A Study of the Generation Gap.* Garden City, N. Y., Doubleday, 1970.

MESSER, A. A.: Ethnocultural identity and mental health. In *Social Work Practice*. New York, Columbia University Press, 1963.

MESSER, A. A.: Family treatment of a school phobic child. *Arch Gen Psychiat, 11*:548-555, 1964.

MESSER, A. A.: The only-child syndrome. *New York Times Magazine,* Feb. 25, 1968, p. 84.

MESSER, A. A.: Dissolution of long-standing marriages. *Ment Hyg, 53*:127-130 1969. (a)

MESSER, A. A.: The "Phaedra complex." *Arch Gen Psychiat, 21*:213-218, 1969. (b)

MILLER, A.: The family in modern drama. *The Atlantic Monthly, 197*:35-41, April 1956.

MILLER, A.: A view from the bridge. In *Collected Plays*. New York, Viking, 1957.

MILLER, N. E.: Learning of visceral and glandular responses. *Science, 163*: 434-445, Jan. 31, 1969.

MOORE, M. E., STUNKARD, A., and SROLE, L.: Obesity, social class, and mental illness. *J Amer Med Assn, 181*:962-966, 1962.

MOORE, R. A., BENEDEK, E. P., and WALLACE, J. G.: Social class, schizophrenia and the psychiatrist. *Amer J Psychiat, 120*:149-154, 1963.

MORGENTHAU, H. J.: Stevenson—Tragedy and greatness. *The New Republic, 153*: Aug. 7, 1965.

MYERS, J. K., and ROBERTS, B. H.: *Family and Class Dynamics in Mental Illness*. New York, Wiley & Sons, 1959.

NASH, N. R.: *The Rainmaker*. New York, Random House, 1955.

NOYES, A. P., and KOLB, L. C.: *Modern Clinical Psychiatry*, 7th ed. Philadelphia, W. B. Saunders, 1968.

ORWELL, G.: *Such, Such Were the Joys*. New York, Harcourt, Brace & World, 1953.

OSTWALD, P. F.: *Soundmaking: The Acoustic Communication of Emotions*. Springfield, Thomas, 1963.

PARLOFF, M. B.: The family in psychotherapy. *Arch Gen Psychiat, 4*:445-451, 1961.

PARSONS, T., and BALES, R. F.: *Family, Socialization and Interaction Process*. Glencoe, Free Press, 1955.

PEALE, N. V.: Prescription for a marriage on the rocks. *Reader's Digest, 85*:89-93, 1964.

PIRANDELLO, L.: Six characters in search of an author. In *Three Plays*. New York, Dutton, 1922.

POWELL, G. F.; BRASEL, J. A., and BLIZZARD, R. M.: Emotional deprivation and growth retardation simulating idiopathic hypopituitarism. *New Eng J Med, 276*:1271-1278, 1967.

PROUST, M.: Swann's way. In *Remembrance of Things Past.* New York, Random House, 1934, Vol. I.

RADO, S.: Hedonic control, action-self, and the depressive spell. In Hoch, P. H., and Zubin, J. (Eds.) : *Depression.* New York, Grune and Stratton, 1954.

RADO, S.: *Psychoanalysis of Behavior.* New York, Grune & Stratton, 1956.

REICH, W.: *Character Analysis.* New York, Noonday, 1949.

ROSENTHAL, R., and FODE, K. L.: The effect of experimenter bias on the performance of the albino rat. *Behavioral Science, 8*:183-189, 1963.

ROSENTHAL, R., and JACOBSON, L.: *Pygmalion in the Classroom: Teacher Expectation and Pupil's Intellectual Ability.* New York, Holt, Rinehart & Winston, 1968.

RUSH, B.: An account of the bilious remitting yellow fever as it appeared in Philadelphia in the year 1793. In *Medical Inquiries and Observations.* Philadelphia, J. Conrad, 1805, Vol. III.

SCHEFLEN, A. E.: The significance of posture in communication systems. *Psychiatry, 27*:316-331, 1964.

SHERRINGTON, C. S: *The Brain and Its Mechanism.* London, Cambridge U. P., 1933.

SNELL, J. E.; ROSENWALD, R. J., and ROBEY, A.: The wifebeater's wife. *Arch Gen Psychiat, 11*:107-112, 1964.

SOLNITSKY, O.: The human lateral geniculate body: Anatomical, functional and clinical considerations. *Georgetown Med Bull, 19*:137-151, 1966.

SONNE, J. C.; SPECK, R. V., and JUNGREIS, J. E.: The absent-member maneuver as a resistance in family therapy of schizophrenia. *Family Process, 1*:44-62, 1962.

SPERLING, M.: Analytic first aid in school phobias. *Psychoanal Quart, 30*: 504-518, 1961.

SPIEGEL, J. P., and BELL, N. W.: The family of the psychiatric patient. In Arieta, Silvano (Ed.) : *American Handbook of Psychiatry.* New York, Basic Books, 1959, Vol. I.

SPITZ, R. A.: Hospitalism. An inquiry into the genesis of psychiatric conditions in early childhood. In *The Psychoanalytic Study of the Child.* New York, International Universities Press, 1945, Vol. I.

SROLE, L.; LANGER, T. S.; MICHAEL, S. T.; OPLER, M. K., and RENNIE, T. A. C.: *Mental Health in the Metropolis: Midtown Manhattan Study.* New York, McGraw-Hill, 1962, Vol. I.

STOLLER, R.: *Sex and Gender: On the Development of Masculinity and Femininity.* New York, Science House, 1968.

SULLIVAN, H. S.: *The Interpersonal Theory of Psychiatry.* New York, Norton, 1953.

SZASZ, T. S.: *The Myth of Mental Illness.* New York, Hoeber-Harper, 1961.

SZASZ, T. S.: *The Ethics of Psychoanalysis.* New York, Basic Books, 1965.

258 The Individual in His Family

VOGEL, E. F., and BELL, N. W.: The emotionally disturbed child as the family scapegoat. In Bell, N. W., and Vogel, E. F., (Eds.) : *A Modern Introduction to the Family.* Glencoe, Free Press, 1960.

WAGNER, N. N., and BAKER, J. Q.: The relationship of socioeconomic variables to the psychiatric treatment of children. *Amer J Orthopsychiat, 36:*271-272, 1966.

WALDFOGEL, S.; COOLIDGE, J. C., and HAHN, P. B.: The development, meaning and management of school phobia. *Amer J Orthopsychiat, 27:*754-780, 1957.

WEINSTEIN, E. A.: *Cultural Aspects of Delusion: A Psychiatric Study of the Virgin Islands.* New York, Free Press, 1962.

WEINSTOCK, A. R.: Family environment and the development of defense and coping mechanisms. *J Personality and Soc Psychol, 5:*67-75, 1967.

WEST, L. J.: The psychobiology of racial violence. *Arch Gen Psychiat, 16:* 645-651, 1967.

WITTENBERG, R. M.: Personality adjustment through social action. *Amer J Orthopsychiat, 18:*207-221, 1948.

WOLFF, H. G.: *Stress and Disease.* Springfield, Thomas, 1953.

INDEX

A

Ackerman, N. W., 140, 220
"Acting-out," 145, case study, 1-2
Adamson, J., 246
Adaptation, 42 ff.
  alloplastic, 10
  analogy to computer, 21-22
  and Freudian theory, 10, 56
  as liability, 45
  autoplastic, 10
  biological, 44-46, in Japanese, 44-45
  definition of, 9
  emotional level, 19, 28-36
  hedonic level, 19, 21-26
  intellectual level, 19, 36-39, 45-46
  reflex level, 19, 22-23
Adaptational frame of reference, 9
Adaptational psychodynamics, 10
Adaptive behavior,
  and cultural factors, 57 ff.
  maladaptive behavior coexisting, 53
Adaptive levels, vs. id-ego-superego, 56
Adaptive mechanisms, 20 ff.
  definition of, 52
  distinguished from defense mechanisms, 52-53
  environmental factors, 11-12
  examples of, 52
  maturational levels, 55-58
  range of, 11
Addiction, treatment of, 27-28
Adolescence, 211, stages in male, 190-191
Affect, withdrawal of, 96-99
Affect hunger, 60
Aggression,
  authoritarian training, 64 n.
  in animals and man, 49
  inhibition of, 64-65
Alcoholism, 27, 70, 75, 105-106, 154
Alexander, F., 38 n., 187 n., 249
Allee, W. C., 49

Alor, natives, 54
Analysis Terminable and Interminable,
  179
Animal studies,
  lack of socialization, 48
  maladaptive behavior in primates, 46-47
  socialization in monkeys, 53
Appetite, 35
Ardrey, R., 49, 50
Artiss, K. L., 200
Assertivity, in child developmental periods, 57-58
Authoritarianism, 64 n.
  in family, 107-108, 113, 149
  training, 64, 64 n.

B

Baker, J. Q., 175
Bales, R. F., 110
Bannister, Roger, 43
Basamania, B., 70 n.
"Battered-child," 96 n.
Battle fatigue, 26, treatment of, 199-200
"Beatles, The," 218
Behavior,
  disturbed vs. disturbing, 204
  ego, coping vs. defensive, 87
  "ego-alien," 166
  integration of, 21
  repetitious, 239
  social evaluation, 204-205
Bell, N. W., 90, 141
Benedek, E. P., 175
Bernard, Claude, 15, 16, 17, 85, contribution to homeostasis, 15
Birdwhistell, R. L., 71, 149
Blizzard, R. M., 75
Born Free, 246
Boszormenyi-Nagy, I., 141
Bowen, M., 70 n.

Bowlby, J., 42, 47, 59
Brain structure, 40-41
Brain washing, 26
Brandeis Manifesto, 202
Brasel, J. A., 75
Bronson, W. C., 191
Bruch, H., 207 n.
Bruner, J. S., 45
Burgess, E. W., 67
Byrd, Admiral Richard, 221

C

Calibration in therapy setting, 149
Cannon, Walter B., 54
  contribution to homeostasis, 17-18
  phenomena, 35
Cantril, H., 60
Character, 39
Charades, 150 n.
Child,
  "acting-out" parental conflict, case study, 123-125
  battered, 96 n.
  developmental periods, 57-58, 76
  emotional deprivation, 75
  infantile omnipotence, 57
  only-child syndrome, 120-123
  separation from mother, 59
Child psychiatry, 249
Child rearing, 54, 58 ff., 75, 76, 82
  affection in, 74, 76
Children, affect hunger in, 60
"Cinderella Married," 217
Civil Rights riots, 74
Civilization and Its Discontents, 61
Cognitive development (Piaget), 41-42
Communes, 211
Communication, 87
Community Mental Health Centers, 247
Complementarity, 118, 127
  definition of, 220
  marital, 218 ff.
  role, 116-118
Compromise, as family homeostatic mechanism, 104-105
Computerized dating, 219 n.
Concentration camp, 99, 127

Conformity, 13
Coolidge, J. C., 139
Cornelison, A. R., 71
Co-therapist, 171 n.
Courtship, adolescent, 213 ff.
Creativity, 77
Crisis,
  family, 83
  intervention, 84
Cultural institutions,
  and traditions, 63
  origins of, 61-65
Culture,
  definition of, 61
  Libyan, 62

D

Defense mechanisms, 80
Defensive alliances, 94-95
Dehumanization, 100, 100 n.
Delegated omnipotence, 57
Delgado, J. M. R., 244
Delinquency, 126
Delusions, cultural factors, 206
Denial, 55
Dentler, R. A., 203
Dependency,
  child, 57
  child developmental periods of, 53-55
Depressive spell, 28
Development,
  critical periods, 47-48
  primordial period, 57 n.
Developmental periods, assertivity, dependency, socialization, 57-58
Deviance, 8, 201-205
  psychiatric evaluation of, 4
  societal evaluation of, 4
Diagnosis, "Social" vs. Medical, 203-204
Divorce, 102, 172
  attitudes toward, 232-233
  causes of, 231-233
  laws in California and New York, 233
Dubos, R., 45
Durkheim, E., 201
Dyscultural anxiety reaction, 2 n.
Dysinger, R. H., 70 n.

E

Ego apparatuses, 10
Ego-behavior, coping vs. defensive, 87-88
Einstein, A., 156 n.
Eissler, R. S., 126
Emergency emotions, 32-33, 113
Emotional level of adaptation, 17, 19, 28-36
  learning, 29
Emotional role, 109-110
  complementarity, 116-118
  definition of, 110
  family, 119
  group therapy, 135-136
  in presidency, 130-131
  learning, 128-132
  vs. rational role, 132-135
Emotional role sets, 115-118
Emotions, 66
  affirmation of, 114
  characteristics of, 113
  communication of, 113
  definition of, 29
  emergency, 32-33, 113
  family, 35-36
  welfare, 32-33, 113
Engagement, 214-216
Environment, and adaptive mechanisms, 20
Equilibrium, homeodynamic, 85
Ergotropic effects, 34
Erikson, E., 11, 186
Erikson, K. T., 201, 203
Ethology, 46-50
"Exclusive possession," 77, 218
Experimentation, bias in, 250-251
Extended family, 132, 193
Extramarital liaison, 241-242

F

Falstein, E. I., 139
Family,
  adaptation to crisis, 83 ff.
  aerospace, 74-75
  authoritarian, 90, 113, case study, 107-108, 149
  autocratic, 189-190
  British, and homosexuality, 132 n.
  care of aged, 77
  communication patterns, 171-172
  conflict, example of, 88 ff.
  defined, 69-70, 86
  division of labor, 79 ff.
  emotional roles in, 119
  emotions, 35-36
  evaluation of functions, 80
  extended, 67-69, 132, 193, 222
  frontier, 83-84
  functions, 72-75
  healer, 99-102
  historical continuity, 165-166
  historical origins, 67-69
  homeostasis, 85-88
  immigrant, 135 n.
  myth, see case study, 105-106
  non-verbal communication, 71
  patriarchal, 67-68
  "protector," see case study, 101-102
  reconstituted, 233-234
  "repressive," 106
  roles, 72-75
  "romance," 71, 233-234
  simulated, 70
  "suicidal," 106
  values, 75-76
Family defense, 86
Family homeostatic mechanisms, 89-108
  defensive alliances or coalitions, 94-95
  family healer, 99-102
  family myth, 105-106
  loosening the family unit, 103
  range of, 86
  "reaction formation," 106-108
  repetitive fighting, 103-104
  "resignation" or compromise, 104-105
  scapegoating, 89-93
  withdrawal of affect, 96-99
Family therapist, 172 ff., 246
  and social class, 174-175
Family therapy,
  and psychoanalysis, 176 ff., 186 ff.
  development of, 140-143
  discouragement during, 171
  individual therapy within, 168-170
  interruption of, 151-152
  neutrality of therapist, 164-165

of patient previously analyzed, case
    study, 180 ff.
of school phobia, case study, 137 ff.
resistance to change, 154-156
techniques of, 144 ff., 162-165
vs. individual therapy, 177-180
with co-therapist, 171 n.
with one member, 70 n.
with several generations, 166-168
Father-daughter relatedness, 145-146
Father-son relatedness, 135, 190-193, case
    study, 180 ff.
"Feared Stranger," 90 n.
Female infanticide, 21, 61
Femininity,
    change in concept, 218
    learning attributes of, 131
Fenichel, Otto, 5
Ferenczi, S., 57 n.
Ferreira, A. J., 105
"Fight or Flight" phenomena, 17
Fleck, S., 71
Fode, K. L., 250
Folklore, 65 n.
Fraiberg, S., 99
Framo, J. L., 141
French, T. M., 187 n.
Freud, A., 11
Freud, S., 176, 179, 180
    and adaptation, 10, 56
    and analysands, 187, 235
    criticism of, 245
    depression, 31
    emotions, 25, 31, 112
    libido theory, 5
    oedipal complex, 61
    orientation to medicine, 20
    phobias, 139-140, 148 n.
    primal parricide, 61
    schizophenia, 141 n.
    sexual instinct, 31
Friedman, A. S., 141

G

Galdston, R., 96 n.
Gaylin, W., 28
Gehrke, S., 106

Gellhorn, E., 34
Gestalt, 38
"Going steady," 213 ff.
Group therapy, 135-136, couples, 242
"Gruesome twosome," 104, 223

H

Haan, N., 87
Hahn, P. B., 139
Haley, J., 239
Hare, R. D., 26 n.
Harlow, H. F., 48, 53
Harlow, M. K., 48
Hartmann, H., 47, contribution to adap-
    tation, 10
Hatcher, C., 248 n.
Healer, family, 99-102
Heath, R. G., 5
Hebb, D. O., 21
Hedonic level of adaptation, 19, 23-28
    clinical disorders, 27-28, 207 n.
    learning, 25
Hellman, L., 156
Helper role, 99-102
Hemingway, E., 152 n.
Heston, L. L., 5
"Hippies," 211
Holland, B. C., 20
Hollingshead, A. B., 200
Homeodynamic equilibrium, 85
Homeostasis, 15-20, 54
    analogy to physical medicine, 85-86
    family, 85-88
    range of reactions, 20
    social, 19, 85, 200-205
Homeostatic mechanisms, vs. defense
    mechanisms, 87
Homosexual panic, see Pseudohomosex-
    uality
Homosexuality, 202, see case study, 94-95
    active and passive obligatory, 119
    female, 119
    male, 133
Horney, K., 6, 13
Humor, 98-99, in families, 150
Hunger, 35
Hysterical woman, 75

I

Ibsen, H., 13
Idiopathic hypopituitarism, 75
Imprinting, 47-48
Individual therapy, in family setting, case study, 168-170
Industrial Revolution, 69
Infanticide, female, 61
Inhibition, 63-65
  cultural, and psychotherapy, 65-66
  of aggression, 64-65
  of masturbation, 63
Instinct of self-preservation (Freud), 10
Instinctual behavior, 47
Intellectual level of adaptation, 19, 36-39, 45-46
  learning, 37-39
Introspection, 196
Ipcress File, 26 n.

J

Jackson, D. D., 85
Jacobson, L., 25 n.
Johnson, A. M., 124, 126, 139
Jungreis, J. E., 70

K

Kallmann, F. J., 5
Kalman, F., 84
Kardiner, A., 18, 21, 31, 54, 58 n., 61, 65 n., 187 n.
Karush, A., 31, 57, 58 n., 251
Kinesics, 71
Kinsey Report, 247
Kirschenbaum, M., 106
Kohl, R. N., 198 n.
Kolb, L. C., 139
Koos, E. L., 99
Kraepelin, E., 4
Kris, E., 10
Krober, T. C., 87

L

Langer, T. S., 4
Langsley, D. G., 84
Lear, M. W., 207
Learning,
  emotional level, 37-39
  hedonic level, 25
  intellectual level, 37-39
Learning theory, 171
Lee, R. V., 212
Levy, D., 18
Libyan culture, 62 n.
Lidz, T., 71
Limbic system, 33-35
Linguistics, 71
"Little Hans," 139-140, 147 n.
Litvak, A., 134
Locke, H. J., 67
Loewenstein, R. M., 10
Lorenz, K. Z., 48, 49
Love,
  adolescent's view, 214
  as voluntary expression in sex, 231
  romantic vs. married, 216-218

M

Mahler, M. S., 78
Malleus maleficarum, 3
Manhattan State Hospital, 206
Marriage,
  adolescent, 273 ff.
  assessment of change, 229
  communication of needs, 222-226
  complementarity, 218-222
  fighting, 103-104, 152, 222, 224-225, 235 n.
  life cycle, 226-230
  likes vs. needs, 219
  motivations for, 213
  "overloaded," 222
  secrecy in, 151, 235-236
  self-made man, 242-243
  social class differences in, 216
  "work" of, 215
Marriage manuals, 231
Marriage therapy, 220-221
  couples group, 242
  efficacy of, 236-243
  growth of partners, 239
  practice, 234 ff.
  sabotage by mate, 236
  sexual problems in, see case study, 194-198
Masculine protest, 180

Masculinity,
  change in concept, 218
  learning attributes of, 13
Masturbation, inhibition of, 63
Mead, M., 135
Mental illness,
  as "emotional disorder," 112
  as "myth," 204
  cultural factors, 14 n., 205-206
  definition of, 244
  environmental factors in, 5-9, 198-200
  history of, 3-9
  neurotic personality (Horney), 6
  psychiatric assessment, 7-8
  social class differences in, 81, 199-200
  sociological assessment, 8-9
Messer, A. A., 102, 121, 135 n., 138, 143,
    228, 234
Michael, S. T., 4
Midtown Study, 4, 6
Miller, A., 127 n., 192
Miller, N. E., 23 n.
Moore, M. E., 207
Moore, R. A., 175
Morgenthau, Hans, on Adlai Stevenson,
    43
Mother,
  hysterical, 75
  obsessive, 75
  surrogate, 75
Mourning and Melancholia, 31, 112
Myers, J. K., 81
Myth, as family homeostatic mechanism,
    105-106

N

Nash, N. R., 131
Neurotic behavior,
  fixation in roles, 80
  personality, 6
  projection, 167-168
Nonconformity, 6, 13
Nonverbal communication, 71, 149
Noyes, A. P., 139

O

Obesity, cultural factors in, 206-208
Obsessional patient, 64 n., 235 n.

Old Testament (Ruth), 68
Omnipotence, primary and delegated,
    57n.
Only child, 239
  syndrome, 120-123
Opler, M. K., 4
Orwell, George, 79
Ostwald, P. F., 34
Overpopulation, 251
Ovesey, L., 31, 57, 58 n.

P

Pain, tolerance for, 26
Paralanguage, 71
Parenthood, 227-228
Parloff, M. B., 141
Parsons, T., 110
Passive-dependent personality, 57
Patient, social environment of, 143-144
Peale, N. V., 172
Personality, passive-dependent, 57
"Phaedra Complex," 233
Phobia, school, case study, 137 ff., 147 n.
  street, 139, 238
Phobias, treatment of, 139-140
Piaget, J., 41-42
"Pill," the, 194, 231
Pirandello, L., 127 n.
Pittman, F. S., 84
Pleasure,
  anticipation of, 82
  mechanism of, 24
"Polymorphous perverse" phantasies, 230
Posture, linked with character, 39
Powell, G. F., 75
Pregnancy, fear of, 194-198
President of the United States, emotional
    preparation for, 130-131
Primal horde, 212-213
Private property, 62-63
Projection, in storytelling, 126
Projective system, 65
"Proprioceptive language," 250
"Protector" in family, see case study,
    101-102
Proust, M., 217
Pseudohomosexuality, 191-192
Psychiatry, training in, 248-249

Psychoanalysis,
  and family therapy, 176 ff., 186 ff.
  as emotional reorientation, 245
  of both parents, 97
Psychoanalyst,
  as family therapist, 141-142, 179
  neutrality of, 250
Psychodynamic system, 18-20
Psychopathology,
  cultural factors in, 205-206
  sexual, 59, 63, 64
Psychosomatic medicine, 134 n.
Psychotherapy,
  and cultural inhibitions, 65-66
  future of, 244-251
  silence in, 200
  team approach, 244-247
  "wrong" patient in, see case study,
    208 ff.
Pumpkin Eater, The, 242

R

Rado, S., 18, 19, 25, 25 n., 30, 32, 38,
  57 n.
Rational role, 132-135
"Reaction formation," as family homeostatic mechanism, 106-108
Reassurance, pathologic need for, 241
Redlich, F. C., 200
Reflex level, 22-23
Reich, Wilhelm, 39
Rennie, T. A. C., 4
Riddance mechanism, 24-25
Roberts, B. H., 81
Robey, A., 14
Role,
  age, 119-120
  change during crises, 83-84
  complementarity, 116-118
  emotional definition of, 110
  emotional influence on, 112 ff.
  experimenting within family, 119
  expressive (emotional), 73, 218
  helper, 99-102
  in Negro family, 80
  instrumental (performance), 73, 218
  neurotic fixation in, 80

"physical," 114
  preparation for, 115
  sick, 110-112
  social, 110-112
Roosevelt, Franklin D., 121, 129
Rosenthal, R., 250, 251 n.
Rosenwald, R. J., 14
Roughhousing, 190
Rush, Benjamin, 55

S

Scapegoating, 12, 70, 91-93, 210, case
  study, 91-93
Scheflen, A. E., 149
Schizophrenia, 28, 34, childhood, 140-141
Schizophrenogenic mother, 141
Schmidt, C. P., 49
School phobia, case study, 137 ff., 147 n.
"Screaming mother," 40 n.
Secrecy,
  in marriage, 151, 235-236
  in psychotherapy, 249
Self-made man, 184-186, and marriage,
  242-243
"Senior girl's panic," 226
Sense organs, 26-27, 34-35
Sensitivity training, 35
Separation anxiety, 220
Sex, sado-masochistic, 117 n.
  conflicts related to contraception, 198
Sexual gender role, 76, 190-191
  impotence, 105
  incompatibility, 241
  instinct, 31
  psychopathology, 63-64
Sexual mores,
  change in, 230-231
  "New Victorianism," 231 n.
Shaw, George Bernard, 216
Sherrington, C. S., 26
"Sickest" person, 70, definition of, 14
Sickle cell anemia, 63 n.
Sleep, 241 n.
Smell, sense organs, 34
Snell, J. E., 14
Social homeostasis, 19, 85, 200-205
Social work, and family study, 142

Socialization,
 in child developmental periods, 53-55
 of child, 58, 76, 78
Societies, preliterate, 82
Sociopath, background, 12, 126
Solnitsky, O., 33
Sonne, J. C., 70
Speck, R. V., 70
Sperling, M., 139, 148 n.
Spiegel, J. P., 141
Spitz, R., 60
Srole, L., 4, 207
Status,
 achieved, 110-111
 ascribed, 110-111
Stoller, R., 76, 190
Stunkard, A., 207
Suicide, 238 n.
Sullivan, H. S., 189
Surrogate-mother, 75
Svendsen, M., 139
Symptom, 189, 247
Szasz, T. S., 204, 245
Szurek, S. A., 124, 126, 139

T

Team-teaching, 136, 193
Television, 34, 211
Territoriality, 49-50
Terry, D., 71
Totem and Taboo, 61
"Touching base," 78
Tourraine, G., 207 n.
Traditions, cultural, 63

Tranquilizers, 238 n.
Transference, 187-188
Trophotropic effects, 34
Twain, Mark, 191
"Twenty-year fracture," 102, 228-229

V

Values,
 family, 75-76
 in marriage, 238, 246
Vietnam veteran, 200 n.
Vogel, E. F., 90

W

Wagner, N. N., 175
Waldfogel, S., 139
Wallace, J. G., 175
Ward, R. S., 20, 56
Weinstein, E. A., 205
Weinstock, A. P., 87
Welfare emotions, 32-33, 113
West, L. J., 90 n.
Who's Afraid of Virginia Woolf?, 242
Wife-beating, 14
Wittenberg, R. M., 100
Wolff, H. G., 199
"Working through," 251
"Wrong" patient in psychotherapy, case
 study, 208 ff.

Y

Yin and Yang, 3
Yoga, 23 n.
"Young wife syndrome," 130